How *Dancing* Really Stops the *Clock*

*How the Capillary Cell's Two Step Dance Step
Anoints Longevity through a Counterbalanced Rhythm*

ROBERT L BUCKINGHAM, MD, FACP

ISBN: 978-1-959483-04-5 (sc)
ISBN: 978-1-959483-05-2 (hc)
ISBN: 978-1-959483-06-9 (e)

Library of Congress Control Number: 2023904479

R Buckingham MD, FACP

HOW DANCING *REALLY* STOPS THE CLOCK

HOW THE CAPILLARY CELL PIVOT AND SWING DANCE ACHIEVES A REVERBERATING ANTI-INFLAMMATORY RHYTHM WHICH ORCHESTRATES WELLNESS

Acknowledgments

To my deceased and beloved parents Bob and Marcella, for their enduring grit and love.

To my grown adult children for their faith in me.

To my professional colleagues for tolerating my weaknesses.

To the deceased Professor Radulovacki, who taught me science research and to find joy in the discovery of small things.

To my wife Kate, for her enduring faith, hope and love.

Table of Contents

Appendix

Figure One:
Interstitial Space (IS) Vascular Inflammatory Free Radicals (VIFRs) and the Capillary Cell's (CC) Continuous Outer Membrane (COM) Permeability Pivot

Figure Two:
(IS) (VIFR) Induced (CC) (COM) Chain Reactions

Figure Three:
The (CC) (COM) Permeability Pivot will Facilitate the Combustion Swing of (CC) Mitochondria to Produce Either Nitric oxide (NO) or Energy (ATP) as the (CC) (COM) makes Multiple Dance Step Related Adjustments to Increase or Decrease its Permeability to Funneled (IS) Inflammatory Mediators (IA)

Figure Four:
The Mechanics of (CC) (COM) Funneled, Sequenced and Precision Purposed (IA) Choreography

Figure Five:
The (CC) Dance Step Rhythm is Dependent upon the Timely (IA) Execution of (VIFR) Removal

Figure Six:
How the (CC) Outer Membrane Complex (OMC) and (COM) in Particular Responds to the (IS) Mesenchymal (M) "All Clear" Inhibitory Signal

Figure Seven:
Pulsed Anti-Inflammatory Signaling Streams and Metabolic Rhythms Chain React a Back-and Forth Pivot and Swing of (CC) (OMC) Permeability and Mitochondrial Combustion that Redirects a Counterbalanced Dance Step Multipurpose

Figure Eight:
The Pulsed Anti-Inflammatory (CC) Mitochondrial (NOCC) and (ECC): A Rhythmic Signaling, Metabolic and Functional Back-and Forth Counterbalance, that Combines with The (CC) (OMC) Permeability Pivots, to Precision Execute Multipurpose

Figure Nine:
(CC) Counterbalanced Mitochondrial Combustion Signaling and Metabolic Rhythms, within the Context of the (CC) Dance Step, will Facilitate and Quality Assure (CC) Multipurpose Execution

Figure Ten:
Counterbalancing a Sequential (CC) Dance Step Rhythm Requires the Timely Execution of Each Sequential Dance Step Purpose

Figure Eleven:
The Linchpin of a Persistent Chronic Inflammatory (IS) Signaling and Metabolic Crescendo: Too Many (IS) (VIFRs) that Cannot be Timely (CC) Dance Step Removed

Figure Twelve:
The Loss of (CC) Dance Step Rhythm, Functional Counterbalance and Multipurpose Execution will Increase (CC) (IA) (IS) Funneling Mistakes from Combinations of (CC) (OMC) Pseudocapillarization, the Reduction of (CC) Mitochondrial Reserve and the Silencing of its Nuclear Chromosomal DNA Coding Capacity (as its Protective Telomeres Shorten)

Figure Thirteen:
The Misappropriated (IS) (IA) Funneling through the Compromised (CC) (OMC) will Outcome an (IS) Purpose Misalignment that will Further Deter (CC) Dance Step Rhythm and Enable the Expression of Chronic Inflammatory Intent

Figure Fourteen:
The Reverberation of Chronic Inflammatory (IS) (IA) Signaling and Metabolic Rhythms will Abort the (CC) (OMC) Dance Step Permeability Pivot which Marginalizes the (CC) Mitochondrial (NOCC) to Result in Loss of (CC) Signaling, Metabolic and Multipurpose Execution

Figure Fifteen:
Persistent (IS) Chronic Inflammatory Signaling Streams and Metabolic Rhythms will Dismantle the Anti-Inflammatory (CC) Dance Step Rhythm and its Execution of Multipurpose

Figure Sixteen:
(IS) Chronic Inflammatory Signaling and Metabolic Consolidation and the "Pseudocapillarization Effect" on the (CC) (OMC) Enables the Chronic Inflammatory (IS) Matrix to Pirate (IS) Intent

Figure Seventeen:
The Maturing of Chronic Inflammatory (IS) Signaling and Metabolic Purpose towards *Anti-Organ* Disease Venues (DVs)

Figure Eighteen:
The Full Expression of *Anti-Organ* (DVs): The Anti-Inflammatory (CC), (IS) and (M) Signaling and Metabolic Capitulation that Enables the Anti-Organ to Divert (IS) Functional Rhythms towards Its Own Purpose

Figure Nineteen:
Breaking the Thread of Chronic Inflammatory (IS) Signaling and Metabolic Chain Reactions: Finding (CC) Dance Step Traction from (IS) (VIFR) Reduction and Decreased (DV) Posturing

Figure Twenty:
Summarizing the Executed Recycling of (CC) Dance Step Rhythms: Integrating the Counterbalanced Anti-Inflammatory Execution of (CC), (IS), (M) and (EOC) Purposes within the Context of (CC) Dance Steps

Introduction

The Crux of End Organ Interstitial Space Signaling Control: Pro Versus Anti-Inflammatory Signaling Streams and Metabolic Rhythms

An Introduction to End Organ Interstitial Space Streaming Signal Momentum

The Signal and Metabolic Engineering of a Reverberating Capillary Cell Dance Step Rhythm

Cytokines, free radicals, electromagnetic wavelets, enzymes, hormones and other assorted proteins are often bundled into functional streams and rhythms within cells, interstitial spaces or blood plasma to cause pulsed chain reactions which provides momentum towards the execution of timely circadian purposes. Within the interstitial space of end organs, these signaling and metabolic streams are flanked by and controlled from either pro or anti-inflammatory influencers, the ladder of which originates from a finely tuned and pulsed capillary cell dance step rhythm. It is within the context of this rhythm that precision choreographed inflammatory mediators are pulsed and funneled into the interstitial space to remove inflammatory breach and secure its hygiene. The success of interstitial space inflammatory breach removal, which typically involves the molecular reduction of vascular inflammatory free radical impediments, will produce sufficient signaling and metabolic momentum to herald the onset of the next endothelial cell dance step which repletes a *completely different* type of *recycled* purpose. When executed the corresponding chain reactions the dance step elicits will complement and purpose fulfill the next "pivot and swing" step.

The back-and-forth rhythm of the capillary (and downstream endothelial) cell dance step *rhythm* becomes integral as to how the nearby abluminal interstitial space will functionally maneuver its own purpose fulfillment that includes the unique functional rhythms of its end organ cell. When pulse orchestrated in a counterbalanced dance step rhythm, each dance step will emanate circadian signaling streams and metabolic rhythms that drive a multipurpose "anti-inflammatory" execution whose fulfillment auto perpetuates the health, integrity and functional direction of the capillary cell, interstitial space and its corresponding molecular and transcellular constituents.

The manifest *health* of these rhythms is intimately linked to and coordinated with everyday behaviors that either favor or disavow the capillary cell dance step continuity. These aforementioned behaviors involve everyday lifestyle decision making which on the surface may appear innocuous towards influencing adverse health outcomes. These subtle but often repetitive behaviors could resonate resistance towards the integrity of the sleep wake cycle, the capacity to manage stress, the capability to regularly exercise, or the motivation to avoid dietary sugars, processed food or red meat. It could also lower the avoidance threshold towards avoiding other addictions such as tobacco products, alcohol, or drugs. The aggregate of these daily proinflammatory lifestyle choices will push reliable compilations of vascular inflammatory free radicals into the systemic circulation and end organ interstitial spaces that will in turn induce chain reactions that eventually nuance chronic inflammatory signaled and metabolic rhythms. Their effects will push signal and metabolic against the capillary cell dance steps and its counterbalanced rhythm to eventually interstitial space enable the maturing of chronic inflammatory outcomes.

This real time confluence between lifestyle choices, vascular inflammatory free radical interstitial space displays and the subsequent capacity of the capillary cell to dance step repulse them defines the anti-inflammatory integrity of the interstitial space in terms of how it manages its sanitation and resists chronic inflammatory overtures while enabling the nearby end organ cell to use the signaling and metabolic format to optimally function. In these potentially anti-inflammatory vulnerable interstitial space settings, the capillary cell dance steps can become unbalanced and desynchronized and subsequently lose their functional verve. As the dance step rhythm falls into functional disarray, its corresponding anti-inflammatory multipurpose fulfillment becomes less satisfying thereby inviting the interstitial space assemblance of chronic inflammatory rhythms as capillary cell funneled space immune arsenal become less anti-inflammatory compliant in executing purpose fulfillment.

The implication from a deteriorating capillary cell dance step rhythm is that its pulsed signaled and metabolic rhythms would be less anti-inflammatory reliable. Given a sufficient chronic inflammatory interstitial space nuance and the capillary cell's dance step rhythm will mirror in the opposite direction as it can no longer reconcile anti-inflammatory multipurpose. When this occurs, the signaled and metabolic interstitial space processes virilize towards a chronic inflammatory conversion.

One early key factor to this foreboding interstitial space transition is how vascular inflammatory free radical interstitial space impingements become relentless to where they cannot be reliably reduced or eliminated. In this proinflammatory scenario, the capillary cell's dance steps begin to flail as its rhythm is forced to spend more of its dance time suspended towards funneling inflammatory mediators into the interstitial space. This persistent dance step delay keeps the capillary cell out of rhythm, decreased its signaling and metabolic counterbalance and longer-term functional viability as chronic inflammatory interstitial space rhythms gather virility and intentionality.

One more key factor that increases chronic inflammatory interstitial space impropriety is how the interstitial space can transition incoming purpose neutral immune arsenal to be signal turned to endorse chronic inflammatory maneuvering. This can occur because the capillary cell's outer membrane complex allows these immune funneling snafus due to its declining capacity to anti-inflammatory choreograph purpose precise immune arsenal into the interstitial space. This occurs as its outer membrane complex loses infrastructure capacity from diminished restitution due to a declining dance step driven nitric oxide combustion cycle. As purpose neutral interstitial space immune arsenal become signal converted from chronic inflammatory signaling rhythms, their purpose gets hijacked to conform towards and further virilize their intent. With persistent forbearance, they will posture a purpose that will enable interstitial space disease consorts.

This conversion of the interstitial space from anti to proinflammatory rhythms will occur over time with the rate of conversion dependent on vascular inflammatory free radical fuel, the degree to which purpose neutral immune arsenal have penetrated the interstitial space, the maturation of chronic inflammatory signaling rhythms, and the decay of the capillary cell itself and its corresponding dance steps. As darker interstitial space signaling and metabolic rhythms consolidate, they will purpose virilize by signal pirating the capillary cell's outer membrane complex to further increase interstitial space funneling of specific immune arsenal that can be signal aligned to a chronic inflammatory revisionist realm. By dumbing down the disabled capillary cell's outer membrane complex into their immune funneling agent, chronic inflammation re envisions the interstitial space towards its own purpose. The signaling and metabolic rhythms it musters become fodder for a variety of interstitial space chronic inflammatory entanglements that prioritize oxygen deficits, hyper coagulopathies, the birthing of infections, the advent of different types of scarring, the increasing displays of immune ignored cancer cells, and the proliferation of tweaked immunoglobulins whose electron exposures forebear autoimmune mishaps.

The scope of these chronic inflammatory bursts will not just involve one end organ's interstitial space but will bisect multiple end organs simultaneously but not necessarily with the same mosaic of disease outcomes. The different end organ chronic inflammatory outcomes will become codependent on how chronic inflammatory signaling and metabolic rhythms opine the interstitial space to subsequently encrypt the nature of the disease outcome or mosaic. In these instances, and in the context of a systemically diffuse capillary and endothelial cell functional decline, upstream oxygen depravity and proclivity towards hypercoagulable states and insulin resistance will forbear how an end organ disease mosaic unfolds in different end organs. In these systemic end organ chronic inflammatory interstitial space outcomes, the signaling and metabolic milieu they portend will deploy disease consorts based on what the end organ cell is most vulnerable to.

The Importance of the Capillary Cell's Dance Step Rhythm *Counterbalance*

The capacity of the capillary cell to extoll sufficient anti-inflammatory multipurpose execution to the interstitial space will depend on how resilient its counterbalanced dance step rhythm has been maintained. Counterbalance becomes dependent primarily on how well the dance steps can timely reduce vascular inflammatory interstitial space free radical impingements. When effective, the next dance step pivot and swing purposed execution can fully manifest without being delayed or aborted. The capacity to timely eliminate vascular inflammatory free radical impediments will require that the capillary cell embodies the fullness of its dance step rhythm as its *pace, ricochet and backwash* align its anti-inflammatory purpose with the blood plasma constituents and interstitial space allies. The timeliness of free radical interstitial space elimination will parlay a signaling and metabolic interstitial space nuance that is intimately linked to the capillary cell's dance steps and its pulsed anti-inflammatory reverberations. Without a timely vascular inflammatory free radical interstitial space removal, the capacity of the dance step rhythm to perform will decline as next dance step signaling and metabolic *counterbalance* is lost. Without counterbalance, dance step infrastructure restitution will get short changed wo here signaling and metabolic rhythms cannot be compensated for. The result will nuance a continued dance step purposed decline whereby funneled immune arsenal into the interstitial space will no longer exclusively cater to anti-inflammatory execution. The funneled immune discrepancies become a chronic inflammatory stepping stone for signal conversion towards a proinflammatory purpose.

When the capillary cell's dance steps no longer pulse anti-inflammatory counterbalance, the rhythm will lose a functional forbearance whereby its outcomes lack multipurpose *quality assurance*. This proinflammatory bias does not occur from isolated dance step deficiencies but rather is a collective of inappropriate funneled immune contingents that become signal purpose realigned as a result of the lack of thorough capillary cell outer membrane complex and infrastructure restitution. Because of this, the capillary cell's outer membrane complex loses functional infrastructure (adhesion receptors, pores, switches, voltage gradients) whereby it can no longer accurately choreograph interstitial space funneled immune contingents that will execute a precise anti-inflammatory purpose of inflammatory breach removal. The loss of this capacity can be blamed on a persistently diminished dance step nitric oxide combustion cycle. As the capillary cell's outer membrane complex *pseudocapillarizes* its anti-inflammatory purpose execution diminishes which becomes a proinflammatory linchpin to interstitial space outcomes.

This theme of interstitial space immune arsenal becoming signal converted to a chronic inflammatory purpose will eventually convey its own *virulence* and *intentionality*. This will enable an interstitial space purpose transition whereby distinct chronic inflammatory signaling and metabolic rhythms will framework a lattice that will elicit disease seeding. The loss of the capillary cell's dance step counterbalance and a quality assured anti-inflammatory multipurpose fulfillment becomes the necessary infrastructure adjustment that is required for disease consorts to become agents to the interstitial space. This chronic inflammatory interstitial space "transitioning" will shift the capillary cell's dance step rhythm and outer membrane complex from a potent anti-inflammatory facilitator to a signal hacked purveyor of chronic inflammatory interstitial space intent.

The capillary-endothelial cell, with its unique blend of purpose sophisticated outer membrane complex receptors and mitochondria that will urgently respond to outer membrane complex energy requirements, that when combined with a cellular infrastructure that functions without oxygen combustion, becomes the primary facilitating entity for pacing and distributing interstitial space anti-inflammatory outcomes. With an elegant and functionally distinct set of outer membranes and sub membranes, the capillary cell's luminal and abluminal surfaces parlay sophisticated arrays of interstitial space and blood plasma signaling and metabolic crescendos that permutate endo and exocytic anti-inflammatory rhythms that purpose execute its dance steps. When this occurs as a counterbalanced circadian rhythm, the pulsed dance steps execute multipurposed rhythm while at the same time providing for a signaled and metabolic framework for the next dance step's purpose fulfillment. When this occurs, the dance step rhythm becomes an anti-inflammatory powerhouse that is methodical, recurring, signal and metabolically counterbalanced, and functionally quality assured.

The elicited dance step rhythms will stream cytokines, enzymes, electromagnetic wavelets and even their own blend of anti-inflammatory free radicals that will purpose fulfill while laying the signaling framework for the next dance step. When this occurs, the permutated dance step purpose fulfillment will attribute signaling rhythms that will chain react the onset of the next dance step. The pulsed fulfillment of these dance step anti-inflammatory rhythms become harbingers of interstitial space health and end organ cell functional resolve as they also contribute towards the prevention of chronic inflammatory disease consorts. The dance step counterbalance and multipurposed execution is supported by a cadre of paced metabolic interstitial space shifts that involve pH, osmolality and osmotic pressure gradients, oxygen and carbon dioxide tensions and pyruvate/ fatty acid distribution ratios. These dance step pulsed metabolic rhythms become additive towards the anti-inflammatory purposed execution of all end organ interstitial spaces and their corresponding allied cells as they conform their rhythms and purpose to the capillary cell dance steps and the metabolic fluxes they convey.

The Importance of the Timely Interstitial Space *"All Clear"* Signal

When vascular inflammatory free radical interstitial space elimination becomes "a *fait accompli*", the compilation of metabolic and signaled rhythms will reverberate an "***all-clear***" signal whose chief architect becomes a mesenchymal cell subset. The signaling crescendo will induce the capillary cell's basement membrane to shift its outer membrane complexes' permeability away from further interstitial space immune funneling. The all-clear signal will find additional traction within the interstitial space's landscape from a host of pulsed metabolic indicators that will occur within the all-clear signaling entourage. Once the capillary cell's basement membrane receives this inhibitory signal, restricted interstitial space immune funneling will occur from signaled chain reactions elicited from the capillary and downstream endothelial cell's continuous outer membrane that is permutated by fluxing cAMP levels. As transmembrane cAMP levels increase, activated switch operatives among other things will restrict luminal access of continuous outer membrane adhesion receptors to its glycocalyx and circulating white blood cells or platelets. This will also coincide with across-the-board reductions of immune arsenal endocytosis through its gap junction orifice, channel, endocytic vesicles and transcellular transport channels as voltage gradients increase and the cell's outer membrane configuration flattens out.

As this occurs, the capillary cell's continuous outer membrane will no longer need extra energy or calcium ions to assist in the transmembrane interstitial space immune funneling efforts. They will in turn form concentration gradients within the capillary cell's cytoplasm and predictably follow these gradients into the nearby mitochondrial inner membrane space. It is here that they become a feedback loop signaling force with the mitochondrial inner membrane as they signal loop inhibit the electron transfer through the cytochromes that will deactivate ATP synthase while simultaneously activating matrix nitric oxide synthase and nitric oxide combustion. The coming and going of mitochondrial calcium, energy and magnesium to and from the capillary cell's continuous outer membrane and mitochondria become important dance step feedback loops that become integral to its pulsed rhythms and multipurpose anti-inflammatory execution.

As the all clear signaling manifesto chain reacts resistance towards additional interstitial space immune funneling, the downward shift in the capillary-endothelial cell's outer membrane complex permeability gradient and its mitochondrial combustion to nitric oxide becomes part of the cell's counterbalancing master plan of functional anti-inflammatory homeostasis. When the dance step rhythm finds an optimal signaling and metabolic counterbalance, its anti-inflammatory functional outcomes will be quality assured and timely executed. The dance step rhythm's resilience becomes an abiding anti-inflammatory reverberation of dance step multipurposed execution as each completed pivot and swing dance step gets paced and backwashed into the interstitial space and systemic circulation.

The dance step's multipurposed execution can be constrained in the short term as the rhythm may struggle to remove vascular inflammatory free radical interstitial space impingements. This rhythm imbalance can be signal and metabolically compensated for by capillary cell infrastructure adjustments. Over time however, a persistent overcompensation of dance steps to purpose execute will cause the rhythms to become unbalanced and lose functional resolve.

Robert L Buckingham, MD, FACP

Why the Capillary Cell's Mitochondrial Combustion Cycles are Critical to Dance Step Purpose Fulfillment

The capillary and downstream endothelial cell's dance step derived pullback of inflammatory mediators from the interstitial space will mean that mitochondrial combustion energy surges will be no longer required to facilitate their interstitial space active transport from blood or lymph plasma. As continuous outer membrane cAMP, transitions permeability calcium and magnesium ions and ATP to and from mitochondria facilitate its execution. In aggregate they form concentration gradients based on outer membrane complex permeability requirements that feedback loop permeability execution on the one hand and mitochondrial combustion preference, be it energy or nitric oxide on the other. These outer membrane complex and mitochondrial "raw materials" will easily penetrate the porous mitochondrial outer membrane to interact with the more voltage potent inner membrane to signal shifts in combustion output based on their intermembrane space concentration gradients. In this fashion, calcium, magnesium and ATP become the equivalent of facile inner membrane on-off switches that facilitate the **rotation** mitochondrial combustion back and forth between energy and nitric oxide gas. Depending on combustion output, there will occur a paradigm shift in the capillary cell 's purpose fulfillment as either energy or nitric oxide gas production facilitate entirely different functional signaling and metabolic rhythms. Their outcomes produce a mitochondrial and transcellular functional divergence but each requires the other to counterbalance and maximize their combustion benefits.

When the dance step's outer membrane complex permeability shifts to inhibit interstitial space immune funneling it will feedback loops to mitochondrial signaling rhythms that will inhibit further energy combustion while stimulating a spurt of nitric oxide production which then causes an entirely different set of signaling, metabolic and purpose derived fulfillments. Interestingly, the nitric oxide derived fulfillment is required to maximize the next dance step's energy combustion purpose fulfillment and so on. These signaling, metabolic and functional transactions that occur with each permeability pivot and combustion swing dance step will not only permutate fulfillment through the capillary cell, but will also signal and metabolically facilitate its functional rhythm into the interstitial space. In this manner the dance step's purpose fulfillment becomes an interstitial space (and blood plasm) footprint that EXECUTES *AN ANTI-INFLAMMATORY* interstitial space purpose that conforms to the intent of the capillary cell dance step rhythm. When the *pivot and swing* capillary cell's dance step rhythm is timely and purpose fulfilled it forms an aligned signal and metabolic counterbalance that algorithms a quality assured purpose that is transmitted to the interstitial space, its cellular allies that reside there as well as to the blood plasma as the rhythm longer term success requires that it prepares its interstitial space domain and blood plasma for the next step's purposed execution.

The timely and purpose precise dance steps will to and from the interstitial space and blood plasma will chain react rhythms of activated anti-inflammatory cytokines, enzymes, proteins, hormones, free radicals and electromagnetic wavelets that will produce a collective execution of anti-inflammatory multipurpose. Their reverberation becomes the backdrop towards a counterbalanced and functionally-quality assured multipurposed outcome that is to the mutual benefit of the capillary cell itself, its interstitial space domain, the mesenchymal and end organ cells that reside there as well as with distant endothelia and end organ cells.

The anti-inflammatory capillary and endothelial cell dance step rhythm will at the same time *subvert* the interstitial space towards a chronic inflammatory signaling and metabolic manipulation. The *reverberation of the anti-inflammatory* dance step rhythm will contrive a signaling and metabolic wall that will buttress the interstitial space and blood plasma from chronic inflammatory overtures. The back-and-forth pulsed dance step rhythm will integrate itself with its interstitial space partners to precision purpose outcomes that are beneficial to all cellular parties. The derived anti-inflammatory rhythms will inherently suppress chronic inflammatory seeds thereby preventing their escalation towards disease consorts.

The Importance of Dance Step Derived Anti-inflammatory Outcomes

Anti-inflammatory end organ interstitial space signaling and metabolic rhythms become jeopardized when chronic interstitial space inflammation jams the timing of the capillary cell's dance step rhythm. This can be as simple as not timely removing vascular inflammatory free radical interstitial space impingements or can be more sinister as immune funneling errors into the interstitial space become increasingly de rigueur. Their resilience will cause the capillary cell to minimize its infrastructure reconstitution thereby placing its functional reserve in a tailspin. Chief among its organelle outliers will be its increasingly destitute outer membrane complex, as its lack of restitution increases pseudocapillarization, meaning it no longer has the functional capability to precision choreograph tangible immune remnants into the interstitial space to eliminate all forms of inflammatory breach. This loss of anti-inflammatory outer membrane complex transparency will delay and minimize the next dance steps critically important rhythm, the nitric oxide combustion cycle it permeates, and all of the signaling and metabolic fallout that occurs from its less than stellar purposed execution.

As anti-inflammatory purpose inept immune contingencies are persistently pushed into the interstitial space, the dance step rhythm will continue to break down from chronic inflammatory chain reactions. The process creates an increasingly anti-inflammatory divergent interstitial space rhythm that keeps vascular inflammatory interstitial space free radicals in play and creates an interstitial space signaling and metabolic milieu that increasingly virilizes chronic inflammatory intent to where the disabled capillary cell outer membrane complex becomes a signaling attribute towards chronic inflammatory interstitial space outcomes. The persistent block in the capillary cell's dance step rhythm will uncouple its anti-inflammatory benefits which become the linchpin to interstitial space decline and capillary cell functional senescence.

The Vascular Inflammatory Free Radical *"Pester and Fester Effect"* and Subsequent Chronic Inflammatory Interstitial Space Contingencies

Given sufficient *diversity, volume and persistence,* vascular inflammatory free radical interstitial space impingements can increasingly marginalize the capillary cell's dance step circadian rhythm by not getting timely removed thereby preventing or delaying the next dance step. Their *"pester and fester effect"* will require the capillary cell's outer membrane complex to keep immune funneling into the interstitial space even if they are not capable of eliminating the free radical. This immune ineptness becomes a boon to chronic inflammatory interstitial space rhythms as these bungling immune remnants will signal convert to enhance proinflammatory rhythms thereby increasing capillary cell dance step ineffectiveness. The inability of the capillary cell to subdue the increasing displays of chronic inflammatory rhythms will eventually lead to the conversion of the interstitial space from an anti to proinflammatory signaling rhythm. It is in this context where the capillary cell's outer membrane complex loses its capacity to choreograph funneled immune arsenal into the interstitial space that will execute an anti-inflammatory purpose. Over time and as the capillary cell's outer membrane complex pseudocapillarizes and interstitial space chronic inflammatory signaling and metabolic rhythms virilize, the purpose of the capillary cell's declining infrastructure will convert to a chronic inflammatory cause. The maturing of chronic inflammatory interstitial space intent is executed by its *matrix* and *anti-organ.*

The chronic inflammatory-matrix will begin to scale a proinflammatory interstitial space transition by signal pirating the capillary cell's basement membrane and subsequent outer membrane complex. Doing so will elicit a different type of immune funneling into the interstitial space that will cater to a chronic inflammatory expression rather than to interstitial space hygiene. This *purpose transitioning* within the interstitial space virilizes chronic inflammatory intentionality as its blended rhythms become a signaling and metabolic edifice for disease seeds. As chronic inflammatory signaling and metabolic rhythms rewire the interstitial space their nomenclature to a different purpose identity, the scope and power of anti-inflammatory rhythm identity diminishes.

The outcome to this interstitial space transitioning is a considerably anti-inflammatory purpose weakened capillary cell that is no longer capable of choreographing or pacing anti-inflammatory rhythms that keep the interstitial space sanitized and the end organ cell functionally optimal. As the chronic inflammatory interstitial space anti-organ builds out it signaling and metabolic hierarchy, disease venues will seed the interstitial space. When this occurs, the capillary and true end organ cell will become senescent as their outer membranes divorce functional intimacy with each other. The chronic inflammatory interstitial space transitioning will require a *metabolic rhythm* follow through as non-pulsed but increasing insulin resistance, reduced oxygen tensions, acid-base abnormalities and hypo osmolality gradients mature.

With a chronic inflammatory interstitial space transformation, anti-organ disease consortiums take root by signal dialing into these rhythms. In this manner infectious agents, cancer cells, scar tissue, hypercoagulable states, and autoimmune complexes find integrative virulence as they take advantage of chronic inflammatory signaling platitudes, favorable metabolic conditions, and an increasingly complacent anti-inflammatory interstitial space functional hierarchy. The struggle for control of this end organ interstitial space domain is high stakes but can very easily slip into a chronic inflammatory takeover as its signaling and metabolic rhythms competitively silence those that are occurring from an increasingly diminished anti-inflammatory immune hierarchy. The *rate and degree* of anti-inflammatory surrender is defined by multiple factors that include the volume and diversity of vascular inflammatory free radical interstitial space exposures, the degree to which the capillary cell's outer membrane complex has pseudocapillarized, the volume and type of funneled interstitial space immune arsenal that have been signal converted and the inherent functional priorities of the end organ cell and how they predispose to being marginalized by certain chronic inflammatory disease venues.

The Importance of the Capillary Cell's Dance Step *Cadence*

When capillary cells pulse and optimal pivot and swing dance step rhythm, they will signal and metabolically reinforce anti-inflammatory interstitial space outcomes that become the basis for the dance step's **ricochet, pace, stem and backwash** to and from the interstitial space, its allied cellular cohabitants and the blood/lymph plasma. The pulsed and fluxing anti-inflammatory rhythms of the capillary cell's outer membrane complex permeability pivots and mitochondrial combustion swings produce a reverberating signal and metabolic precipice that communicates dance step multipurpose as it communicates, supplies sustenance and procures next step functional countenance to and from the interstitial space and blood/lymph plasma. In the case of its interstitial space mesenchymal and end organ cells, the capillary cell dance steps will signal and metabolically align anti-inflammatory rhythms that lock and key dance step purpose fulfillment to these cells which integrate their functional rhythms to dance step purpose. That is, the capillary cell's dance steps will rhythm an anti-inflammatory interstitial space fulfillment that will also enhance the functionality of its interstitial space mesenchymal and end organ cell neighbors.

In the case of the end organ cell, the capillary cell's pulsed outer membrane complex permeability and mitochondrial combustion rhythms will purpose outcomes that are functionally opposite to those of its nearby end organ cell partner. That is when capillary cell outer membrane complex permeability increases to inflammatory mediator interstitial space penetration, the end organ cell's outer membrane will increase resistance to the inflammatory assaults coming from the interstitial space thereby forming a barrier between them and its infrastructure. In likewise fashion, as the capillary cell revs up mitochondrial energy combustion to support active transport of immune contingents into the interstitial space, the end organ cell's mitochondria are being signaled to do the opposite; that is to shut down their energy combustion (and functional rhythms) to instead focus on sustaining its nitric oxide production.

As the interstitial space' becomes dance step sanitized, all clear signals will emanate from mesenchymal cells to the capillary cell's basement membrane that will pivot and swing the next dance step. In this manner, the capillary cell's dance step rhythm delivers a sequential and purpose defining string of *anti-inflammatory signaling and metabolic rhythms* that execute a multipurpose fulfillment to and from the blood plasma, interstitial space and its cellular allies. The pulsed reverberation of purpose specific anti-inflammatory cytokines, enzymes, hormones, proteins, free radicals and electromagnetic wavelets, and the corresponding metabolic rhythms they cause and effect, become signaled manifestations of timely dance step purpose fulfillment. Each dance step's purpose fulfillment will threshold the success of the next dance step's purpose which gets signal and metabolic messaged to and from the interstitial space and blood plasma.

Another important key to capillary cell dance step fulfillment is its *backwash effect* into the blood and lymph plasma. The pulsed rhythms it generates from the interstitial space, through the capillary cell and into the blood and lymph plasma will serve as a signaling and metabolic backdrop that will immune enhance to increase their future proficiency towards anti-inflammatory interstitial space immune funneling efforts. With each consecutive dance step rhythm multipurpose fulfillment, the prevailing signaling and metabolic momentum to and from the interstitial space will reverberate through the capillary cell a *backwash* into the plasma/lymph circulation that both immune refurbishes while establishing a backdrop towards a successful capillary cell anti-inflammatory choreographed interstitial space immune funneling effort. In this context, the dance step rhythm will seamlessly interconnect its anti-inflammatory multipurpose fulfillment with the end organ cell, interstitial space and blood/lymph plasma.

The Direct Relationship Between the Power of the Capillary and Downstream Endothelial Cell's Dance Step Rhythm and a Systemic Multi-End Organ Anti-Inflammatory Trajectory

"How Dancing Really Stops the Clock" provides a clear descriptive of how the capillary cell's dance steps defend the functional integrity of its interstitial space domain and its end organ cellular partners. The pulsed capillary and downstream endothelial cell dance step rhythms will signal and metabolically lead a mosaic of interlocking anti-inflammatory chain reactions from different immune cells and their activated cytokine rhythms that support interstitial space hygiene, transcellular restitution and end organ cell functional resolve as it conveys these outcomes to the blood/lymph plasma for future dance step success. In this conveyance, its backwashed anti-inflammatory rhythms will outcome next step purpose fulfillment as they intercept with circulating white blood cells, immunoglobulins, clotting factors, platelets and inflammatory proteins to tweak their molecular identity prior to being next dance step capillary cell choreographed and interstitial space identified. As this is occurring, anything that is chronic inflammatory circulating will become

victims to the systemic anti-inflammatory backwash. This would include infectious agents, cancer cells, rogue immunoglobulins, or activated clotting factor contingents.

Thus, the capillary-endothelial cell's dance step rhythm will not only signal loop anti-inflammatory crosstalk and purpose clarity to its interstitial space domain but will also extend this fulfillment towards a backwash that will systemically provide for further anti-inflammatory immune enhancement as backwashed cytokines, enzymes and assorted free radicals enter the blood and lymph plasma to molecularly tweak the configurations of circulating immune contingents in preparation for future interstitial space deployment. "**How Dancing Really Stops the Clock"** clarifies how the endothelial cell dance step rhythm renders anti-inflammatory salvos to and from the interstitial space that both connects and clarifies multipurpose management. This trans endothelial cell pluripotent *immune holism* will nurture a continuous flow of optimizing multi-end organ interstitial space hygiene and cellular refurbishment which in turn will allow for the expression of exceptional multi-end organ functional rhythms. The maintenance of this "anti-inflammatory *tone"* from the trans-capillary- and downstream endothelial cell's dance step processes will require:

❖ The timely (circadian) removal of vascular inflammatory free radical interstitial space impediments.

❖ A recurring signal and metabolic counterbalanced and functionally quality assured capillary and downstream endothelial cell dance step rhythm that will cater multipurpose fulfillment.

❖ A funneled interstitial space anti-inflammatory purpose precise immune contingents that are vigilant towards removing vascular inflammatory free radical impediments.

❖ The recurring dance step anti-inflammatory rhythm that ricochets, paces, stems and backwashes timely functional outcomes.

❖ Supplies an interstitial space "surveillance system" that prevents the disbursement of chronic inflammatory disease seeding.

The Importance of Capillary and Endothelial Cell Dance Step "Clock Management"

As each dance step pulses a timely anti-inflammatory algorithm, the functional outcome it procures will quality assure the purpose fulfillment of the next dance step. This is because of what the signaling and metabolic confluences purvey within the context of the dance step rhythm. That is, all the moving dance step signaled and metabolic parts will counterbalance each other as they purpose fulfill. The offsets they create becomes a quality assurance measure towards next dance step functional fulfilment. The *maintenance* of dance step counterbalance and a subsequent quality assured functional outcome can be termed dance step "**clock management** ". Without the dance step circadian clock management, its rhythm will *desynchronize* and lose optimal multipurpose fulfillment. This outcome can occur when a willful confluence of proinflammatory lifestyles increase anti-inflammatory resistance within end organ interstitial spaces. This interstitial space chronic inflammatory conversion process becomes noticeable in midlife as the capillary cell's dance step rhythm strains to find counterbalance and anti-inflammatory functional outcomes. The loss of midlife capillary and downstream endothelial cell dance step rhythms can be traced to many different issues that conspire to work against its multipurpose anti-inflammatory fulfillment but chief among them is the declining capacity of the dance step to timely remove vascular inflammatory free radical interstitial space impingements. The process becomes self-fulfilling as its critically important outer membrane complex strains to choreograph suitable funneled interstitial space immune contingents that will timely remove various and sundry inflammatory breaches.

The process of interstitial space inflammatory breach removal unravels as different levels as the capillary cell's dance step rhythm cannot provide sufficient immune funneling efficacy. As capillary cell dance steps disharmonize and mitochondrial energy combustion outstrips nitric oxide combustion, increased ROS free radical mitochondrial exhaust will crosslink and code silence nuclear chromosomal DNA. When this effect is coupled with an insolvent capillary cell mitochondrial nitric oxide combustion cycle that subsequently minimizes protein synthesis and infrastructure repair, the capillary cell's outer membrane complex becomes increasingly dysfunctional thereby causing immune funneling gaps that are delivered to the interstitial space. When this occurs in midlife, when vascular free radical interstitial space contingents are peaking, the combination emboldens the interstitial space towards a chronic inflammatory identity.

This midlife multi end organ chronic inflammatory interstitial space debacle can be countered by a rigorous reduction in vascular inflammatory free radical interstitial space impingements that virilize the decline of the capillary cell's dance steps and can be achieved primarily through simple yet comprehensive lifestyle adjustments that confront their interstitial space reduction at many different levels. This lifestyle adjustment package will enable the systemic endothelial cell network to rekindle their respective dance step tone as they will collectively find it easier to remove vascular inflammatory free radical impingements from their interstitial spaces. This midlife free radical awareness and mitigation becomes the mainstay of reversing a potentially catastrophic multi end organ chronic inflammatory onslaught of virilized disease consorts. In this manner, the end organ cell's **"aging clock"** will be directly linked to and proportional with the functional decline of the capillary cell's dance steps and the incipient increase in chronic inflammatory interstitial space rhythms they enable. In this context, the silencing of the capillary cell's nuclear chromatin to code becomes the equivalent to the cell's "aging clock" which outcomes an increasingly marginal dance step performance that is further self-fulfilled by virilizing chronic inflammatory interstitial space rhythms.

The Capillary Cell's Pivot and Swing Anti-Inflammatory *Formula*

The method by which the capillary cell's pivot and swing dance step rhythm prevents chronic interstitial space inflammation is simple yet complex at the same time as its rhythms support anti-inflammatory multipurpose execution yet are signal and metabolically vulnerable to being overridden by proinflammatory rhythms. By pulsing a counterbalanced and quality assured anti-inflammatory rhythm from its dance steps, the interstitial space sanitation that it produces will keep end organ cell functional reserve intact while at the same time negating the risk for overt chronic inflammatory interstitial space signaling crescendos. In this context, the capillary cell's second dance step phase will backwash a systemic anti-inflammatory reserve that will immune enhance interstitial space outcomes. In this manner the immune enhancing backwashed cytokines will surrogate subsequent next dance step fulfillment. At the same time, the dance step rhythm will also pulse anti-inflammatory *metabolic strings* that adjust interstitial space pH, oxygen and carbon dioxide tensions, osmolar gradients, as well as glucose, pyruvate and fatty acid distributions that will collectively chain react the interlocking rhythms of anti-inflammatory confluence towards purpose fulfillment.

In the world of a perfectly anti-inflammatory reflective capillary and downstream endothelial cell dance step rhythm, the streams it conveys are continuous and multipurpose fulfillment predictable. Simply stated, there are no anti-inflammatory dance step pause buttons. In fact, a dance step pause will usually occur from persistent proinflammatory interstitial space encumbrances which in turn will push the loss of rhythm counterbalance and loss of functional utility as nitric oxide combustion diminishes. Rather, It is the pulsed back and forth rhythm of the counterbalanced capillary cell dance steps that produces a powerful multipurposed anti-inflammatory procurement whose rhythm and functional outcomes maintain its vigor. The dance step reverberation will posture an anti-inflammatory immune defensive mechanic that foreshadows interstitial space hygiene as it supports functional utility of the end organ cell within its domain as it simultaneously resists proinflammatory beachheads. When this occurs, the resolve of the capillary and downstream endothelial cell's dance step rhythm will *forestall the aging clock.*

Chapter One

The Signaling and Metabolic Vulnerability of the End Organ Cell's Interstitial Space

The Foundation for a Chronic Inflammatory Expression within an End Organ Cell's Interstitial Space: The Persistent Engagement within the Space of Vascular Inflammatory Free Radical Impingements

The persistent penetration of vascular inflammatory free radical displays within end organ interstitial spaces (Figures one and eleven, appendix) becomes a quintessential mechanic that lends to increasing capillary and downstream endothelial dance step rhythm vulnerability [4,5,6,7,14]. Their capacity to "***pester and fester***" on various interstitial space transmembrane surfaces or cellular infrastructure will eventually harm the capacity of the capillary cell's outer membrane complex to levy a precision choreographed dispersal of immune arsenal into the interstitial space that is capable of eliminating them. In other words, the more they pester and fester, the greater the likelihood that it will not only continue but will get worse before it gets better. In this chronic inflammatory compromising interstitial space context, the capillary cell becomes increasingly incapable of manifesting dance step precision as its infrastructure and outer membrane complex fails to remain fully operational. The breakdown of its infrastructure will allow purpose neutral immune contingents access to the interstitial space that do more harm than good in so far as removing vascular inflammatory free radicals.

This revolving door of chronic inflammatory interstitial space signaling and metabolic disruption not only robs the capillary cell's outer membranes from doing their anti-inflammatory job, but at the same time produces condescending anti-inflammatory signals that further transgresses what remains of the dance step rhythm. In this setting consecutive dance steps do not support the anti-inflammatory rhythms of the previous step but instead become rhythm disconnected and functionally absorbed into an increasingly virile chronic inflammatory interstitial space signaling and metabolic amalgam. Each dance step becomes less anti-inflammatory functionally viable as it loses supportive infrastructure from lack of restitution. When this occurs, the functionally jeopardized capillary cell dance steps must try to compensate for lost anti-inflammatory reserves. However, if consecutive dance steps continue to hemorrhage lack of anti-inflammatory purpose execution, the capillary cell's infrastructure will continue to become moribund and less anti-inflammatory purpose compliant. The interstitial space domain it serves will harbor an increasing virilization of chronic inflammatory signaling and metabolic intent.

The persistence of a "locked in" chronic inflammatory interstitial space will render the capillary cell's pivot and swing dance step rhythm increasingly non pulsed of anti-inflammatory purposed execution as recurring dance step delays continue to transport anti-inflammatory noncontingent immune arsenal into the interstitial space and the capillary cell continues down the path of losing its infrastructure restitution form a disabled nitric oxide combustion cycle. Without the timely production of this gas not only is capillary cell infrastructure restitution placed on hold but the delivery of upstream oxygen to facilitate the management of end organ cell functional reserve is also diminished.

The loss of interstitial space oxygen tension is typically associated with increasing insulin resistance and acidic interstitial space conditions, all of which gain most favored status to chronic inflammatory disease consorts. As a result, continued immune funneling into the interstitial space becomes even less anti-inflammatory engaged and more purpose prone towards affiliating with chronic inflammatory outcomes (Figure 11-appendix) [4,5,6,7,10]. In this persistent anti-inflammatory interstitial space decrescendo, vascular inflammatory free radicals will thrive to become a form of chronic inflammatory fuel, incoming immune arsenal will continue to ignore diminished anti-inflammatory signaling rhythms, the interstitial space metabolic momentum will continue to favor chronic inflammatory disease consorts, and the capillary cell will become increasingly anti-inflammatory functional deficient. This persistent proinflammatory overture becomes the chronic inflammatory interstitial space formula of converting multi-end organ interstitial spaces to its own designs.

How Capillary Cells Transition Accelerated Senescence

A persistent proinflammatory interstitial space signaling bias is brought forth by persistent vascular inflammatory free radical impingements and a declining capacity of a pseudocapillarized capillary cell outer membrane complex to choreograph anti-inflammatory purpose precise immune arsenal into the interstitial space. This interstitial space penetration allows chronic inflammatory signaling and metabolic rhythms to increase as the capillary cell transitions to becomes a proinflammatory immune funneling facilitator. This capillary cell *pseudocapillarization effect* is accentuated by a diminished capillary cell mitochondrial functional reserve as their volumes, mass and size shrink within the cell in concert with the declining capillary cell dance step anti-inflammatory outcomes and increased chronic inflammatory interstitial space penetration. This will mean that within capillary cell mitochondria and even though their combustion apparatus will remain stuck in energy, their reduced functional capacity will net less energy surge to accommodate the cell's outer membrane complex requirement to actively transport certain immune contingents into the interstitial space. The lack of ATP surge becomes a further drag on the capacity of the capillary cell's outer membrane complex to execute what remains of its anti-inflammatory immune funneled choreography into an interstitial space that is already suffering from increasing chronic inflammatory signaling and metabolic rhythms.

Within this increasing chronic inflammatory interstitial space context, the functionally diminished capillary cell loses its anti-inflammatory swagger to instead become an immune funneling conduit of chronic inflammatory intent. The loss of capillary cell dance step rhythm usurps its capacity to signal and metabolic lead a multipurpose precise anti-inflammatory rhythm which in turn contracts its capacity to functionally quality assure its operations. In this situation, the dance step derived anti-inflammatory rhythms become weak and are interstitial space replaced by overriding chronic inflammatory processes that become increasingly purpose intentional as signal converted immune arsenal contingents are added into their rhythms.

With the loss of the capillary cell's dance step rhythm, the increasing functional depravity of sequential pivot and swing dance steps will have a catastrophic effect on the cell's mitochondrial combustion of nitric oxide [4,5,6,7]. The persistence of the dance step energy combustion cycle, and the system wide fallout of reduced functional counterbalance, becomes the driving force that derails multipurposed anti-inflammatory outcomes (Figures 3 and 12, appendix) [3,6,7]. The capillary cell's persistent loss of its mitochondrial nitric oxide combustion cycle eventually creates an uncompensated *functional shift* within the cell's infrastructure that will reduce the effectiveness of its dance step outcomes. As the capillary cell's nitric oxide combustion cycle gets increasingly marginalized, the volume, distribution and purposed equity of nitric oxide gas gets reduced. This in turn reduced the signaling and metabolic chain reactions that is it processes which will then minimize functional outcomes that execute specific anti-inflammatory effects. This will result in a reduction in dance step rhythm functional counterbalance as well as its capacity to quality assure the current and future dance step outcomes.

One disastrous outcome is the loss of capillary cell *infrastructure refurbishment.* As nitric oxide combustion diminishes, its infrastructure does not get renewed thereby making their functional utility increasingly ineffectual. This has particular reference to the capillary cells elaborate and functionally ultra-sophisticated outer membrane complex whose array of receptor and specialized immune arsenal transport mechanics require ongoing refreshment in order to optimally manage anti-inflammatory choreography into and out of the interstitial space. With the loss of the cell's dance step counterbalance and subsequent inability to refresh its outer membrane complex or mitochondrial infrastructure, anti-inflammatory choreographed immune funneling gaps into the interstitial space will occur that will lend themselves to becoming signal converted to increasing arrays of chronic inflammatory signaling and metabolic rhythms. The loss of interstitial space anti-inflammatory resolve creates an atmosphere that will enable purpose neutral immune contingents to signal convert to a chronic inflammatory purpose thereby lending themselves towards the identity of evolving disease consorts. This immune conversion will eventually pirate funneling content into the interstitial space that will conform towards disease expression to make the increasing debilitated capillary and downstream endothelial cell transition from an anti to proinflammatory facilitator. The interstitial space becomes a chronic inflammatory signaling and metabolic *beacon* that disease expresses through the increasingly moribund capillary cell as its end organ cell partner atrophies from being functionally ignored[13].

As a result of the progressive endothelial cell dance step slide. the upstream capillary cell will zombie into various levels of functional senescence as its infrastructure dwindles from lack of dance step coordinated restitution that is headlined by the functional loss of its outer membrane complex, mitochondrial reserve and nuclear chromosomal DNA coding capacity[6,7]. The loss of the capillary cell anti-inflammatory rhythm will also make its interstitial space allied cells (mesenchymal and end organ cells) less capable of purpose fulfillment (Figures 13,14,15, appendix). This occurs as the disabled capillary cell transmits a signaled and metabolic language through its weakened dance steps that will gap anti-inflammatory discrepancies that make the functional efficacy of its allied cellular partners less purpose capable. The diminished renderings of anti-inflammatory interstitial space signaling and metabolic transmissions, will increase ambiguity in the execution of dance step purpose. As anti-inflammatory interstitial space rhythms contract, their reduced capacity to purpose execute creates opportunities for proinflammatory rhythms to birth and expand their functional priorities.

The Direct Relationship Between an Eclipsed Capillary Cell Dance Step Rhythm, Chronic Interstitial Space Inflammation and the Disintegration of its Outer Membrane Complex Functional Utility

The loss of capillary cell dance step rhythm mojo will chain react the diminishment of its infrastructure to functionally counterbalance which becomes malevolent to the cell's capacity to perform its multipurposed anti-inflammatory rhythms. Chief among its infrastructure declines is the functional decay of its outer membrane complex [5,6,7]. It is here that the capillary cell manages its anti-inflammatory rhythms and multipurposed execution through the interstitial space endo and exocytosis of precision choreographed inflammatory mediators and their released cytokines, enzymes and free radicals. Without a durable dance step derived mitochondrial nitric oxide combustion cycle (Figure 14, appendix), the capillary cell outer membrane complex loses functional efficacy in performing its timely and elaborate anti-inflammatory immune funneling choreography. Not only does this make dance step anti-inflammatory multipurposed execution into the interstitial space less reliable, but will also increase vulnerability within the interstitial space for virilized chronic inflammatory expressions. The diminished capillary cell's nitric oxide combustion cycle robs the outer membrane complex from suitably replacing its elaborate infrastructure with the subsequent effect being the pseudocapillarization of its capacity to convey an anti-inflammatory will on interstitial I space functional outcomes. With declining numbers of functionally relevant pores, adhesion receptors, switches, and other operatives that manage permeability, the capacity to funnel purpose precise immune constituents into the interstitial space fades thereby enabling proinflammatory rhythms to fester, become authentically chronic and increasingly resistant to anti-inflammatory resistance[5,7,13].

As proinflammatory signaling and metabolic rhythms increasingly evoke their own interstitial space consciousness, they will posture an increasingly intentional interstitial space transitioning that will facilitate the propagation of disease consorts (Figure 16, appendix). As these rhythms virilize, they will signal harness the capillary cell's pseudocapillarized outer membrane complex and moribund infrastructure to funnel its own brand of immune reserves into the interstitial space that will cater to the advancement of disease expression. (Figure 16, appendix) [5,6,7].

The Unhinged Capillary Cell Dance Step Rhythm, Excessive Mitochondrial Energy Combustion and Increased Infrastructure Disability from Excessive *Reactive Oxygen Species* (ROS) Attachments

The persistence disparity of a counterbalanced capillary cell's dance step rhythm will increase its mitochondrial energy combustion cycle which in turn will escalate the production of toxic levels of ROS (reactive oxygen species-superoxide and hydrogen peroxide) exhaust. The ROS will overextend antioxidant capacity to reduce them thereby making these molecularly reactive residues capable of attaching to and effacing membrane surfaces to chain react their functional disability with relation to dance step rhythm protocols. When the attachments are to nuclear chromosomal DNA, the code silencing effect they enable diminishes protein synthesis and infrastructure refurbishment[6,7]. This makes undeterred and molecularly unstable ROS within the capillary cell a powerful membrane and DNA damaging free radical Figures 14 and 15, appendix)[7]. These attachments will produce membrane and chromosomal disfigurement that can produce long lasting effects to their functional integrity. Without a complete cellular restitution from a fully functioning DNA coding apparatus, cellular infrastructure will evolve functional gaps that will make the processing of dance step chain reactions that support anti-inflammatory rhythms less effective.

With capillary cell nuclear chromosomal DNA becoming increasingly ROS code silenced from the combination of increased ROS cross linkage and a reduced nitric oxide combustion cycle, infrastructure refurbishment will become disabled on multiple fronts (Figures 8 and 14, appendix). As the cell progressively loses functional integration from lack of infrastructure replacement, it will cascade reductions in anti-inflammatory *signaling, metabolic and functional* rhythms that will gap loss of *interconnected responses* from transmembrane switches, enzymes, free radicals and other dance step rhythm surrogates. This in turn will alter the anti-inflammatory function of organelles and capillary cell's outer membrane complex as well as its mitochondrial and cytoplasmic infrastructure [5,6,7]. It is when the elaborate capillary cell's outer membrane complex becomes a functional misfit that the cell will accelerate losses to its anti-inflammatory rhythms and dance step functional utility thereby enabling chronic inflammatory interstitial space rhythms to pick of the signaling and metabolic slack. Chief among these risks is the failure of the outer membrane complex to continue choreographing anti-inflammatory purpose precise immune arsenal into the interstitial space t timely remove inflammatory breach (Figure 16, appendix)[5,6,7].

In this insipid chronic inflammatory interstitial space setting, signaling streams, metabolic rhythms and functional outcomes will develop into *auto perpetuated cycles* that further stymie the capillary cell's anti-inflammatory dance step rhythm. In so doing, its reduced signaling and metabolic pitch places the nearby and also functionally compromised end organ cell on notice that its purpose fulfillment will diminish, as interstitial space signaling and metabolic rhythms develop sufficient impetus to favor chronic inflammatory outcomes[5,6,7]. This evolving chronic inflammatory interstitial space signaling and metabolic consortium will evoke a darker signaling and metabolic mosaic that will become functionally responsive to the manifestation of disease consorts while at the same time ignoring the functional requirements of the nearby end organ cell (Figures 16 and 17, appendix).

The Interstitial Space Chronic Inflammatory Functional *Conversion* becomes the Death Knell Towards the End Organ Cell's Functional Utility

With the build-up of chronic inflammatory purpose converted interstitial space immune arsenal, their elicited signaling and metabolic momentum will support the escalation of disease consortiums. The evolving process will simultaneously feature a decay of capillary cell infrastructure that is MOST pronounced by the loss of its elaborate *outer membrane complex's capacity* to choregraph immune arsenal into the interstitial space for purposes of removing inflammatory breach. The increasing capillary cell infrastructure decay will escalate and increasingly ineffectual anti-inflammatory dance step responses towards it multipurposed execution. It is this uncoupling of outer membrane complex anti-inflammatory multipurpose execution that creates opportunity for chronic inflammatory interstitial space signaling and metabolic expressions. With less anti-inflammatory interstitial space *signaling reserve,* the functionally compromised capillary cell outer membrane complex and infrastructure becomes prone towards becoming manipulated by an increasingly virilized chronic inflammatory interstitial space signaling hierarchy.

This means that interstitial space funneled and anti-inflammatory purpose imprecise white blood cells, immunoglobulins, platelets, complement, clotting factors and inflammatory proteins will become prone towards being chronic inflammatory signal converted from the ladder's increasing interstitial space rhythms[6,7]. In this sense purpose vulnerable interstitial space immune arsenal become *signal played* by preexisting chronic inflammatory signaling streams to operationally *hitch* their signaling rhythms with those of chronic inflammation. As they integrate into the chronic inflammatory signaling and metabolic hierarchy, they virilize intentionality which in turn will lead to the build-out of disease consorts[7].

As these chronic inflammatory immune operatives consolidate purpose, they will also signal convert other interstitial space cells, including the families of mesenchymal cells (Figure 13, appendix) [6,7]. These interstitial space conversions will define and refine the intentions of chronic inflammatory purpose as the anti-inflammatory disabled capillary cell outer membrane complex facilitates their requests (Figure 16, appendix). In this increasingly foreboding chronic inflammatory interstitial space posturing, the anti-inflammatory functionally senescent capillary cell becomes a chronic inflammatory immune funneling conduit as it surrenders its pseudocapillarized outer membrane complex to chronic inflammatory interstitial space prerogatives [6,7].

The proinflammatory signaling and metabolic *manipulation* of the interstitial space and its subsequent chronic inflammatory consolidation, will become dependent on many moving signaling targets that include their increasing mismanagement of vascular inflammatory free radical impingements[5,6,7]. The signaling and metabolic pace towards a chronic inflammatory interstitial space transitioning will be dependent upon:

- ❖ the *level* of vascular inflammatory free radical penetration and their capacity to delay their elimination
- ❖ the *rate* of capillary cell outer membrane complex, mitochondrial and nuclear chromosomal DNA chronic inflammatory capitulation that is directly correlated to a persistently compromised capillary cell pivot and swing dance step rhythm
- ❖ the *speed* in which funneled and purpose misaligned immune arsenal signal convert
- ❖ the capacity of chronic inflammatory interstitial space rhythms to *leverage and consolidate* their signaling and metabolic conduits
- ❖ the capacity of these increasingly virilized rhythms to signal *pirate* immune funneling intent from the capillary cell's disabled outer membrane complex into the interstitial space
- ❖ the furthering of chronic inflammatory rhythm enhancement from the maturation of interstitial space disease consorts
- ❖ the inherent functional and genetic culpability of the end organ cells as the chronic inflammatory interstitial space procurement will feed off the cell's functional utilities[7]

As chronic inflammatory signaling and metabolic rhythms gain interstitial space traction, they will likely posture the birthing of disease seeds (Figure 6 and 17, appendix). It is in this setting the disabled capillary cell's outer membrane complex becomes a functional prisoner to the signaling and metabolic overtures of expanding chronic inflammatory interstitial space rhythms and purpose. The chronic inflammatory build-out, regardless of the end organ involved, will have certain similarity patterns that become universal indicators. These include abundant displays of vascular inflammatory interstitial space free radicals, capillary and downstream endothelial cell infrastructure and dance step decline, increasing interstitial space displays of immune arsenal that are prone to becoming signal converted, and the subsequent birthing of disease mosaics that place a final stamp on chronic inflammatory intent. The advent of which disease consort becomes interstitial space preeminent will depend on all of the above transitions within the interstitial space. In aggregate, the evolving chronic inflammatory virilization of interstitial space intent will arbitrate specific disease consorts based on the unique metabolic, signaling and functional heritage that is conferred within each end organ cell's functional rhythms *(Figures 14-17 appendix)*[5,6,7].

The Chronic Inflammatory End Game: *Disease Clusters*

The end organ's interstitial space transitioning from a synchronized anti-inflammatory signaling, metabolic and functional machine to one that caters to disease venues will require the confluence of several chronic inflammatory initiatives that include:

➤ A vascular inflammatory free radical pester-fester effect (Figure 11, appendix).

➤ A progressively declining capillary and downstream endothelial cell dance step rhythm (Figure 12, appendix).

➤ Along with that decline, the loss of capillary (and downstream endothelial) cell functional infrastructure that is most notable with its outer membrane complex, mitochondrial reserve and inability of its nuclear chromatin to code comprehensively.

➤ The purpose consolidation of chronic inflammatory interstitial space signaling and metabolic rhythms from signal converted immune arsenal and mesenchymal cells (Figure 13, appendix).

➤ The loss of the capillary cell outer membrane complex to convey an anti-inflammatory immune context to the interstitial space (Figure 14 and 15, appendix).

➤ The funneling momentum of signal turned immune arsenal that will output increasing chronic inflammatory intentionality to the interstitial space (Figure 15, appendix).

➤ The execution of chronic inflammatory intentionality by signal pirating the capillary cell's anti-inflammatory disabled outer membrane complex (Figure 16 and 17, appendix) [6,7]

As interstitial space immune arsenal signal convert to chronic inflammatory purpose, their rhythms will necessitate the birthing of disease mosaics. Initially, their interstitial space signaling and metabolic rhythms are functionally primitive and will only cause anti-inflammatory disruption, but as they virilize and become chronic inflammatory *purpose intentional* they transition from being a disrupter to becoming a purpose facilitator. Regardless of how chronic inflammatory interstitial space rhythms are interstitial space staged, they will weaponize delays in the capillary cell's dance steps and diminish its nitric oxide combustion cycle to create a venue that is conducive to its interstitial space expression. This chronic inflammatory interstitial space transitioning to become an intentional provocateur of expressed purpose is what enables disease consorts to position access as chronic inflammatory processes gain control of the signaling and metabolic mechanics of the interstitial space. The outcome will enable the completion of the chronic inflammatory build-out of disease consorts (Figure 16, appendix)[7].

Depending on how these chronic inflammatory signaling and metabolic rhythms mature within the interstitial space will determine the speed and type of the disease mosaic. The process of conjoining chronic inflammatory interstitial space signaling and metabolic rhythms to virilize intent will likely produce a sequential display of disease consorts [5,6,7]. As chronic inflammation intensifies, the signaling and metabolic salvos it generates will create opportunities for multiple disease entity escalation. That is, end organ *scarring, coagulopathies, thrombosis/hypoxia-ischemia, infections, cancers and autoimmune complexes* could find simultaneous refuge within the same end organ's interstitial space[4,5,6,7].

The Battle for Control of Interstitial Space Purpose

The signaling battle for what entity ultimately controls an end organ's interstitial space will depend on many integrating factors with the chief mechanic being the integrity of the capillary and downstream endothelial cell's dance step rhythm. To the extent that the pivot and swing dance steps remain anti-inflammatory purpose effective is to the extent that the interstitial space and end organ cell stay functionally joined at the hip. The job of maintaining the unique functional counterbalance between all adjoined interstitial space cells is many splendored but ultimately depends on the capillary cell and its dance step rhythm for all the moving parts to come together as a unified functional whole. This counterbalanced amalgam will allow the persistence of the capillary cell's nitric oxide combustion cycle, which becomes the rate limiting factor it's the maintenance of the dance step rhythm and anti-inflammatory multipurposed execution (Figure 5,6 appendix) [6,7].

In robust anti-inflammatory interstitial space settings, the signaling impulses that generate either the mesenchymal cell's "all hands-on deck or all clear signals" will be supported by a cascading expression of signaling streams and metabolic rhythms that comingle anti-inflammatory cause and effect [6]. Their precision to increase or decrease interstitial space immune funneling will be a signal coordinated package that is conveyed by and through the outer membranes of mesenchymal cells and how they read the interstitial space context and then convey their findings to the capillary cell's basement membrane. Depending on the message the capillary cell's basement membrane will trigger the continuous outer membrane's cAMP to increase or decrease which in turn will facilitate a permeability adjustment based on a crescendo of activated or deactivated switch operatives that will increase or decrease immune funneling into the interstitial space (Figures 6 and 7, appendix). It is the adjustment of continuous outer membrane cAMP that provides the signaling backdrop to *flip* the purpose of the capillary cell's continuous outer membrane from interstitial space immune facilitator to inhibitor [5,6,7]. As this permeability adjustment is executed transmembrane ATP, magnesium and calcium ion concentrations will increase or decrease based on the intention of the permeability flip. This circulating intracellular raw materials will in turn feedback loop with the mitochondria to swing its combustion towards energy or nitric oxide (Figure 8, appendix) [5,6,7].

The Small Particle LDL Cholesterol Effect and How it Boosts Chronic Interstitial Space Inflammation

One type of vascular inflammatory free radical has garnered significant attention within the chronic inflammatory universe, the so-called small particle LDL cholesterol [4,5,6,7, 20,26,28]. These ubiquitous molecules that are manufactured primarily in the liver actually have a place within the context of anti-inflammatory rhythms as they help facilitate clotting counterbalance. When produced within the context of anti-inflammatory interstitial space rhythms, they attach, membrane effect and then are timely degraded through the capillary cell dance step process. However, when overproduced or elimination delayed their interstitial space basement membrane attachments become a nest for a bevy of chronic inflammatory immune processes levied against them. With delays in their removal, the mesenchymal cell's "all clear signal" becomes inconsequential thereby keeping the capillary cell's dance step stuck to convey ongoing immune funneling and energy combustion.

The small size of the LDL particle couples with its lipophilic solubility characteristics to become a perfect interstitial space penetration molecular with a predilection for basement membrane attachment. Because of its unique physical characteristics, LDL cholesterol mobilization into interstitial spaces will not require energy or special transport mechanics. Once within the interstitial space, their molecular configuration is likely tweaked to further accommodate attachment to membrane surfaces with a predilection for basement membrane ligands. Depending on how intense and focused the signaling and metabolic anti-inflammatory rhythms are within the interstitial space, these basement membrane attachments will be dance step responsive towards being removed and components recycled. If not timely removed, they could pester and fester effect a chronic inflammatory effect on the endothelial cell's basement membrane that will auto perpetuates a rhythm of monocyte, macrophage and clotting factor movement towards their attachment. When this occurs, the basement membrane becomes increasingly dysfunctional as it thickens from layers of ineffective and degraded immune components. The chronic inflammatory immune response will not only delay the capillary cell's dance steps but will make next dance step purpose execution increasingly less reliable.

If the LDL particle basement membrane attachment is timely dance step *degraded and* molecular constituents *recycled, the process* should conform to *an efficient* anti-inflammatory interstitial space signaling and metabolic reset that facilitates the functional execution of the capillary and downstream endothelial cell's dance step rhythm. The LDL basement membrane attachment and subsequent dissolution will become part of an anti-inflammatory signaling and metabolic rhythm that will facilitate a robust mesenchymal "all clear" signal and timely next dance step. The signaling and metabolic execution of LDL reduction becomes part of a potent pacing rhythm of anti-inflammatory purposed fulfillment to and from the capillary cell, interstitial space and central circulation (Figure 9, appendix) [5,6,7].

Within the dance step process, the small particle LDL basement membrane attachment, reduction and molecular recycling of its basic molecular constituents becomes part of the bigger picture of dance step multipurposed execution. The processing of its basement membrane attachment and removal, the mesenchymal response to each and the subsequent chain reactions it elicits back to the capillary cell's outer membrane complex to signal an adjustment to its dance step purpose become part of a much larger dance step processing of multipurpose. This processing becomes part of the dance step rhythm that gets signal and metabolically transmitted through its infrastructure, the interstitial space, allied cells within the interstitial space, the central circulation, and other endothelium that could be near or farther away. In this manner, the nature of the dance step response gets communicated to adjacent and downstream endothelium as well as near and far end organ cells. When dance step effective, these timely and pulsed dance steps will pace, stem, ricochet and backwash *anti-inflammatory* salvos that will interconnect a dance step rhythm multipurposed fulfillment. The multipurpose execution becomes a self-sustaining reverberation of sequential dance step fulfillment as any semblance of proinflammatory rhythms are quickly snuffed out a robust anti-inflammatory resolve. In this dance step setting the recurring basement membrane LDL attachment and removal becomes part of a much larger revolving anti-inflammatory dance step rhythm. On the other hand, when small particle LDL cholesterol becomes basement membrane burdensome, it will enable malevolent signaling rhythms to manifest within the interstitial space that will contribute to the maturing of chronic inflammatory intent (Figure 9, appendix)[5,6,7].

The Expanding Chronic Inflammatory Interstitial Space Expression from Less than Effective Small Particle LDL Cholesterol Basement Membrane Removal

If small particle LDL-cholesterol cannot be timely basement membrane removed, the capillary cell dance step rhythm stalls out to sequentially lose its counterbalancing outer membrane permeability pivot and nitric oxide mitochondrial combustion cycle. The pivot and swing dance step delay puts signaling pressure on capillary and downstream endothelial cell mitochondria to persist in their energy combustion cycle (Figure 8 and 14, appendix) [5,6,7]. The subsequent diminishment of the cell's nitric oxide combustion cycle will cascade a host of transcellular imbalances that will include the loss of infrastructure refurbishment that will conspire against subsequent dance step purpose execution. The functional disparity between capillary and downstream endothelial cell mitochondrial combustion cycles becomes part of a much larger signaling thread of miscalculations and lost counterbalance which will portend poorly towards subsequent dance step purpose fulfillment. Anti-inflammatory interstitial space purpose execution will become increasingly haphazard as functional rhythms gap communication mistakes which will only make interstitial space immune funneling less anti-inflammatory effective [7]. As chronic inflammatory interstitial space processes transition intentional outcomes, anti-inflammatory functional rhythms diminish and disease venues become an increasingly viable alternative to the decay of the end organ cell.

The inability to *timely reduce and molecularly recycle* small particle LDL cholesterol from the capillary and downstream endothelial cell's basement membrane will *transition, scale and unify* significant proinflammatory signaling and metabolic momentum to eventually qualify the expression of disease consorts [5,6,7,12]. As the capillary cell's infrastructure self-destructs, a progressive chronic inflammatory signaling and metabolic malfeasance will interstitial space escalate that will transition and reorganize the its outcomes. As this transitioning process unfolds, the progression of proinflammatory interstitial space signaling and metabolic rhythms will chain react their own brand of purposes intention, as immune, mesenchymal and end organ cells conform to their signaling hierarchy. Within the construct9oe of the LDL particle, downstream endothelium this will mature basement membrane fatty streaks, thickening and obstructive plaque that will cause upstream interstitial spaces sufficient oxygen deficits to preclude various disease consorts as the capillary cell dance steps unravel and cede their disabled outer membrane complex to rhythm chronic inflammatory interstitial space intentions[20,26,31].

The chronic inflammatory interstitial space signaling and metabolic transitioning will always involve the conversion of funneled immune remnants into the interstitial space towards their purposes. Signal turned white blood cells, immunoglobulins, platelets, other blood plasma constituents and mesenchymal cells will respond by eliciting proinflammatory signaling rhythms that ignite a chronic inflammatory purposed fulfillment. The process will escalate further cascading small particle LDL cholesterol-basement membrane malfeasance as incoming immune arsenal accelerate a collision course with the expanding expressions of basement membrane thickening and obstructive plaque development [4,5,6,20]. As the maturation of the chronic inflammatory interstitial space process unfolds, it will begat further marginalization of anti-inflammatory rhythms as increasing numbers of disenfranchised immune arsenal participate in the chronic inflammatory response.

The Persistence of the Capillary-Endothelial Cell *Mitochondrial Energy Combustion Cycle* becomes a Chronic Inflammatory Signaling and Metabolic Hinge

When the capillary cell's dance step rhythm deconstructs, its increasingly unbalanced circadian rhythms will contrive a counterproductive signaling, metabolic and functional interstitial space disclosure that will limit the resolve of anti-inflammatory multipurposed execution. This fundamental change in signaling nomenclature will bias increases in chronic inflammatory interstitial space intentionality that will virilize the expression of their outcomes (figure 15, appendix) [5,6,7]. The elicited chronic inflammatory signaling and metabolic interstitial space chain reactions will bias a persistent capillary cell mitochondrial energy combustion as the energy required to push additional interstitial space immune funneling becomes relentless[6,7]. As this unbalanced capillary cell combustion rendering persists, nitric oxide combustion diminishes as does all of its counterbalancing functional attributes.

With capillary cell dance step slippage, the cell will sacrifice functional mojo to where it can no longer pace anti-inflammatory purpose fulfillment as the mediocrity of its dance steps begin contributing to chronic inflammatory interstitial space chain reactions. As the dance step rhythm decommissions anti-inflammatory purpose, the signaling and metabolic rhythms it produces will procure a chronic inflammatory tone. This will make the capillary and downstream endothelial cell increasingly more reactive and conciliatory to chronic inflammatory interstitial space rhythms[6,7]. When these rhythms obtain a certain interstitial space pitch, the virulence of their intentions will self-fulfill disease consorts [6,7].

When the capillary cell switches sides, their disabled outer membrane complex and mitochondria become complicit to chronic inflammatory intent. Not only does capillary cell mitochondrial energy combustion enable the active transport of immune arsenal that will cater to chronic inflammatory outcomes, but similar byproducts will also occur with downstream endothelium. When this occurs, trans endothelial cell interstitial spaces will require the capillary cell's infrastructure to cater to their requests for specific types of immune arsenal that will tether to their functional outcomes. The persistent capillary and downstream endothelial cell dance step slide will enable a diminished anti-inflammatory interstitial space *consciousness* whose diminished presence becomes the signaling and metabolic calling card for the expression of darker chronic inflammatory interstitial space intentions[7].

The Anti-Inflammatory Expression of a Counterbalanced Capillary Cell Mitochondrial ROS/RNS Combustion Exhaust

When capillary cells lose signaling and metabolic counterbalance, the subsequent disturbances in dance step rhythm will bias a prolonged mitochondrial energy combustion cycle which in turn will generate excessive **ROS (reactive oxygen species) combustion exhaust** (Figure 9, appendix) [5,6,7]. Under an optimal signaling, metabolic and functional dance step hierarchy, energy combustion and its ROS exhaust products, will be *time limited by the outcome success of the dance step* and will be turned off by signaled and metabolic feedback loops that will bias the initiation of the next dance step that will include the mitochondrial nitric oxide combustion cycle. In this dance step setting, the cause and effect of mitochondrial ROS exhaust becomes part of a *self-limited continuum of purpose execution,* as it participates *in the* t anti-inflammatory dance step effort to convey a specific signaling purpose on attached membrane surfaces. Within the dance step context, as they membrane attach to become an anti-inflammatory signaling agent, their attachment lifespan is short lived as antioxidants will degrade them with the residuals becoming metabolic signaling agents for the next pivot and swing dance step and nitric oxide combustion. In this counterbalanced rhythm both ROS and RNS, generated by both types of mitochondrial combustion, will afford additive anti-inflammatory benefit to their respective dance steps. Their metabolic degradation will also be supportive towards the signaling of the next dance step. In this scenario, its mitochondrial exhaust attachment and degradation cycles become viable functional addendums of the fluxing dance step rhythm and multipurposed anti-inflammatory outcome. In this context, the recycled ROS and RNS contingents become akin to *anti-inflammatory free radicals* that are *additive* to their respective dance step multipurposed execution.

With regards to the ROS exhaust, its production and membrane attachment within the capillary cell becomes part of the overall anti-inflammatory commitment that virilizes precision of the capillary cell's outer membrane complex to choreograph incoming interstitial space immune arsenal towards a timely degradation of a specific vascular inflammatory free radical. In this context, the ROS "membrane attachment" will switch regulate the luminal continuous outer membrane's infrastructure to express specific displays of adhesion receptors that will facilitate an immune funneling into the interstitial space that will target the rem oval of an invading vascular inflammatory free radical. When the dance step purpose fulfills elimination of the free radical, the signaling momentum will incentivize subsequent ROS antioxidant degradation with its reduced elements (water, carbon dioxide) becoming part of a metabolic rhythm that signaling facilitates the next dance step. In this capillary cell counterbalanced dance step format, all the moving signaling and chemical displays of each dance step, that even include mitochondrial exhaust products, will integrate into the dance step functional outcomes with their respective molecular reduction becoming a signaling agent that incentivizes the induction of the next dance step and rhythm continuity. In this dance step signaling reach to the interstitial space, ROS and RNS become valuable adjuncts that will facilitate the clarity of interstitial space anti-inflammatory outcomes and the subsequent mesenchymal cell's "all hands-on deck or all clear" signaling reverberations (Figure 9, appendix). In this manner, both ROS and RNS displays become *pegged* dance step lock and key anti-inflammatory fixtures that potentiate dance step multipurpose fulfillment (Figure 9 and 10, appendix)[7,22,23].

When the capillary cell's dance step rhythm becomes misaligned, mitochondrial ROS exhaust will accumulate, form concentrations gradients within the cytoplasm, and attach to membranes and other infrastructure that become malevolent to anti-inflammatory purpose fulfillment. In this proinflammatory setting, ROS will affix to inappropriate surfaces that include nuclear chromatin that *are not* prescriptive to precision to the goal of vascular inflammatory free radical removal [6,7]. The misaligned ROS attachments will instead silence or will chain react a membrane or DNA signaling discourse that will under or overexpress intentions that will facilitate the outer membrane complex to make mistakes towards interstitial space immune funneling. These misguided funneling outcomes will foster a breakdown in vascular inflammatory free radical removal, further aggravate the loss of dance step counterbalance, and will incentivize an interstitial space proclivity towards proinflammatory signaling momentum.

The over expression of capillary cell ROS will couple with the functional underperformance of a minimized RNS exhaust which will have a significant impact on the efficacy of anti-inflammatory interstitial space multipurposed outcomes (Figure 16, appendix) [7]. In this evolving chronic inflammatory context, the increasing ROS/RNS disparities and the corresponding functional rhythms they over or underperform, will produce corresponding outer membrane complex switch operatives and subsequent infrastructure maneuvering that will fall short of purpose precise anti-inflammatory interstitial space signaling, metabolic and functional prerogatives. As a result, excessive capillary cell mitochondrial ROS production becomes part of a chronic inflammatory signaling faux pax that will induce constant expressions of funneled immune arsenal that are refractory to anti-inflammatory purposes that involve the removal of vascular inflammatory interstitial space free radicals.

In addition, a sustained capillary cell mitochondrial ROS production will increase nuclear chromosomal DNA cross linkage. As DNA becomes code silenced DNA, what remains of protein synthesis for infrastructure repair or replacement becomes increasingly marginalized. The loss of transcapillary (and mesenchymal) cellular infrastructure will further marginalize the effectiveness of interstitial space anti-inflammatory execution. The persistence of these processes becomes chronic inflammatory outliers that contribute to the maturing of interstitial space disease consorts (Figure 17, appendix)[7].

Making matters worse, excessive capillary cell ROS production will bias metabolic chain reactions that promote gluconeogenesis (and subsequent insulin resistance) over glycolysis, the utilization of fatty acids over pyruvate in the mitochondrial combustion of acetyl CoA, and the shuttled push of this molecular hub to the Krebs cycle rather than to ribosomes. In addition, liposomes within the capillary cell's cytoplasm will bias lipolysis rather than lipogenesis thereby favoring shorter chained fatty acids entering the mitochondrial matrix for beta oxidation (Figures 9 and 14, appendix) [7]. All of these transcapillary metabolic perturbations will extend loss of dance step signaling and metabolic counterbalance as the rhythms they anoint become part of a chronic inflammatory amalgam that transfixes the purpose of the interstitial space to disease consorts (Figure 17, appendix) [5,6,7].

The Diminishing Functional Returns of the Capillary Cell's Mitochondrial Combustion Performance is in Direct Proportion to Increasing Discrepancies in Energy and Nitric Oxide Combustion Counterbalance

In relation to the chronic inflammatory loss of the capillary cell's dance step rhythm and progressive outer membrane complex pseudocapillarization of its infrastructure, the functional plight of nearby mitochondria becomes equally deranged as their combustion output diminishes from loss of size, mass and volumes[5,6,7]. Unique to other intracellular organelles, mitochondria have their own *rudimentary clumps* of telomere naked DNA nestled within their matrix that when at full code capacity will mRNA transfer to ribosomes instructions to synthesize roughly 29 proteins that are used to refurbish its inner membrane and cytochrome infrastructure. Within the context of the capillary cell's dance step rhythm and functional mitochondrial counterbalance, it is during a robust nitric oxide combustion cycle whereby these proteins are coded and ribosome synthesized and whereby the DNA clumps are made whole again vias the processes of *fusion and replication*. The combination of nitric oxide driven mitochondrial DNA repair and protein synthesis refurbishment of its infrastructure keeps mitochondria on track to manage the optimization of its combustion performance within the context of a counterbalanced capillary cell dance step rhythm that proportions energy and nitric oxide combustion more or less equally. The optimization of the capillary cell's diverse dance step multipurpose fulfillment requires that its mitochondria maintain a robust combustion cycling of energy and nitric oxide. To do so, requires its nitric oxide combustion cycle to stay relevant and counterbalanced to its energy production rhythms.

Within the capillary cell is funneling immune arsenal into the interstitial space to support elimination of vascular inflammatory free radicals, its mitochondrial energy combustion cycle is providing energy for their active transport while at the same time some of its matrix DNA clumps denature to become code silenced from ROS cross linkage. In dance step fashion, it is during this cycle that culling of the crosslinked DNA clumps by fission and autophagy occurs which in turn is followed by fusion and replication in the nitric oxide combustion cycle thereby restoring its capacity to code for 29 proteins. The fission/fusion and autophagy/replication format of DNA and infrastructure recycling is counterbalanced and optimized based on combustion counterbalance that manifests as an outcome of the dance step rhythm.

When capillary cell energy combustion becomes excessive, as during the processes of interstitial space chronic inflammation, the fission/ autophagy of mitochondrial DNA increases as the fusion/replication cycle diminishes thereby making the DNA clumps less code reliable for protein synthesis and its ribosomes signal silenced even to enable an attempt at protein synthesis, thereby producing a double whammy effect on mitochondrial infrastructure repair, replacement or replication. As fission and autophagy increase and fusion/replication diminishes, and with no signal to refurbish or replace ineffectual infrastructure proteins, mitochondrial mass, volumes and size will diminish and as it does, so will its capacity to perform any type of combustion. Its reduced "anti-inflammatory" performance, along with the pseudocapillarization of its outer membrane complex, becomes the chronic inflammatory interstitial space calling card to manifest increased signaling and metabolic virulence and purpose intentionality.

When capillary cell mitochondrial infrastructure denatures, an early functional compromise will involve the maintenance of its inner membrane voltage gradient and its efficacy of promoting cytochrome electron transfer. The inner membrane's capacity to prevent hydrogen ion leaking back into the matrix is what keeps its cytochrome electron transfer apparatus energy production efficient. In this pivotal area of energy production, where the inner membrane must be able to hold its voltage gradient, where lack of infrastructure inner membrane replacement proteins will enable enough hydrogen ion leaking to prevent the efficient production of energy as cytochrome electron transfer weakens. The loss of inner membrane protein replacement will be caused from a reduced capacity of matrix chromatin to code for the maximum number of protein replacements as well as the reduced stimulus to push ribosomes to actually facilitate protein synthesis. Not only dies increased inner membrane hydrogen leaking occurs to poison the efficiency of electron transfer through the cytochromes, but the membrane becomes less effective in its capacity to regulate fluid, electrolyte, mineral and energy diffusions to and from the inter membrane space and matrix making all of its combustion grid less effective[6,7]. The decline of the mitochondrial inner membrane voltage gradient will further marginalize the efficiency of dance step pulse execution as each mitochondrial combustion cycle becomes increasingly uneven and less performance capable. In the setting of chronic interstitial space inflammation, the capillary cell's mitochondrial combustion cycles become energy redundant and production inefficient which will enable even further declines in its capacity to combustion perform,[6,7].

In the Setting of a Conforming *Anti-inflammatory* Capillary Cell Dance Step Rhythm, its Mitochondrial Fusion and Replication *Nitric Oxide Combustion Cycle* will Counterbalance its *Energy Combustion* Fission and Autophagy Cycle

When chronic inflammation invades the interstitial space, capillary cell mitochondrial fission and autophagy dominate its infrastructure landscape due to a prominent and excessive energy combustion push[6,7,25]. The denaturing of mitochondrial infrastructure will limit the entirety of its functional capacity to execute appropriate combustion responses or to process other outcomes associated with the combustion rhythms. Within capillary cell mitochondria, the persistence of energy combustion pushes increased fission and autophagy of its DNA and infrastructure which in turn diminishes the capacity of either energy or nitric oxide combustion cycle to perform making dance step outcomes less anti-inflammatory reliable.

Within the functionally counterbalanced capillary cell dance step rhythm, mitochondrial fission and autophagy become critically important culling processes that enable its DNA and infrastructure to stay purpose comprehensive as long as its nitric oxide combustion can muster enough functional impetus to fuse and replicate what was culled from fission and autophagy. Without a counterbalancing dance step rhythm, fission and autophagy will dominate fusion and replication thereby contracting mitochondrial functional performance. The maturation of chronic inflammatory interstitial space signaling and metabolic algorithms will eventually make the capillary cell's mitochondria a less reliable dance step partner to the also functionally compromised outer membrane complex (Figure 16, appendix)[7].

Wen mitochondrial combustion becomes less robust and dance step responsive, interstitial space anti-inflammatory rhythms becomes less purpose fulfilled and more apt to be chronic inflammatory coopted. Implied within this increasing chronic inflammatory interstitial space formulation are concomitant metabolic machinations that tie into the signaling reverberations which involve reduced oxygen tensions, increasing acid base imbalances, osmolality disparities and increasing insulin resistance (Figure 16 and17, appendix).

In summary, smaller, fewer and less combustion capable capillary cell mitochondria will foment the following chain reactions:

> Will reduce combustion output to where anti-inflammatory dance step outcomes cannot be signal and metabolic purpose clarified.
> Will reduce the capacity of the mitochondrial combustion apparatus to respond to shifting capillary cell outer membrane complex permeability feedback loops.
> Will relinquish its capacity to maintain its inner membrane voltage gradient which will cascade hydrogen ion leaking into the matrix and push numerous deficiencies in the diffusion and facilitated diffusion of minerals, electrolyte sand energy transport through it.
> Will reduce all production tied to either energy or nitric oxide production including the synthesis of heme, antioxidants and mitochondrial matrix infrastructure proteins[7].

The loss of energy and nitric oxide combustion counterbalance will also secondarily facilitate the loss of "anti-inflammatory consciousness" within the interstitial space while providing signaling rhythms that fortify chronic inflammatory utilization of the functionally moribund capillary cell outer membrane complex. The reduction of capillary cell mitochondrial reserve become part of the chronic inflammatory interstitial space expression that will transition both its virulence and intentionality [6,7] (Figures, 13, 15, 16,16, appendix). The sustained downdraft of anti-inflammatory interstitial space rhythms has many moving parts but chief among them is the degree in which capillary cell mitochondria have become functionally vulnerable. The preponderance of a puny and less combustion responsive capillary cell mitochondria reserve becomes one of several cascading proinflammatory mediators that will cause foreclosure of the capillary cell's dance step rhythm. As their mitochondria become increasingly combustion inept, the interstitial space feedback loop signaling and metabolic outcomes will favor chronic inflammatory outcomes[6,7].

Interstitial Space Chronic Inflammatory Rhythms: *Proinflammatory Outcome Addition by Anti-Inflammatory Subtraction*

With increasing salvos if chronic inflammatory interstitial space signaling and metabolic arbitrage, anti-inflammatory crosstalk between the capillary cell's infrastructure, outer membrane complex, systemic circulation, interstitial space and its cellular allies becomes increasingly less purpose reliable (Figure 13, appendix) [3,4,5,6,7]. The basis for this interstitial space transitioning will involve the emerging momentum of several chronic inflammatory confluences that include:

> A persistent prodrome of vascular inflammatory free radical interstitial space impingements that fuels their *"pester and fester effect"*.
> The diminution of capillary cell dance step *precision mechanics.*
> A persistent deficiency of the capillary cell's *nitric oxide combustion cycle.*
> An increase in outer membrane complex *pseudocapillarization that couples with* reduced mitochondrial combustion *reserve* and code silencing of its nuclear chromatin from increased ROS cross linkage.
> The increase in funneled and potentially purpose diverted immune arsenal into the interstitial space that can be signal turned by preexisting chronic inflammatory rhythms.
> The subsequent deployment of these purpose converted immune remnants and their released cytokines to become chronic inflammatory purveyors of intent.

> ➤ The subsequent capacity to auto-perpetuate these newly contrived interstitial space rhythms into chronic inflammatory purpose intentionality (Figures 16 and 17, appendix) [6,7].

As the capillary cell's capacity to procure anti-inflammatory rhythms into the interstitial space fades, the subsequent signaling and metabolic void it produces is replaced by chronic inflammatory rhythms that when transition intentionality, begin to signal pirate immune funneling into the interstitial space through the dance step disabled capillary cell's outer membrane complex. This procurement of chronic inflammatory virilization of interstitial space intent is a natural outcome to the serial decline of the capillary cell's dance step rhythm and the subsequent diminution of replaced worn out infrastructure that ensues. When this occurs, chronic inflammatory interstitial space signaling and metabolic rhythms will be further propagated by the signal pirating effect on the capillary cell's outer membrane complex. This process of maturing an interstitial space chronic inflammatory signaling *consciousness* is contextually known as the *chronic inflammatory matrix effect* (Figure 16, appendix) [5,6,7]. As the interstitial space signaling and metabolic mechanics are remastered, their virilizing effects increase to where disease venues are propagated with this level of intentionality heretofore known as the *chronic inflammatory anti-organ effect* (figure 17, appendix). In this interstitial space chronic inflammatory progression, the anti-organ will signal lead an interstitial space purpose identity that will build-out disease consorts. When this occurs, anti-inflammatory resistance has waned such that signaling and metabolic rhythms within the interstitial space will cater to the anti-organ rather than the muted efforts of the atrophied end organ cell [5,6,7].

The Direct Functional Link Between Interstitial Space Chronic Inflammatory *Transitioning* and a Declining Capillary Cell Dance Step Rhythm

When chronic inflammatory interstitial space transitioning occurs, funneled and existential immune arsenal will signal convert to cytokine deploy proinflammatory signaling displays that will intensify chronic inflammatory outcomes. This will occur as a result of:

> ➤ Reduced capillary cell dance step anti-inflammatory processing.
> ➤ Increased capillary cell outer membrane complex pseudocapillarization.
> ➤ Reduced capillary cell mitochondrial volumes, mass and size.
> ➤ Increased nuclear chromosomal DNA-ROS cross linkage and its code silencing effect that will mute protein synthesis for infrastructure replacement.
> ➤ The reduction of functional capillary cell infrastructure quality assurance due to lack of restitution.
> ➤ The increasing selectivity of interstitial space proinflammatory signal and metabolic rhythms to pirate immune content into the interstitial space.
> ➤ The conversion of interstitial space mesenchymal cells towards serving chronic inflammatory intent
> ➤ The progressive and diminished functional reserve of the end organ cell

When this transition of the interstitial space occurs, chronic interstitial inflammation will virilize build-out its purpose identity by signal pirating specific immune content form the blood plasma that it can utilize to subsequently magnify its expression. It is at the pseudocapillarized capillary cell's outer membrane complex where the immune pirating effect is enabled. This pirating transition will require:

❖ Signal converting the functionally diminished luminal glycocalyx and adjacent continuous outer membrane complex towards chronic inflammatory purposes.

❖ Utilizing the full complement of the outer membrane complex pseudocapillarization effect including the signal mummified basement membrane and the reduced range of continuous outer membrane voltage gradients to affect the enablement of chronic inflammatory enhancing metabolic gradients within the interstitial space (aberrant pH, osmolality, glucose to fatty acid ratios, oxygen tensions).

❖ Nullifying the dance step derived precision choreography of anti-inflammatory funneled immune arsenal that would mount resistance to proinflammatory signaling and metabolic rhythms.

❖ Minimizing the anti-inflammatory gate and choreography effects of immune funneling through the gap junction orifice and channel.

❖ Reducing the precision and integrity of anti-inflammatory active transport mechanics of funneled immune arsenal through endocytic vesicles, pores or transcellular transport channels[5,6,7]

When capillary cell outer membrane complex signaling, metabolic and functional rhythms cater to chronic inflammatory intent, the interstitial space will have surrendered purpose control to an increasingly intentional anti-organ that will process a disease build-out [6,7].

The Mechanics of the Signal Hijacked Capillary Cell Outer Membrane Complex

As proinflammatory signaling rhythms begin to process an identity, they will transition the interstitial space into a chronic inflammatory signaling and metabolic *nebula* that will coalesce its *identity. The h*ow and *rate* of this transition will depend on the how ineffectual the capillary endothelial cell's dance step rhythm has become, the degree of vascular inflammatory free radical penetration within the interstitial space, the maturation of chronic inflammatory interstitial space signaling and metabolic rhythms, and the functional context of the end organ that is involved. When chronic inflammatory interstitial space signaling and metabolic rhythms have gained full access and are in full pursuit of disease consorts, the speed of the transition will depend on how much anti-inflammatory resistance can still be manifested to counter the progression (Figure 13, 16 and 17, appendix) [5,6,7]. It turns out that the functional and genetic identity of the end organ cell itself will provide an interstitial space microenvironment that will be conducive towards the expression of specific types of disease consorts. When these interstitial space rhythms are in full swing, the capillary and downstream endothelial cell dance steps have lost a substantial amount of anti-inflammatory functional resolve as their pseudocapillarized outer membrane complex will cater to the signaling rhythms of chronic inflammatory interstitial space requests.

When the capillary cell's outer membrane complex becomes a functional conduit of chronic inflammatory intent (Figure 9, appendix) its compromised receptors, switches, pores, gates, voltage gradients and transport vesicles become chronic inflammatory immune funneling tools that will process interstitial space purpose identity [6,7].

In summary, the end organ interstitial space chronic inflammatory functional conversion will become dependent upon:

> - The specific end organ cell's functional purpose and its inherent or acquired genetic risks that enable specific disease consorts to propagate.
> - How the proinflammatory cytokine streams and metabolic rhythms from signal converted immune arsenal coalesce into a chronic inflammatory identity.
> - The degree of functional compromise to the capillary cell's dance step rhythm.
> - The degree to which interstitial space metabolic rhythms have conformed to a chronic inflammatory purpose (acidic pH, osmolality pressure gradients, reduced oxygen tensions, increased insulin resistance)[7]

Chapter Two

How the Capillary Cell's Dance Steps Execute Precision Multipurpose

The Proposed *Antidote(s)* that Limit Chronic Inflammatory Interstitial Space Expression

Countering the potential for interstitial space chronic inflammatory signaling and metabolic rhythms will require a well-executed and signal communicated capillary and downstream endothelial cell dance step rhythm. The pulsed rhythm will portend a solid multipurposed *anti-inflammatory* signaling and metabolic portfolio to and from the blood plasma and interstitial space that will outcome optimal interstitial space hygiene, allied transcellular interstitial space restitution and an enduring end organ cell functional resolve. At the same time, the reverberating salvos of multipurposed anti-inflammatory rhythms will increase resistance towards the development of any chronic inflammatory interstitial space signaling or metabolic constituency that will abort disease consorts [6,7]. The consecutive dance step multipurposed fulfillment will architect substantial resistance towards chronic inflammatory interstitial space seeding (Figures 7 and 9, appendix).

Included in this recurring anti-inflammatory capillary cell dance step reboot is a pivot and swing momentum that incentivizes a durable mitochondrial nitric oxide combustion cycle. It is the self-perpetuation of this cycle that becomes critical to dampening the possible impact of proinflammatory interstitial space signaling seeds. It is the functional resolve of the capillary cell's nitric oxide combustion cycle that drives capillary and downstream endothelial cell refurbishment which in turn becomes the purveyor of its comprehensive dance step multipurposed anti-inflammatory fulfillment [5,6,7]. The infrastructure revitalization that occurs form the capillary cell's nitric oxide combustion cycle will footprint the cell's capacity for a genuine processing of anti-inflammatory functional outcomes while at the same time laying out the pulsed signaling and metabolic infrastructure that subverts chronic inflammatory interstitial space infringement [6,7]. The "in rhythm" pulsed (circadian) and reverberating capillary cell dance steps when anti-inflammatory fulfilling, will require a robust nitric oxide combustion cycle that enables:

> An optimal ingress and egress of the necessary immune funneling agents and cytokine rhythms through the capillary cell's outer membrane complex that will process multipurpose fulfillment.

> Precision anti-inflammatory communication exchanges within the interstitial space involving immune, mesenchymal, end organ and capillary cell outer membranes that process and facilitate the timing of dance step multipurposed execution.

Robert L Buckingham, MD, FACP

The Optimization of *Endo and Exocytic* Transport Processes to and from Blood Plasma and the Interstitial Space that Prepares Circulating Immune Arsenal for a Precision Anti-Inflammatory Interstitial Space Transaction.

The foundation of the capillary cell's anti-inflammatory dance step rhythm is multipurpose, interconnect purpose fulfillment of the interstitial space with its allied cells, and link the fruits of purpose fulfillment to circulating immune elements. Doing so keeps the dance step rhythm functionally precise over time as all the pieces of the immune puzzle remain purpose alert and infrastructure rejuvenated. The capillary cell dance step rhythm functional outcomes not only serve to quality assure its infrastructure restitution, but also that of its interstitial space allied cell partners as it simultaneously prepares, through its exocytic cytokine backwash, circulating immune remnants for next step purpose fulfillment.

When dance step multipurpose fulfillment is timely and counterbalanced, the rhythm stays robust thereby keeping each dance step's purpose fulfillment comprehensive. It is in the context of a *resuscitated* capillary cell dance step rhythm that preexisting and existential chronic inflammatory interstitial space signaling and metabolic rhythms can be unwound by an increasing anti-inflammatory recincarnation[6,7]. When chronic inflammatory unwinding is required, the signaling and metabolic anti-inflammatory reconversion of the interstitial space may take time and may not be able to complete a full makeover due to recalcitrant chronic inflammatory resistance. Even so, a sufficient anti-inflammatory resistance can keep the chronic inflammatory interstitial space residues at bay thereby prevent them from channeling progression (figure 17,18,19, appendix). The capacity to recover a pristine anti-inflammatory interstitial space that places chronic inflammatory rhythms in functional remission will require adjustments in many moving targets but principally the comprehensive return of the capillary cell's dance step rhythm.

The Anti-inflammatory Importance of Capillary Cell Dance Step *Counterbalance*

Anti-inflammatory execution of the capillary cell's dance step rhythm requires a recurring and comprehensive restitution of its infrastructure. In the dance step context, its mitochondrial nitric oxide combustion cycle is pivotal to this end and must stay purpose counterbalanced with the dance step's energy combustion cycle. When this occurs, the capillary cell will be able to sufficiently refurbish its infrastructure to where it can dance step rhythm multipurpose (Figure 5, appendix) [6,7]. This will bias the interstitial space away from any chronic inflammatory signaling or metabolic sway. When in a satisfactory dance step cadence, serial dance steps will execute a purpose fulfillment that will also support the signaled and metabolic foundation for execution of the next step's purpose. Capillary cell dance step counterbalance is facilitated by:

> The timely elimination of vascular inflammatory free radical interstitial space impingements.
> The recurring and buoyant return of its mitochondrial nitric oxide combustion cycle.
> The timely expression of counterbalanced anti-inflammatory expansile and inhibitory cytokines, free radicals, enzymes, and electromagnetic wavelets that cameo a timely dance step purpose fulfillment.
> The pacing of these rhythms to and from the interstitial space (ricochet effect) and blood plasma (backwash effect) to coincide with dance step multipurpose execution (Figure 7, appendix)

The dance step's multipurpose fulfillment will ultimately become dependent upon how well the capillary cell can maintain its infrastructure refurbishment which is conveyed through its mitochondrial nitric oxide combustion cycle[6,7]. This in turn becomes dependent on how timely and well executed the previous dance step purpose fulfilled optimal interstitial space hygiene which in turn requires the removal of vascular inflammatory free radical interstitial space impingements [5,6,7].

As the capillary cell's sequential dance steps restore and rhythm anti-inflammatory outcomes, each pivot and swing dance step will interconnect purpose fulfillment with its infrastructure, interstitial space domain, allied cellular partners and central circulation. These sequential dance steps will rhythm and anti-inflammatory pace – *stem, ricochet* and *backwash* (Figure 10, appendix) of **pervasive** and clearly delineated intent that is multipurpose procured through the permeability mechanics of its outer membrane complex and the pulsed mitochondrial combustion of energy and nitric oxide. The dance step's outcomes will always optimize the end organ cell's functional health and longevity while preventing the development of anti-organ interstitial space impediments.

With a counterbalanced capillary cell pivot and swing dance step rhythm, the interstitial space will remain sanitized as the end organ cell receives credible supplies of on demand oxygen and optimal nutrient to support its purposed execution. At the same time, the dance step effect will rejuvenate the infrastructures of the capillary and interstitial space allied cells while rhythming a cytokine and enzyme backwash into the systemic circulation that will hinge anti-inflammatory immune enhancement as it also chronic inflammatory disease suppresses,[6, 7].

The Anti-Inflammatory Capillary Cell Dance Step Rhythm Requires Optimal Signaling Clarity from its Nearby Interstitial Space Mesenchymal Cell Partner

When interstitial space mesenchymal cells are functionally responsive to the capillary cell's dance step rhythm, their signaled nomenclature into the interstitial space and to the capillary cell's basement membrane will clarify intent regarding the shuffling or postponing of immune remnants into the interstitial space, which in turn will push contextual precision of the next pivot and swing dance step [6,7]. The mesenchymal cell's capacity to receive and respond with purpose clarity to interstitial space signaling rhythms regarding inflammatory breach becomes critically important to the capillary cell's dance step cadence and multipurposed execution. In this interstitial space anti-inflammatory context, the mesenchymal cell provides a signaled clarity to the capillary cell's outer membrane complex to increase or decrease specific types of immune funneling to remove vascular inflammatory free radical impingements and manage interstitial space hygiene. In this manner, the *urgency, scale and sequencing* of inflammatory mediator interstitial space penetration is taken into account with their messages to the capillary cell's basement membrane. These signals will elicit variations the "all hands-on deck" response to the capillary cell's outer membrane complex to funnel-mediate specific displays of immune arsenal into the interstitial space to eliminate the inflammatory breach. When the immune response has completed the task, an equal and opposite "all clear" signaling salvo of inhibitory cytokines that is mesenchymal elicited that will turn off the capillary cell's immune funneling spigot and begin processing the purpose execution of the next dance step.

The "all clear" cytokine inhibitory signaling stream will cause the capillary cell's continuous outer membrane to turn off the utilization of cAMP the *master switch of permeability mediation*. As **CAMP** (cyclic adenosine monophosphate) levels transmembrane accumulate, it will become a facilitator of other outer membrane complex switch chain reactions that will shift the infrastructure and purpose of the cell's continuous outer membrane away from further interstitial space immune funneling. The **"all clear" signaling message** becomes part of a dance step's counterbalancing algorithm that enables an enduring, timely and purpose precise permeability pivot and mitochondrial combustion swing.

When capillary cell continuous outer membrane cAMP levels accumulate, activated switch operatives within the membrane's infrastructure will bend or twist cytoskeleton proteins to reduce exposures of luminal adhesion receptors, increase the membrane voltage gradient, narrow the width of the gap junction orifice and channel, and reduce endocytic vesicle and transcellular active transport mechanics. This *about face* realignment of outer membrane complex permeability will cause the accumulation of transmembrane *ATP and calcium ions*, which in turn will form feedback loop concentration gradients with the nearby mitochondrial inner membrane that will signal arbitrate a combustion swing to nitric oxide gas production.

The precision and purpose executed mesenchymal cell "all hands-on deck and all clear" signals become a capillary cell dance step foundational piece that spells out what is required to manage interstitial space hygiene which is operationally conveyed to the capillary cell's outer membrane complex[6,7]. When interlocked with the capillary cell's dance step rhythm, the pulsed expansionary and inhibitory immune funneling signals will functionally counterbalance and quality assure interstitial space sanitary outcomes and dance step multipurpose. .

Why is Interlocking Capillary and Downstream Endothelial Cell Dance Step Rhythm Important?

The capillary and downstream endothelial cell's dance step rhythms are purpose interconnected to coordinate similar responses to interstitial space inflammatory breach involving the removal of vascular inflammatory free radical impingements as they also service their respective end organ cell's functional requirements (Figures 9 and 20, appendix) [6,7]. That is, anti-inflammatory multipurpose fulfillment of downstream endothelium and upstream capillary cells are dance step related as their executed dance steps potentiate each other's outcomes[7].

The key to the capillary cell's dance step anti-inflammatory signaling and metabolic hierarchy and pulsed functional efficacy is similar to that of its downstream larger arterial vessel endothelial cell cousins [5,6,7,8,9,10,11]. The timely removal of vascular inflammatory free radical interstitial space impediments will key an effective execution dance step rhythm counterbalance and purpose regardless of where the endothelial or capillary cell resides within the arterial tree. Doing so keeps their vulnerable nitric oxide combustion cycles purpose execution on track and most important combustion counterbalanced with its energy combustion cycle. The anti-inflammatory language that is transmitted from this trans endothelial cell pivot and swing rhythm is universal to all vascular endothelial cells and will convey a circulating immune enhancement that will suppress chronic inflammation and disease prevent.

The capillary and downstream endothelial cell dance step reverberation will form endo and exocytic rhythms through their respective cytoplasm that optimize interstitial space hygiene and their end organ cell functional rhythms as they simultaneously dance step refurbish their infrastructure and become purveyors of circulating anti-inflammatory immune enhancements. The ladder effect becomes a potent chronic inflammatory *inhibitor* that sharpens circulating anti-inflammatory immune resolve that denies chronic inflammatory access to interstitial space signaling mechanics [5,6,7]. As the dance step rhythm generates its multipurposed execution, the procured anti-inflammatory rhythms become a welcomed insurance policy that will further resist chronic inflammatory attempts at interstitial space disease processing. In this manner, dance step execution *incentivizes auto perpetuating* anti-inflammatory feedback loops that become the signaling and metabolic framework for its rhythms to percolate effects both within the interstitial space and blood/lymph plasma[7].

The Dance Step Multipurpose *Foundation:* The Timely Pulsing of Outer Membrane Complex Permeability Adjustments

The back-and forth fluxing of capillary cell outer membrane complex permeability becomes a *rate and time-based* circadian anti-inflammatory signaling and metabolic confluence to and from the interstitial space and blood plasma that ratifies multipurpose execution. When coupled with the swinging of mitochondrial energy and nitric oxide gas combustion, the dance step rhythm produces a powerful anti-inflammatory multipurposed outcome [6,7]. In this sense the capillary cell's optimal management of its interstitial space and end organ cell functional requisites becomes akin to an elite football quarterback or basketball point guard and how they manage the tempo of the offense and the distribution of the ball to score points. To win, both quarterback and point guard require a consistent and well-coordinated effort amongst of all the players to achieve enough points to win a game. In the case of the capillary and downstream endothelial cell, optimizing interstitial space hygiene by utilizing all the Other "team players" (immune and mesenchymal cells) will I similar fashion enable a sanitized interstitial space that will incentivize a win for end organ cell functional utility.

The effectiveness of the capillary cell, and the execution of its dance steps being similar to a quarterback or point guard's execution of plays to score points, will hinge on how well its highly evolved continuous outer membrane receptor apparatus can execute precise permeability gradients to sequence-funnel specific immune forays into the interstitial space that will timely eliminate vascular inflammatory free radical impediments. This pulsed anti-inflammatory management of interstitial space hygiene will determine the functional well-being of the interstitial space and ergo the efficacy of end organ cell purpose execution[5,6,7,8,9].

The capacity for the capillary cell's outer membrane complex to optimally manage its permeability to multipurpose execute anti-inflammatory outcomes over time will require that all its infrastructure has a refurbishing mechanic that is not happenstance but part of the dance step anti-inflammatory rhythm [6,7]. This means that existentially, the dance step rhythm must provide the necessary refurbishment incentives for a resourceful outer membrane complex infrastructure makeover such that its complex signaling, metabolic and immune funneling gear remain purpose precise. Anything short of a recurring outer membrane complex refurbishment reboot will limit its capacity to dance step choreograph its anti-inflammatory responsibilities to the interstitial space or end organ cell. Said differently, the loss of outer membrane complex permeability functional precision will chain react a series of misaligned transmembrane switch and metabolic misadventures that will likely miscue interstitial space immune interstitial space funneling and subsequent efficacy in eliminating inflammatory breach thereby producing a signaling wrinkle that can be utilized by predatory proinflammatory rhythms to beachhead chronic inflammation.

In contrast, a robust dance step rhythm will provide for a purpose precise capillary cell outer membrane complex that maintains its resolve to sustain anti-inflammatory permeability fluxes that will:

> ➤ Precision clarify and execute capillary cell-interstitial space functional intent.
> ➤ Optimize and future *quality assure* the dance step rhythm's multipurposed functional resolve.
> ➤ Auto-perpetuate capillary cell infrastructure restitution.
> ➤ Keep interstitial space allied cells infrastructure functionally refurbished and on the same operational page.
> ➤ Keep interstitial space metabolic rhythms *in sync* with pulsed anti-inflammatory signaling cues.
> ➤ Clarifies its anti-inflammatory crosstalk to adjacent capillary cells and interstitial space mesenchymal cells with interconnecting gap junction connexins and interstitial space microtubules as well as signaling streams (of cytokines, enzymes, free radicals and electromagnetic wavelets) and metabolic rhythms (involving pulsed adjustments to interstitial space pH, osmolality, oxygen tensions and glucose/fatty acid differentials)[7].

How Capillary Cell Dance Step Processed Functional "Short Cuts" Reduce its Nitric Oxide Combustion Cycle to Increase Chronic Inflammatory Interstitial Space Risk

Signaling, metabolic or purpose derived dance step rhythm processing shortcuts will limit timely anti-inflammatory interstitial space outcomes which in turn impairs dance step functional counterbalance and its capacity to generate a suitable *nitric oxide combustion cycle* (Figure 14, appendix) [5,6,7]. As this cycle degenerates, infrastructure restitution becomes less than adequate which over time reduces anti-inflammatory purpose execution that further disharmonizes the dance step rhythm. The persistence of the capillary cell's mitochondrial energy combustion cycle will bias excessive production of ROS exhaust which in turn negatively impacts its nuclear chromosomal DNA via cross linkage and increased code silencing. This will make infrastructure restitution even less reliable as essential protein synthesis for infrastructure replacement is severely diminished from the combination of fewer proteins being synthesized and less time attempting to synthesize them. The compilation will translate into an increasingly signal and metabolic hostile interstitial space environment that will wedge a maladjusted dance step rhythm.

Most important, the reduction of the dance step derived nitric oxide combustion cycle will place harsh clamps on the capillary cell's outer membrane complex to remain anti-inflammatory multipurpose viable infrastructure as the refurbishment of adhesion receptors, switches, pores, vesicles and infrastructure proteins become less than ideal (Figures 14 and 15, appendix)[6,7]. Not only does anti-inflammatory precision based choreography of funneled immune arsenal into the interstitial space come under attack, but dance step pulsed metabolic rhythms run amok as osmolality gradients, pH, oxygen tensions and excessive glucose levels make the interstitial space more proinflammatory rhythm friendly. As the capillary cell outer membrane complex atrophies, it loses the capacity to transact dance step anti-inflammatory multipurpose which in turn creates an interstitial space functional milieu that fosters a chronic inflammatory signaling and metabolic interface.

Without a genuine nitric oxide combustion cycle, the capillary cell's infrastructure declines to where it will no longer bidirectionally convey a robust anti-inflammatory sentiment. The bidirectional signaling and metabolic void to and from the interstitial space and blood plasma will bias chronic inflammatory interstitial space rhythms that will eventually make the disabled capillary cell its functional conduit towards its virilized disease consorts[6,7].

It is *Not* the Capillary Cell's Energy Combustion Cycle that Determines Anti-inflammatory Interstitial Space Purpose Fulfillment but Rather Combustion Cycle Counterbalance

The management key to capillary cell anti-inflammatory dance step rhythm success is the ongoing maintenance of its infrastructure and functionally elaborate outer membrane complex which in turn requires an optimal and recurring nitric oxide combustion cycle. Infrastructure refurbishment keeps the dance step rhythm purpose robust with particular reference to the ongoing restitution of its outer membrane complex infrastructure as well as the maintenance of mitochondrial volumes, mass and size. All of these infrastructure attributes require nitric oxide combustion which is biased to diminish with increasing chronic interstitial space inflammation. When the nitric oxide combustion cycle becomes diminished, the capacity for infrastructure renewal will proportionally decline and as it does the dance step rhythm and anti-inflammatory multipurpose execution diminishes. This loss of capacity to renew infrastructure will determine the future capabilities of the capillary cell's dance steps and its ability to execute anti-inflammatory purposed rhythms[4,5,6,7].

On the other hand, when the capillary cell's mitochondrial nitric oxide combustion cycle remains fully engaged, its dance steps are likely executing powerful anti-inflammatory rhythms where outer membrane complex permeability shifts and mitochondrial combustion swings are operating at facilitating a timely multipurposed execution. Within this rhythm context, the mitochondrial combustion of energy or nitric oxide gas stays more or less counterbalanced thereby keeping all of its signaling and metabolic cascades in counterbalanced rhythms. As a counterbalanced nitric oxide combustion cycle fortifies capillary cell infrastructure refurbishment, it will confer future dance step anti-inflammatory multipurposed fulfillment as interstitial space sanitation remains optimal, which in turn provides a qualifying signal and metabolic basis for an effective end organ cell functional resolve [5,6,7].

Capillary Cell Dance Step Execution of Interstitial Space Hygiene in Turn Pushes its Nitric Oxide Combustion Cycle Which Drives Infrastructure Repair and Visa-Versa

The timely removal of vascular inflammatory interstitial space free radicals sets up a capillary cell dance step outer membrane complex permeability pivot and mitochondrial combustion swing that enables the induction of the nitric oxide combustion cycle and infrastructure refurbishment. The satisfactory fulfillment of infrastructure restitution in turn will make the next dance step's processing of precision immune funneling into the interstitial space to remove accumulated vascular inflammatory free radical inflammatory breach more likely which in turn will dance step process the return of the nitric oxide combustion cycle and additional infrastructure refurbishment and so on. In this dance step jurisprudence, the satisfactory completion of one dance step fulfillment will usher in the next dance step and will make its purpose fulfillment more likely. On the other hand, if the dance step does not purpose fulfill or is late in its fulfillment, the next dance step will eventually not be able to compensate for its tardiness or lack of fulfillment. When this happens, nitric oxide combustion diminishes and infrastructure repair does not get completed and subsequent dance step fulfillments are increasingly unsatisfactory. As interstitial space sanitation diminishes, end organ cell functional capacity will do likewise[5,6,7]. In this manner the decay of the capillary cell's dance step fortitude becomes dependent on its nitric oxide combustion cycle which in turn is vulnerable to the capacity of the previous dance step's removal of vascular inflammatory free radical interstitial space impingements. In this context the dance step anti-inflammatory resolve will decline to where chronic interstitial space inflammation will become capable of virilizing intent.

The basis for a capillary and downstream endothelial cell dance step failure is directly linked to a persistent block in its counterbalanced rhythm which in turn reduces dance step functional quality assurance as all anti-inflammatory purpose executions become maladjusted. When this occurs, chronic interstitial space inflammation will mojo control of the prevailing signaling and metabolic landscape to facilitate its own fulfillment[7]. The dance step derailment becomes chronic inflammatory self-fulfilling as the continued capillary cell functional slippage increases the likelihood that its outer membrane becomes transmitting vestiges towards chronic inflammatory intent (Figure 10, appendix) [7].

How the Capillary Cell *ROS and RNS* Mitochondrial Exhaust Become Anti-Inflammatory *Switches* or Proinflammatory Free Radicals

One of many important outcomes to the capillary cell's dance step rhythm is the pulsed production of ROS or RNS mitochondrial combustion exhaust[6,7]. When in a counterbalanced dance step rhythm both exhausts will facilitate a membrane attachment that will activate anti-inflammatory chain reactions that favor dance step execution. When this occurs, it becomes more likely that the attached exhaust products will be antioxidant degraded before they become deleterious free radicals that would otherwise antagonize the effectiveness of dance step purpose execution. In dance step rhythm their chemical denigration to water and carbon dioxide (and nitrogen in the case of RNS) become metabolic hub signals that will facilitate the onset of the next dance step. In this fashion, the *timely* production, attachment and degradation of ROS (reactive oxygen species) and RNS (reactive nitrogen species) combustion exhaust will participate in anti-inflammatory dance step purpose fulfillment *without* increasing risk for either exhaust product to initiate proinflammatory rhythms. When the dance step purpose is executed, their reduced molecular forms will become metabolic switches that for subtle readjustments in cytoplasmic and organelle osmotic and pH membrane gradients that bias the initiation of the next dance step. When the ROS combustion exhaust dance step membrane attaches, specific sets of switch operatives will be activated that will both facilitate *expansion and specificity* of blood plasma immune funneling prerogatives into the interstitial space. As this occurs and commensurate with dance step outcomes, the ROS circadian lifespan will be timely thwarted as they become antioxidant degraded with their reduced metabolic remnants forming intracellular gradients that hub signaling reversals towards the initiation of the next dance step. With the next pivot and swing dance step and activation of the nitric oxide combustion cycle, *RNS exhaust* will increase (as ROS decreases). Its increased presence within the cell will also form a concentration gradient and membrane attach to facilitate the activation of a different set of switch operatives that will enhance nitric oxide purpose execution. When the dance step purpose (cellular restitution, increased oxygen delivery to the interstitial space) is executed, the RNS is antioxidant degraded to form its own metabolic hub that will facilitate the onset of next dance step.

As the capillary cell "ages", chronic inflammation will establish a foothold within the interstitial space and will cause the dance step rhythm's counterbalance to decay which manifests as an increased energy combustion cycle, increased ROS production, underperformance of antioxidant ROS reduction, and increased attachments of ROS to anti-inflammatory misaligned membrane surfaces and nuclear chromosomal DNA surfaces. The loss of combustion and exhaust counterbalance will potentiate further capillary cell senescence as it becomes a malingering proinflammatory free radical[5,6,7].

The obvious implication with regard to aborting capillary cell senescence requires that the capillary cell maintain its dance step counterbalanced rhythm even when it loses some of its multipurposed anti-inflammatory steam. As it does, the interstitial space must be made more dance step inducible by limiting the *volume and diversity* of vascular inflammatory free radical impingements that would otherwise enter and disrupt an already less robust dance step process. In this setting, dance step pulsed and counterbalanced ROS/RNS production, can remain anti-inflammatory compliant when less pressure is placed on the capillary cell outer membrane complex to funnel immune arsenal into the interstitial space for their elimination[6,7].

How Dance Step Mechanics Slow Down Capillary Cell Nuclear Chromosomal DNA Cross Linkage and Transcellular Aging

The anti-inflammatory signaling momentum generated by the capillary cell's counterbalancing dance step rhythm will bias a *reduction* in nuclear chromosomal DNA free radical cross linkages that will also rhythm similar reductions to the DNA of its interstitial space allied cellular partners [6,7]. The basis for these reduced DNA encumbrances will involve the dance step's capacity to efficiently process the elimination of free radicals such as ROS thereby reducing their risk for risk adverse membrane or nuclear chromosomal DNA attachments. Instead, infrastructure produced or cell penetrated free radicals become an essential membrane attachment display to the processing of dance step anti-inflammatory multipurposed outcomes whereby their attachment and subsequent antioxidant degradation become interlocking cogs towards the execution of interstitial space free radical removal. In the case of RNS or the processing of free radicals during the nitric oxide combustion cycle, the optimizing of infrastructure rejuvenation will occur as increased oxygen and end organ cell functional performance escalates. In these settings, the timely membrane attachment and removal of free radicals will both enhance dance step functional rhythms and reduce risk for malignant cross linkages to nuclear chromatin thereby inhibiting potential senescence.as the cell remains fully protein synthesis capable for infrastructure replacements. This back-and forth tethering of intracellular free radical membrane attachment, their timely degradation and subsequent dance step performance becomes a quintessential anti-inflammatory and anti-aging signaling feature of the pivot and swing dance step rhythm which in turn ensures signal compensation against any proinflammatory signaling or metabolic incursions [6,7].

In this manner, the processing of mitochondrial exhaust products and other free radicals within the context of a capillary cell dance step rhythm becomes part of a functional signal and metabolic recycling effort that enhances the endurance of the dance step process. In this context, ROS/RNS and other free radical disbursements linked to the cause or effect of capillary cell anti-inflammatory dance step prerogatives, will optimize the rhythm's signaling and metabolic counterbalance as it channels outcomes to process interstitial space hygiene and end organ cell performance. Doing so increases the capillary cell's endurance to over time to optimally perform while at the same time reducing the risk for chronic interstitial space inflammatory anachronisms[5,6,7]. It can be implied that the capillary cell's capacity to protect and enhance its functional landscape from free radical cross linkage is derived from minimizing free radical malingering through the mechanics of dance step execution which places time constraints on how, what and where free radicals may malevolently attach[7]. In this manner produced or penetrated free radicals, enzymes, cytokines and even electromagnetic wavelets become signaling and metabolic cogs within the dance step rhythm that optimize its anti-inflammatory multipurposed performance. This will in turn antidote the cell from chronic inflammatory influences, and vis-a-vis, its interstitial space allies against premature senescence[5,6,7].

Robert L Buckingham, MD, FACP

The Capillary Cell Dance Step Rhythm's Anti-inflammatory Arc Triggers a Reverberating *Transcellular Restitution* as its Multipurposed Execution Creates an Interstitial Space Signaling and Metabolic Counterbalance that Incentivizes its Sanitation which Optimizes its End Organ Cell *Functional Reserve*

The capillary cell's outer membrane complex, consisting of a luminal g*lycocalyx* mesh, *continuous outer membrane* and abluminal *basement membrane*, when functioning in dance step rhythm, facilitate an endo and exocytic ebb and flow of cells, cytokines, enzymes, free radicals and electromagnetic wavelets through the capillary cell and into the interstitial space and blood plasma that sparks precise, pulsed and timely anti-inflammatory outcomes to its infrastructure as well as that of the interstitial space and allied cells within its domain. The pulsed anti-inflammatory rhythms generated by the capillary cell's outer membrane complex are feedback loop attached to the back and forth swinging of mitochondrial energy and nitric oxide combustion. This *permeability-combustion* rhythm that unites form and function is what enables a precise and immune funneled recipe into the interstitial space that counters malevolent alternatives. When interstitial space sanitation is timely processed, the signaling and metabolic rhythms it generates become purpose transactional to the next dance step.

The process of pulsing the capillary cell's outer membrane complex permeability gradients to achieve anti-inflammatory outcomes is fine-tuned in part by how the continuous outer membrane manages its luminal permeability options. The immune funneling process is further refined by the fluctuating adhesive properties of the luminal glycocalyx as it becomes sticky to specific circulating immune remnants. The arc of interstitial space immune funneling is further processed on the capillary cell's abluminal side by the "all clear or all hands-on deck" cytokine signals resonating to its basement membrane from well-placed mesenchymal cells that provide expert intelligence on the processes that are removing inflammatory breach within the interstitial space. The permeability process if further refines at the capillary cell's continuous outer membrane by the dance step fluxing of cAMP concentrations which in turn will switch chain react membrane infrastructure adjustments that align adhesion receptors, transmembrane voltage gradients, as well as the receptivity of the gap junction orifice, channel, pores, budded vesicles and transcellular transport channels to its permeability thresholds[6,7]. In aggregate, the capillary cell's continuous outer membrane, glycocalyx, basement membrane and sub membrane infrastructure collectively contribute resonating dance step input that enables the continuous expression of its anti-inflammatory outcomes (Figure 9, appendix)[7].

The interstitial space immune funneling processes will utilize a variety of transmembrane passive and actively transported mechanics that are either activated or suppressed based on the dance step processing of it anti-inflammatory multipurpose (Figure 7, appendix)[6,7]. These recurring dance step transmembrane permeability fluxes will enable:

- ✓ Capillary cell transmembrane anti-inflammatory metabolic rhythms that pulse adjustments in acid-base balance, electrolyte and mineral incursions based on dance step performance outcomes and will include both exo and endocytic rhythms through the cell's outer membrane interface utilizing the mechanics of diffusion, facilitated diffusion and active transport.
- ✓ The processing of interstitial space precise oxygen delivery that will also include nutrient displays of glucose, pyruvate, fatty acids, ketone bodies and albumen.

- ✓ The active transport of bulkier immune proteins (immunoglobulins) whose size, shape and molecular properties require energy for their interstitial space dispersal as their interstitial space mobilization often works against osmotic concentration gradients.
- ✓ The accurate and timely choreography of interstitial space funneled cytokines, enzymes, white blood cells, platelets, complement and clotting factors to mitigate the various vascular inflammatory free radical challenges (Figure 7, appendix)[7]

The pulsed dance step rhythm derived immune consortiums, when precision packaged into the interstitial space by the capillary cell's outer membrane complex, will be complementary to the dance step's timely multipurposed execution [5,6,7]. The *process* will ritualize a precise and well-coordinated effort between the capillary cell's outer membrane complex and its pulsed permeability gradients and the binary combustion efforts of nearby mitochondria [5,6,7]

The Continuous Outer Membrane's Execution of Permeability Gradients will Hinge on its Master Switch

The reverberation of pulsed capillary cell continuous outer membrane signal and metabolic chain reactions that unleash its multifaceted and purpose specific permeability weapons begin with master switch cAMP (cyclic adenosine monophosphate). Based on mesenchymal cell signals from the interstitial space, capillary cell continuous outer membrane cAMP concentrations will transmembrane flux which in turn will induce that activation or deactivation of switch chain reactions that gate and route the regulation of outer membrane complex permeability via multiple different permeability mechanics. These maneuvers will increase or decrease transmembrane voltage gradients, hide or expose luminal adhesion receptors, activate (or deactivate) luminal pores or transport vesicles and increase or decrease the width of the gap junction orifice aperture (and channel). The *cAMP effect* will cause the continuous outer membrane's protein laminated infrastructure to *bend and twist* as it processes *metabolic chain reactions* that reduce or increase its voltage gradient, expand or inhibit luminal adhesion receptor exposures and activate or deactivate its pores and vesicle transport mechanics [5,6,7]. This fluxing cAMP continuous outer membrane infrastructure makeover is parlayed by signaling loops that predicate the mobilization of calcium and magnesium ions and energy to and from nearby mitochondria that facilitate:

- ➢ the fluxing of transmembrane voltage gradients that processes adjustments in diffusion and facilitated diffusion of gases, water, electrolytes, minerals, smaller free radicals and cytokines
- ➢ incentivizes (or inactivates) the continuous outer membrane's *actin-myosin fibrils* to contract (slide) or relax, making the cell's outer membrane configuration flat or oval thereby further lending the exposure of its basement membrane surface areas to maximal interstitial space exposures of either the mesenchymal or end organ cell depending on dance step purpose
- ➢ the fibril contractility process will in turn expand or contract the width of the gap junction orifice and channel to increase or decrease immune funneling
- ➢ bias either endocytic or exocytic transcapillary mobilizations processes to (backwash) and from (ricochet) the blood plasma and interstitial space
- ➢ the exposure (or hiding) of luminal adhesion receptors and the activation/deactivation of luminal transport vesicles, pores or transcellular transport channels

The refinement of the continuous outer membrane's immune funneling processes is further buttressed by *transcapillary cell crosstalk* through gap junction channel *connexins* that are communication busy when the capillary cell is pacing and immune response to the interstitial space. These transcapillary cell communication channels when is dance step rhythm will further incentivize funneling precision of immune arsenal into the interstitial space as they facilitate vascular inflammatory free radical removal.

When capillary cells dance steps an anti-inflammatory multipurposed continuum, its outer membrane complex will dramatically flux its permeability gradients with each step purposed fulfillment. This back-and-forth display of permeability mediation not only is critical to interstitial space immune, mesenchymal and end organ cell operatives, but also in aligning circulating immune arsenal with its dance step backwash to anti-inflammatory interstitial space prerogatives[6,7](Figures 7-10, appendix). The timely, sequential and "in rhythm" shifting of the capillary cell's outer membrane complex permeability (and mitochondrial combustion) become the driving force of a successful signal and metabolically counterbalanced, quality assured and timely multipurposed anti-inflammatory fulfillment.

The Enduring Persistence of the Capillary Cell's Mitochondrial *Nitric Oxide Gas Combustion Cycle* Over Time is what Keys End Organ Cell Functional Longevity

The "in rhythm" and robust capillary cell's nitric oxide combustion cycle will induce chain reactions that facilitate a comprehensive *replacement-repair and replication (also* known as *3 R repair)* of worn-out capillary cell infrastructure. As the same the nitric oxide gas production will permeate metabolic rhythms that will pulse increases in upstream oxygen delivery that will augment the end organ cell's functional prerogatives[5,6,7]. This multipurpose of the capillary cell's nitric oxide combustion cycle is a unique *bidirectional asset,* that when timely and of sufficient *length and magnitude,* will facilitate an enduring quality to the cell's capacity to multipurpose fulfill a recurring dance step rhythm. With the robust distribution of capillary cell nitric oxide gas, activated growth factors will implore infrastructure renovations while as increased oxygen delivery to the interstitial space begs for optimizing functional performance from the nearby end organ cell.

When interstitial space immune funneling efforts are suppressed, the capillary cell's outer membrane complex requires that it undergo repair of spent adhesion receptors, pores, switches and transmembrane infrastructure. Within mitochondria nitric oxide gas production will activate *fusion and replication* of its infrastructure and DNA clumps to increase their volumes, mass and size and functional utility[5,6,7]. The nitric oxide combustion cycle's *biogenesis effect* will also play out within the capillary cell organelles and cytoplasm and will include the activation of *telomerase* to facilitate the re lengthening of the protective telomere sheath over the cell's nuclear chromosomal DNA. Within the dance step context, the nitric oxide combustion cycle becomes an *equal combustion partner and collaborator* to the very purpose different mitochondrial energy combustion cycle. It is only when these combustion cycles are dance step *counterbalanced* does the capillary cell fend an optimal operational homeostasis.

The nitric oxide combustion cycle will also induce a critically important exocytic anti-inflammatory metabolic and cytokine backwash that will reach into the systemic circulation to become a systemic *immune stimulus* that potentiates *a further extension of* anti-inflammatory benefits into the interstitial apace when the next immune funneling dance step occurs. The backwashed cytokines, enzymes and free radicals will tweak circulating immune remnants rendering them even more inducible to anti-inflammatory rhythms and amenable to next dance step removal of vascular inflammatory free radical impingements. The recurring dance step push and pull of rhythms through the capillary cell will resonate an anti-inflammatory meme that simultaneously counterbalances and quality assures an enduring multipurpose fulfillment[7].

The *Harmonizing Effect* of the Capillary Cell's Anti-Inflammatory Dance Step *Pace, Ricochet and Backwash*

The recurring adjustment of capillary cell outer membrane complex permeability and mitochondrial combustion functions as a reverberating *signal, metabolic and functional anti-inflammatory loop* of paced rhythms between the blood plasma and interstitial space. In this manner, the capillary cell dance step rhythm becomes an anti-inflammatory multipurpose *pacemaker* that signal and metabolic leads chain reactions which interstitial space *ricochet* the mechanics of purpose execution (Figure 10, appendix)[6,7]. The interstitial space ricochet effect will pulse anti-inflammatory chain reactions that facilitate execution of dance step purpose that are precision clarified by the capillary cell's outer membrane complex permeability adjustments. The interstitial space dance step ricochet effects will also include signaled and metabolic input from both mesenchymal and end organ cells. When this occurs, the dance step rhythm produces a potent anti-inflammatory signaling and metabolic confluence that outcomes a precision purposed execution.

As the capillary cell dance step rhythm pulses interstitial space anti-inflammatory chain reactions, the crosstalk it generates will pace and stem purpose distribution to its allied mesenchymal and end organ cells (Figure 9, appendix)[6,7]. The process is transcapillary *endocytic* to the interstitial space as it distributes anti-inflammatory signaling and metabolic content to the interstitial space from a variety of different and funneled immune contingents. When the dance step process has completed its interstitial space hygiene function, an equally important anti-inflammatory *exocytic* signaling rhythm will backwash through the capillary cell cytokine and enzyme rhythms into the blood plasma which in turn will "set-up" circulating immune operators to optimally perform when they are dance step called up as funneling agents into the interstitial space. In this reverberating dance step mechanic, the interstitial space signaled and metabolic ricochet and blood plasma backwash become equal anti-inflammatory partners towards the maintenance of interstitial space hygiene and end organ cell functional utility (Figure 10, appendix).

When downstream larger vessel endothelial cell dance steps are in a similar anti-inflammatory rhythm with their upstream capillary cell brethren, their rhythms will support each other's dance step prerogatives. In terms of their collective anti-inflammatory backwash effect, there will be a seamless rhythm of cytokine, hormone, enzyme and free radical communication that will restock circulating immune arsenal preparedness as they are subsequently funneled into the interstitial space for inflammatory breach removal. As such the dance step ricochet and backwash effect becomes a transcapillary cell rhythm that coordinates dance step anti-inflammatory multipurpose to their interstitial space and end organ cell with circulating blood plasma immune contingents[5,6,7]. In the distribution of these anti-inflammatory rhythms and because of the functional nature of their receptor elaborate outer membrane complex, the upstream capillary cells become the de facto pacemakers of the endothelial cell network's endo and exocytic dance step processing of multipurposed execution. When coupled with mitochondrial combustion mechanics, the capillary cell pivot and swing dance steps become the functional ring masters of pervasive anti-inflammatory rhythms into and out of their interstitial spaces and blood plasma[6,7].

Robert L Buckingham, MD, FACP

The Importance of Endothelial Cell *Fermentation*

On contrast to all end organ cells within the human organism, endothelial cells have made a powerful metabolic adaptation to its pivot and swing dance steps by limiting the amount of oxygen they utilize to manage their infrastructure maintenance. In this manner, rather than subjecting their mitochondria for this task, capillary and downstream endothelial cells will extensively utilize anaerobic *fermentation mechanics* for much of their basal energy requirements[4,5,7]. When endothelial cells utilize oxygen it will be utilized by mitochondria for the active transport of immune arsenal into the interstitial space against variable concentration gradients or for nitric oxide production. This unique capillary and downstream endothelial cell functional arrangement keeps oxygen utilization within the cell at a very low ebb meaning that 90-95% of its maintenance energy requirements is processed *anaerobically* with the remaining 5% of its energy production processed through mitochondrial combustion as part of facilitating the dance step rhythm.

When oxygen sparing is endothelial cell optimal, the vast majority of oxygen delivered to upstream capillary cells gets diffused into the interstitial space to be subsequently utilized by the oxygen dependent for end organ cell combustion apparatus. In the setting of chronic interstitial space inflammation, capillary cells still only anaerobic metabolism to produce 95% of its energy however its mitochondrial combustion apparatus is utilizing all the energy within the cell to produce energy as the dance step rhythm has lost functional counterbalance with very low nitric oxide combustion reserves[5,6,7]. The capillary cell processing of delivered oxygen is In sharp contrast to the that of the end organ cell whose infrastructure and functional rhythms are very oxygen-combustion dependent. When in an ideal dance step rhythm, the capillary and downstream endothelial cell will utilize oxygen delivery to optimize the performance of its dance step while saving the majority of oxygen delivery for the end organ cell. In the setting of chronic interstitial space inflammation both the dance step rhythm and the volume of upstream oxygen delivery is impaired making the interstitial space prone to infection and other disease consorts and the end organ cell prone to functional deficits and nitric oxide induced oncogenesis.

The Definition of Endothelial Cell *"All for One and One for All"*

When the upstream capillary cell dance step rhythm is counterbalanced, functionally quality assured and anti-inflammatory multipurposed, optimal fulfillment requires *all endothelium* to be on the same functional page. When this occurs their interconnected signaling and metabolic rhythms potentiate anti-inflammatory feedback loops that involve how upstream blood flow and oxygen delivery is managed, how circulating immune arsenal are anti-inflammatory tagged for purpose precision and how the various interstitial spaces remain sanitation solvent. When these processes are seamless the so-called pan endothelial cell "all *for one and one for all*" functional paradigm is elicited[5,6,7]. The process with synergize the anti-inflammatory reconciliation of trans endothelial cell dance step purpose execution with the upstream capillary cell acting as the functional pacemaker. The dance step reconciliation enables trans endothelial cell *endo and exocytic chain reactions* to anti-inflammatory rhythm a transcendental multipurpose that optimizes all of their interstitial space sanitation and facilitate a multi end organ functional resolve that immune calibrates chronic inflammatory and disease suppression.

However, when capillary and vis-a-vis downstream endothelial cell dance steps become chronic inflammatory disrupted, the anti-inflammatory "all for one and one for all" functional resolve will diminish. This will contrast declines in interstitial space sanitation, enable a reduction of end organ cell functional capacity and pressure the interstitial space to become a disease coordinate as funneled immune arsenal become increasingly anti-inflammatory incapable to remove inflammatory breach. In these settings, the pan endothelial cell system will convey an "all for one and one for all" chronic inflammatory message that will eventually sting interstitial spaces with disease consorts [5,6,7].

In this chronic inflammatory interstitial space setting, the pan endothelial cell "all for one-one for all" will posture disease consorts in *all end organs*. Included in this multi-end organ interstitial space chronic inflammatory decline are:

- ❖ the enhancement of vascular inflammatory free radical expression as they are no longer immune reduced
- ❖ the reversal of immune funneled purpose from anti to proinflammatory
- ❖ the increasing expression of chronic inflammatory interstitial space signaling and metabolic rhythms that are no longer anti-inflammatory mitigated
- ❖ the progressive loss of a pan endothelial cell counterbalanced anti-inflammatory dance step rhythm
- ❖ the decline of functional intimacy between the capillary and downstream endothelial cell's outer membrane complex to its interstitial space connected end organ cells outer membrane [6,7].

In these chronic inflammatory scenarios, all endothelial outer membranes will become subservient to chronic inflammatory interstitial space signaling and metabolic rhythms. When this occurs, the disabled endo and exocytic trans endothelial cell signaling rhythms will foment a chronic inflammatory lingo will be purpose transition funneled interstitial space immune cells into chronic inflammatory contingencies[7].

The Pulsed Flipping the Capillary Cell Permeability: The Shifting Anti-Inflammatory Adjustment of *Transcellular* Purpose

Within the dance step rhythm, vascular inflammatory free radical interstitial space impingements are timely recognized and removed by precision choreographed immune arsenal thereby setting up the interstitial space for the next dance step. [5,6,7]. The process will eventually repeat itself as vascular inflammatory free radicals reaccumulate within the interstitial space requiring additional immune funneling for their removal and the conversion of the capillary cell dance step to be outer membrane complex permeable to the precision choreography of these incoming interstitial space immune remnants. When these pulsed permeability adjustments are being made, there are corresponding interstitial space metabolic rhythms that are also occurring that will facilitate further clarification of the executed purposes. The pulsed and purpose executed anti-inflammatory rhythms generated by the capillary cell dance steps provide the necessary interstitial space signaling fodder for assembled mesenchymal, monocyte, lymphocyte, polymorphonuclear and platelet cells to release arrays of either *excitatory* (interleukin 1 or 6) or *inhibitory cytokines* (interleukin 10 or IL-10), enzymes, free radicals or electromagnetic wavelets depending on the timing of the completed dance step cycles.

These signaling exchanges coupled with dance step pulsed metabolic rhythms become the expression of anti-inflammatory multipurposed execution (Figure 6, appendix). It is within this dance step context that the capillary cell's outer membrane complex will increase or decrease its permeability mechanics to elicit or inhibit specific types of immune funneling into the interstitial space[5,6,7]. The height, depth and breadth of this immune funneling effort will determine the effectiveness of vascular inflammatory free radical removal. That immune response is calibrated to the fluxing of the capillary cell's outer membrane complex permeability gradient which becomes a manifestation of fluxing cAMP concentrations and the quality of previous outer membrane complex infrastructure refurbishment. This will include its capacity to flux its transmembrane voltage and diffusion gradients, correctly attach immune funneling displays via its luminal adhesion receptors, regulate the pace of immune funneling by the precise manipulation of the width of its gap junction and orifice, and to activate the correct volume of active transport mechanics through luminal vesicles, pores and transcellular transport channels.

As the capillary cell dance step rotates its outer membrane complex configuration back and forth from oval to flat, the process accentuates the inclusion or exclusion of immune interstitial space funneling as it approximates or alienates its basement membrane to that of the nearby end organ or mesenchymal cell. Within this context, the more the capillary cell remains oval, the more likely its basement membrane will become functionally intimate with the mesenchymal cells to facilitate removal of inflammatory breach.

All of the capillary cell outer membrane complex anti-inflammatory permeability nuances will be dance step facilitated by the efficacy of its functional outcomes. This will be further purpose clarified by the anti-inflammatory readiness of funneled immune remnants from the blood/lymph plasma, the precision of mesenchymal cell purpose integrative rhythms, and the capacity of the capillary cell's outer membrane complex to fulfill its permeability outcomes. The fluxing of the capillary cell's continuous outer membrane master switch cAMP concentration gradients will mediate permeability shifts through various mechanics that include:

> The management of pulsed voltage and diffusion gradients, with help from shifting calcium ion concentrations elicited from nearby mitochondria that either will adjust the continuous outer membrane voltage gradients by affecting the mechanics of membrane potassium and sodium pumps.

> The mitochondrial pumping of calcium ions to the continuous outer membrane will also increase the contractility (sliding) of attached actin-myosin fibrils which in turn adjust the outer membrane complex configuration from flat to oval which will bias an increased signaling intimacy with nearby mesenchymal cell outer membranes with a corresponding reduction in functional interaction with the end organ cell. The process reverses when calcium ions are returned to mitochondria as capillary cell outer membrane complex permeability resists further interstitial space immune funneling.

> The capillary cell "ovoid shape" will be linked to increased luminal exposures of continuous outer membrane purpose specific adhesion receptors that are readied for immune attachment with similar adjustments occurring to luminal pores, vesicles and transcellular transport channels as well as the width widening of the gap junction orifice and channel.

> The calcium ions continuous outer membrane surge is connected with the mitochondrial production of energy, which is stabilized by a magnesium attachment and readied for transport to the continuous outer membrane to facilitate the active transport of immune funneling mechanics into the interstitial space. This process reverses when outer membrane complex permeability gradients diminish immune funneling and mitochondrial nitric oxide combustion is stimulated.

> The pulsed permeability shifts of the continuous outer membrane towards immune funneling are supported by the abluminal basement membrane (and the mesenchymal cell responses) and the luminal glycocalyx (Figures 6 and 7, appendix)[6,7]

The adjustments in capillary cell outer membrane complex master switch cAMP become the facilitating influence towards outer membrane complex permeability execution as switch and gate chain reactions within the continuous outer membrane process the infrastructure mechanics of the permeability shift. The full capacity of these capillary cell permeability adjustments requires that all of its outer membrane components are fully engaged with nearby mitochondria supplying the raw materials of permeability execution.

Why Capillary Cell Dance Step Mitochondrial Combustion *Counterbalance* is Required

When capillary cell mitochondrial combustion shifts between energy and nitric oxide, entirely different sets of activated precursors, enzymes, cofactors and engagement proteins within the mitochondrial inner membrane and matrix and the capillary cell's cytoplasm will be set into motion. When the pulsing of combustion is in counterbalance with precise capillary cell dance step rhythm anti-inflammatory outcomes, the cause and effects of energy and nitric oxide combustion offset each other making their engagement of signaling and metabolic chain reactions purpose precise yet complementary to each cycle. This regularly pulsed combustion rendezvous also allow for the efficient production and subsequent utilization of antioxidants and other matrix functional rhythms (heme synthesis and reduction) that include the restitution of mitochondrial infrastructure. This process is delicately managed by the counterbalancing effects of dance step driven mitochondrial fission/fusion and autophagy/replication. The mitochondrial matrix will also utilize combustion counterbalance to surge the distribution of calcium and magnesium ions, and ATP as they facilitate the outer membrane complex fluxing of its permeability gradients.

What makes anti-inflammatory dance step rhythms challenging is that execution of each dance step may look different that the prior. This means that for execution the length or intensity of the dance step may need up or down adjustment in immune funneling requirements and subsequent energy dispersals from mitochondria. These on-the fly dance step adjustments can typically be compensated for by increased outer membrane complex and mitochondrial functional reserve, which requires that the dance steps stay functionally counterbalanced so as to enable optimal transcellular infrastructure restitution. Typically, when permeability persistently increases towards the immune funneling of interstitial space immune arsenal it should ideally be followed by an equally and more sustained next step nitric oxide combustion cycle to account for the additional repairing of infrastructure that suffered losses as a result of the sustained fission/ autophagy of the previous energy combustion cycle. In the next dance step sequence, the pivot and swing rhythm and subsequent manifestation of the energy combustion cycle may again be different than the composition of the previous step as the dance step execution reflects a different tone of outer membrane complex permeability and postured energy combustion. Each energy combustion cycle should therefore be countered with an equally proportional nitric oxide cycle combustion cycle that will keep the infrastructure functionally intact and facilitate an anti-inflammatory multipurposed and counterbalanced execution.

The capillary cell mitochondrial combustion rhythm becomes a cytoplasmic counterbalancing metabolic facilitator that feedback loop shifts in fermentation glycolysis/ gluconeogenesis and liposomal lipogenesis/ lipolysis cycles which in turn manifest as fluctuating pyruvate, glucose concentrations as well as and short and longer chained fatty acid levels. All of these machinations will feed into mitochondrial combustion cycles as dance step combustion substrates or utilized as precursors for protein synthesis. Other mitochondrial matrix functions will also be affirmed by the combustion shifts and will include the production or degradation of heme, infrastructure proteins and antioxidants (Figure 8, appendix) [6,7].

The bullets below summarize the contrasting signaling and metabolic rhythms within the capillary cell that result from the dance step derived combustion cycles:

> The production (nitric oxide cycle) and degradation (energy cycle) of heme, mitochondrial infrastructure proteins and antioxidants.
> The fission/fusion, autophagy/replication of trans capillary cell infrastructure.
> The fermenting of glucose via glycolysis (nitric oxide) or gluconeogenesis (energy).
> The mitochondrial utilization of pyruvate (nitric oxide) or fatty acids(energy) in the production of acetyl CoA.
> The shuttling of acetyl CoA to ribosomes (nitric oxide) or Krebs cycle (energy combustion).
> The shuttling of matrix hydrogen ions towards cytochromes via FAD or NAD (energy) or to nitric oxide combustion via NADP.

The utilization of liposomes to *lipolyze* fatty acids to shorter chains to be beta oxidized to acetyl CoA (energy combustion) or to *lipogenesis* as longer chains in the eventual ribosomal production of lipoproteins (nitric oxide combustion) (Figure 9, appendix) [7].

The back-and forth rhythms of the capillary cell mitochondrial combustion cycles chain react a series of interconnected and counterbalancing signal and metabolic rhythms that interloop with the cell's circadian anti-inflammatory functional purposes[5,6,7]. Depending on gathered dance step contingencies within the interstitial space, the pulsed magnitude and duration of each dance step's outer membrane complex permeability cycle will change but the pulsing of each mitochondrial combustion cycle should be of similar dance step magnitude and duration[7]. When the capillary cell's dance rhythm is fully engaged and purpose counterbalanced the stature of both its mitochondrial energy and nitric oxide combustion cycles should remain purpose counterbalanced (Figure 9, appendix).

Complementary Fuel for Capillary Cell Anti-Inflammatory Multipurposed Dance Step Execution: The Systemic Immune Stimulatory *Backwash Effect*

The pivot and swing capillary-endothelial cell dance step rhythm will signal and metabolically stream anti-inflammatory strings of pulsed and counterbalanced rhythms that execute multipurpose. A critical piece of the timely pivot and swing dance step execution comes from the *exocytic anti-inflammatory backwash* from the interstitial space through the capillary cell and into the blood plasma[7]. The *backwash effect,* which occurs during the nitric oxide combustion cycle, will pulse a *consortium* of anti-inflammatory cytokines and other immune derivatives that have been derived from the successful completion of interstitial space inflammatory breach removal. The subsequent anti-inflammatory exocytic streaming through the capillary cell in turn becomes a signaling barometer of the dance step's nitric oxide combustion cycle as well as to the health and purpose readiness of circulating immune contingents. The anti-inflammatory cytokine streaming into the blood and lymph plasma will interconnect with other anti-inflammatory backwash from elsewhere to form molecular interactions with circulating immune contingents to ready them for the next immune funneling cycle of precision purpose within end organ interstitial spaces.

The backwash effect is to equip circulating immune arsenal, by tweaking their molecular exoskeletons, to become anti-inflammatory ready for interstitial space purpose execution. As the dance step process repeats itself, the backwash effect will contribute to enhanced dance step anti-inflammatory execution as circulating immune arsenal will stay purpose aligned and will not be subject to signaling distractions within the interstitial space. The result creates a dance step process that firmly aligns with anti-inflammatory resolve as outcomes posture against the possibility of chronic inflammatory interstitial space hyperbolas[6,7]. The backwash effect molecularly prepares circulating immune arsenal for their anti-inflammatory interstitial space purposes (Figure 10, appendix)[6,7]. This will interstitial space portend:

✓ A more precise dance step and counterbalanced circadian rhythm as free radical inflammatory interstitial space impingements are efficiently removed.

✓ A timely, robust and dance step clarifying mesenchymal cell "all hands-on deck and all clear" signaling salvos.

✓ An unmitigated capacity of the capillary cell's continuous outer membrane *cAMP* to master switch to chain react an infrastructure proforma of switch operations that precisely executes outer membrane complex permeability adjustments.

✓ A similar reverberating follows-through of counterbalanced mitochondrial combustion cycles which in bridge anti-inflammatory metabolic rhythms within the cell and interstitial space.

✓ The timely completion of dance step multipurposed execution.

✓ The fusion of backwash from other interstitial space sources to fuse a continuum of circulating anti-inflammatory immune enhancing rhythms (Figure 10, appendix) [7.]

The reverberating capillary and downstream endothelial cell backwash effect creates a global blood plasma anti-inflammatory resolve that makes subsequent interstitial space immune funneling efforts in all end organs more anti-inflammatory perfunctory. The backwash effect amounts to an anti-inflammatory molecular prepping arm that enables circulating immune arsenal to gain a functional edge when funneled into an interstitial space. When the backwash is optimal it enhances the capillary cell dance step rhythm. When fully integrated into the dance steps, the systemic endothelial cell pivot and swing rhythm become the quintessential purveyor of capillary cell-interstitial space anti-inflammatory functional homeostasis, which will extend its purview to include the lengthening of multi end organ cell functional reserve and longevity (Figure 9, appendix)[5,6,7].

Chapter Three

How Chronic Inflammatory Interstitial Space Signaling Streams and Metabolic Rhythms Secede Anti-Inflammatory Signaling Control

How the Capillary Cell's Outer Membrane Complex Becomes a Purveyor of Chronic Inflammatory Interstitial Space Purpose

When capillary cell's outer membrane complex is dance step robust, the counterbalanced rhythm it generates will convey powerful anti-inflammatory interstitial space signaling and metabolic salvos that protect interstitial space sanitation and end organ cell functional resolve as it rejuvenates the infrastructure to itself and its interstitial space transcellular allies(Figures 1-5, appendix) [5,6,7]. In the scenario the mesenchymal cells emerge as the clarifying agent to the capillary cell's dance step pivot and swing direction with its perfunctory "all hands-on deck" and "all clear" cytokine stimulating and inhibitory signals to the capillary cell's basement membrane. These signaling permutations delivered to the capillary cell's basement membrane will flux master switch continuous outer membrane cAMP levels which becomes the purveyor of infrastructure switch chain reactions that preside over outer membrane complex permeability gradients. The sequential execution of dance step anti-inflammatory multipurpose becomes dependent on how signal *timely,* metabolically *counterbalanced* and functionally *quality assured* each dance step has remained which becomes dependent on the previous dance step's purpose fulfillment.

When capillary cell dance steps become delayed, its outer membrane complex will begin to lose signaling power to execute anti-inflammatory multipurpose. This occurs primarily when chronic interstitial space inflammation finds a sufficient signaling threshold within the interstitial space that prevents the capillary cells dance step rhythm from eliminating inflammatory breach. The process will place a functional drag on subsequent capillary cell pivot and swing dance steps as the rhythm loses counterbalance with a reduction in its mitochondrial nitric oxide combustion cycle and purpose execution. The anti-inflammatory fall-out that follows makes the capillary and downstream endothelial less capable of executing dance step multipurpose (Figures 11-14, appendix) [5,6,7].

The chronic inflammatory interstitial space bias will inherently favor an increasing disparity in counterbalanced capillary cell mitochondrial combustion cycles as its signaling rhythms become the driving force of capillary cell functional senescence. Without effective capillary cell outer membrane complex, mitochondrial and other organelle restitution, interstitial space immune funneling mistakes through the capillary cell will increase thereby reducing anti-inflammatory resolve. This will eventually make the interstitial space, mesenchymal and end organ cells that reside there subservient to chronic inflammatory signaling and metabolic rhythms. The capillary cell becomes the *functional conduit* to this newly direction of chronic inflammatory intent. The chronic inflammatory interstitial space divestiture will induce signaling and metabolic chain reactions that will master proinflammatory intent as anti-inflammatory rhythms dissipate. This interstitial space transitioning is associated with capillary cell outer membrane complex pseudocapillarization, diminished mitochondrial reserve and increased nuclear chromosomal DNA code silencing from ROS cross linkage (Figure 15, appendix) [6,7].

The loss of anti-inflammatory dance step rhythms will cause numerous capillary cell signaling and metabolic infrastructure imbalances that will involve metabolic intermediates, fermentation derivatives, antioxidant displays, and unbalanced ROS/RNS mitochondrial combustion outputs to name a few (Figure 15, appendix)[6,7]. At some level of transitioning, the chronic inflammatory interstitial space signaling and metabolic processes will take control of interstitial space purpose to where it marks the space for disease consorts via signal pirating immune influence through the disabled capillary cell's outer membrane complex (Figure 16, appendix) [6,7].

The Virilization of Chronic Inflammatory Interstitial Space Chain Reactions

Without a robust, counterbalanced and purpose decisive anti-inflammatory capillary and downstream endothelial cell dance step rhythm, chronic inflammatory interstitial space rhythms can eventually obtain a signaling and purpose threshold (Figure 10, appendix) [7]. It does so by signal manipulating the capillary cell's outer membrane complex as it hales purpose neutral immune remnants into the interstitial space to be purpose converted to express the intent of disease consorts. When repeated over time, it becomes a duplicitous shift in end organ interstitial space purpose as signaling and metabolic expressions increasingly favor chronic inflammatory intentions.

The maturing of these wayward interstitial space rhythms to express an anti-organ purpose becomes akin to the birth of a new type of end organ that requires its own signal and metabolic enhancements to express its growth and functional fulfillment. As these rhythms interstitial space consolidate, they will posture its own *brand* that selfishly caters its expression at the expense of the nearby end organ cell [6,7]. The rebranding of the interstitial space not only restructures its signaling and metabolic rhythms towards the expression of disease consort(s) but will at the same time subvert end organ cell influence on the interstitial space and capillary cell. As this occurs, the functionally depleted capillary cell becomes a compromised shell capable of only reactive responses to chronic inflammatory prerogatives (Figure 18, appendix)[5,6,7].

The interstitial space outcomes to this increasing chronic inflammatory signaling and metabolic hierarchy will be the expression of anti-organ outcomes (Figure 17, appendix) [7]. With proper interstitial space chronic inflammatory tone, the intentional signaling and metabolic rhythms will *facilitate, expand and organize purposes* that cater to a diversified portfolio of disease outcomes. This interstitial space anti-orgna procurement will utilize funneled and signal turned immune remnants as its purpose facilitator as their rhythms override the increasingly diminished anti-inflammatory resolve to recalibrate the purpose of a signal and metabolically vulnerable interstitial space. Chronic inflammatory outcomes involving increasing oncogenesis, the spreading of infectious agents, fibrous and amyloid scarring, functionally unhinged immunoglobulins and a hyperresponsive clotting and thrombosis portfolios will increase and often in aggregate [5,6,7].

Once the interstitial space has been purpose converted to a certain level, the capillary and its mesenchymal cell ally will become functional minions to the transition (Figure 17, appendix) [6,7]. The purpose conversion will involve in similar fashion *all endothelia* within the arterial tree from the largest to the smallest of capillary vessels[6,7].

The Chronic Inflammatory Repression of the Mesenchymal Cell's Clarity of the "All Clear" and "All Hands-on Deck" Signals

Within the context of the counterbalanced capillary cell dance step rhythm, anti-inflammatory interstitial space rhythms will multipurpose fulfill which in turn accentuate the mesenchymal cell signaling clarity for either the "all clear cytokine inhibitory" or "all hands-on deck cytokine excitatory" signal. Both signals are critical towards the expression of next dance step transitioning as their clarity will cause the capillary cell to shift its outer membrane complex permeability and mitochondrial combustion output with dance step fervor.

With the subsequent adjustment of continuous outer membrane cAMP levels, powerful switch chain reactions are elicited that recalibrate the membrane's protein and tyrosine kinase switches within its infrastructure that cascade shifts in voltage gradients, luminal pore and vesicle portability, the exposure of adhesion receptors to the glycocalyx , and the width and receptivity of the gap junction orifice and channel towards interstitial space immune funneling [5,6,7]. As capillary cell's continuous outer membrane realigns its permeability purpose, nearby mitochondria are feedback loop called upon to alter its combustion output based on the permeability shifts of the capillary cell's outer membrane complex. In this context it will release streams of calcium ions and energy into the cytoplasm to support the immune funneling process into the interstitial space to remove inflammatory breach, or in the case of the "all clear signal", switch directions and begin producing nitric oxide gas to further infrastructure restitution and increased upstream oxygen delivery. The enduring nature of the capillary cell's dance step permeability pivot and combustion swing process is linked to its capacity to timely fulfill anti-inflammatory multipurpose interstitial space outcomes.

The mitochondrial surge of either calcium ions and ATP or nitric oxide gas coincides with the capillary cell's continuous outer membrane directives that involve adjustments to its permeability gradients. These include the manipulation of its sodium and potassium "pump" and the transfiguration of the cell outer membrane morphology from flat to oval so that its basement membrane will cater to either the end organ or mesenchymal cell's outer membranes. The shift in capillary cell outer membrane complex permeability will posture a different tone depending on the end organ involved but the shift adjusts its purpose to perform more as an interstitial space barrier or facilitator of blood plasma and interstitial space exchanges as the dance step bias *endocytic rhythms* into the interstitial space during energy combustion and *exocytic rhythms* into the blood plasma with nitric oxide combustion.

Within this dance step context, the mitochondrial intermembrane space and matrix calcium and magnesium exchanges through the inner membrane are net *voltage neutral* which keeps the voltage gradient potent and will not require the expenditure of energy to maintain the gradient or unduly replenish hydrogens ions to the intermembrane space that may have leaked backed in the matrix. In this manner as calcium ions surge to the continuous outer membrane to liberalize its voltage gradient towards increased permeability, magnesium cations of the same molecular charge are transitioning back into the mitochondrial matrix to be attached to newly minted ATP to stabilize the negatively charged molecule for transport out of the mitochondrial matrix as a charge neutral cand stable complex. When interstitial space immune funneling has removed inflammatory breach, the "all clear" signal will raise continuous outer membrane c AMP which will cause the re accumulation of calcium ions and ATP along its subsurface where they will form concentration gradients to eventually reaccumulate within the mitochondrial intermembrane space. This re accumulation will form powerful feedback loops through the cytochromes that that suppress energy production while simultaneously stimulating nitric oxide combustion. When this occurs, calcium and magnesium cations will re exchange at the mitochondrial inner membrane whereby calcium ions will be either matrix stored or utilized as cofactors in other nitric oxide driven restorative operations. In this manner, calcium, magnesium, hydrogen ions and electrolytes within the inner membrane's control get to or stay where they need to facilitate dance step related processes without the need for energy to do so or without disturbing the potency of inner membrane voltage gradient.

When calcium ions reaccumulate within the mitochondrial matrix and smooth endoplasmic reticulum, nitric oxide combustion has been initiated and calcium will be used as a cofactor in various mitochondrial restitution and salvage operations involving heme and antioxidant synthesis as well as fusion and replication scenarios. When calcium reaccumulates within mitochondria, the continuous outer membrane attached *actin-myosin fibrils* will relax thereby enabling the capillary cell's outer membrane configuration to transfigure from oval to flat to become functionally contiguous with that of the end organ cell (Figure 8, appendix) [5,6,7].

When capillary cell dance steps are delayed, the capillary cell's dance step process will eventually lose its anti-inflammatory impetus and functional multipurpose as chronic interstitial space inflammatory signaling and metabolic markers increasingly mosaic a virilized intent (Figures 8 and 15, appendix)[7]. These anti-inflammatory contrarian rhythms will mute the mesenchymal cell's capacity to crescendo an "all clear" or "all hands-on deck" signal, let alone signal convert the cell signal respond to a chronic inflammatory purpose. As anti-inflammatory dance step functional reserve falters, chronic interstitial space inflammatory rhythms become self-sufficient and even self-fulfilling as they consolidate intent[7].

The Importance of Active Transport for Interstitial Space Immune Funneling

The interstitial space immune funneling processes, whereby the capillary cell's outer membrane complex utilizes vesicles, pores and transcellular transport to override osmotic and chemical gradients that preclude their transport to the interstitial space, will require energy surges directed towards the continuous outer membrane's interface in order to execute the active transport processes. The active transporting of *purpose precise* larger and bulky anti-inflammatory immune arsenal, such as immunoglobulins, albumen or inflammatory proteins, becomes increasingly more difficult when there is a systemic immune suppression and the capillary cell's outer membrane complex loses capacity to anti-inflammatory perform due to increasing pseudocapillarization of infrastructure. This will also involve nearby mitochondrial as their reduced volumes, mass and size will reduce their combustion output of ATP and release of calcium ions. For these three reasons, the active transport of immunoglobulins or inflammatory proteins into the interstitial space favors chronic inflammatory interstitial space signaling and metabolic momentum as the immune funneled molecules are prone to losing anti-inflammatory focus and becoming proinflammatory purpose converted. In addition, their timing, rate, depth and breadth of their interstitial space funneling ratios in combination with reduced ATP reserves for active transport makes the *processing* of immune contingents into the interstitial space less anti-inflammatory purpose precise and more proinflammatory purpose vulnerable. The increasing predilection for anti-inflammatory bungling of actively transported immune arsenal into the interstitial space can be further compromised by:

> ➤ An increasingly ineffectual interstitial space mesenchymal/ immune cell anti-inflammatory clarity message(s) to the capillary cell's basement membrane that spur continuous outer membrane cAMP fluctuations and subsequent infrastructure switch chain reactions that blueprint immune funneling mechanics that include active transport.
> ➤ The increasingly insufficient surges of energy from mitochondrial combustion to facilitate active transport mechanics.
> ➤ The increasing inability of the capillary cell's continuous outer membrane (because of pseudocapillarization) to execute active transport processes due to loss of functional reserve
> ➤ The decreased capacity of circulating immune arsenal to be anti-inflammatory prepared for purpose precise interstitial space execution[7].

The processes that doom the anti-inflammatory mechanics of actively transported immune arsenal into the interstitial space can break down at several levels which involve the chronic inflammatory hijacked interstitial space signaling apparatus, the loss of capillary cell infrastructure and functional reserve and the diminution of circulating immune anti-inflammatory preparation, the ladder of which occurs from an increasingly ineffectual dance step backwash effect. It is against this backdrop of across-the board anti-inflammatory decay that chronic inflammatory rhythms will cannibalize interstitial space intent [5,6,7,8,9].

The diminution of anti-inflammatory interstitial space rhythms become a direct reflection of an increasingly disabled capillary cell outer membrane complex and mitochondria whose functional rhythms become so compromised that chronic inflammatory interstitial space processes will begin to signal pirate through the capillary cell their own brand of immune arsenal into the interstitial space for the expression of disease fulfillment. In this manner, the evolving chronic inflammatory interstitial space amalgam will use the capillary cell as an *endocytic and exocytic* funneling process to and from the interstitial space and blood plasma that will resonate a mosaic of disease expressions. The backwashed cytokines and other proinflammatory streams these rhythms emitted from the interstitial space through the capillary cell and into the blood plasma will process a proinflammatory *molecular reconfiguration* of circulating immune arsenal that renders them anti-inflammatory inaccessible and *immunosuppressive* to anti-inflammatory interstitial space outcomes. The crescendo of chronic inflammatory "rhythm control" of the interstitial space allows it to use the disabled capillary cell as its own functional immune conduit to facilitate the build-out of interstitial space disease consorts (Figure 18, appendix).

Chapter Four

The Interstitial Space Signaling and Metabolic Repercussions of an Inconsistent Capillary-Endothelial Cell Dance Step Rhythm

The *Mechanics* of a Successful Anti-Inflammatory Capillary (and Downstream Endothelial) Cell Pivot and Swing Dance Step

When the capillary and downstream endothelial cell are in dance step rhythm harmony there is an *existential* communicated signaling and metabolic processing that establishes counterbalance which in turn facilitates a functional quality assurance to its diversified and multipurposed anti-inflammatory outcomes. This fulfillment gets reflected as an optimally sanitized interstitial space, a recurring and completely reconstituted endothelial and allied cell infrastructure, and an end organ cell that remains capable of functioning at full throttle (Figures 9 and 10, appendix)[7]. When downstream endothelia are signal, metabolic and functionally interlocked with their upstream capillary cell brethren, the pacing effect of the upstream capillary cell's pivot and swing dance step mechanics becomes a virilized and *circadian anti-inflammatory rhythm* of multipurposed fulfillment. The dance steps will push and pull on the endothelial cell's outer membrane complex to rhythm endo and exocytic impulses to and from the interstitial space and blood plasma that facilitate the execution of anti-inflammatory purposes while at the same time suppressing signaling rhythms that might originate from chronic inflammatory seeds. When operationally astute, vascular inflammatory free radical interstitial space impingements will be circadian DANCE STEP eliminated, mesenchymal cells remain functionally capable of eliciting both a robust "all clear" or "all hands-on deck" signaling complex and the aggregate of upstream capillary and downstream endothelial cell lineages will output signaled, metabolic and functional rhythms that foster interstitial space hygiene, transcellular restitution and end organ cell functional resolve.

As part of the circadian endocytic immune-funneling process, the capillary cell dance step will permutate a reduction in continuous outer membrane cAMP that will process its infrastructure to luminally expose specific types of adhesion receptors, that along with pore, vesicle or transcellular transport activation and the dilation of the gap junction orifice and channels width, will increase the funneling of target specific immune arsenal into the interstitial space whose purpose is to eliminate inflammatory breach. These dance step outer membrane complex permeability adjustments will always be signal looped with nearby mitochondria as they facilitate immune active transport with increases in energy combustion.

The sequential dance steps, when properly executed, will outcome the necessary signaling and metabolic tone that will lay the groundwork for a successful next dance step. of the next dance step. This dance step process becomes functionally inclusive to all the endothelial cell outer membrane complex as the effects of the continuous outer membrane to choreograph immune funneling into the interstitial space requires functional input from both the abluminal basement membrane and luminal glycocalyx. As the capillary cell outer membrane complex regulates its endo and exocytic rhythms, based on its execution of dance step anti-inflammatory multipurpose, continuous outer membrane switch chain reactions will occur that will affect permeability to include the diffusion of gases, the facilitated diffusion of electrolytes, minerals and small molecules, and the active transport of larger more difficult to mobilize molecules or cells as well. When this occurs, the continuous outer membrane will process the utilization of mitochondrial produced ATP to support the active transport of immune arsenal into the interstitial space which in turn will further advocate for anti-inflammatory purposed fulfillments (Figures 5, 7 and 9, appendix)[5,6,7].

The rhythm of the capillary cell dance steps, in conjunction with interstitial space immune and mesenchymal signaling to its basement membrane, will turn up ("all hands-on deck") or down ("all clear" the volume of continuous outer membrane protein kinase-tyrosine kinase switch operatives that in turn increase or decrease immune funneling sequences. Critically important amongst all the anti-inflammatory detail of the capillary cell's permeability pivot is how its outer membrane complex operationally maneuvers the *specific expressions of its immune funneling apparatus* in order to channel the timely removal of inflammatory breach from the interstitial space. The immune funneling process requires that the entirety of the capillary cell's outer membrane complex package an immune consortium that eliminates the vascular inflammatory free radical interstitial space compilation. In particular, it is the continuous outer membrane's elaborate array of luminal adhesion receptor exposures that define its immune funneling purpose precision, facilitate the maintenance of dance step counterbalance and help to pace the cohesiveness of dance step purposed distribution to downstream endothelium[6,7].

How the Capillary Cell Mitochondrial Inner Membrane Protects its Potent Voltage Gradient: Facilitated Diffusion of Calcium-Magnesium Exchanges

An important operational component towards dance step homeostasis is how mitochondria's inner membrane remains voltage gradient potent. It does so by preventing hydrogen ion leakage from its intermembrane space to the matrix, and keeping the dance step rhythm's multipurposed execution intact and counterbalanced so that the inner membrane's infrastructure can be continuously refurbished from a recycled and robust nitric oxide combustion cycle. In addition, facilitating the inner membrane's facilitated diffusion of exchanged calcium and magnesium cations is also an important contributing factor. [6,7]. These exchanges should occur in dance step rhythm, enhance the executed purposes of the dance steps and should not require energy as they effortlessly move in and out of the matrix following dance step derived feedback loops and concentration gradients. These mitochondrial inner membrane cation exchanges facilitate the *operational rotation* of the capillary cell's outer membrane complex permeability execution of multipurpose *without* materially impacting the inner membrane's voltage gradient. As such, when mitochondrial matrix and smooth endoplasmic reticulum calcium ions are signaled to leave from the authority of capillary cell continuous outer membrane feedback loops (which are pushing immune arsenal into the interstitial space,) the outbound flux of calcium through the mitochondrial inner membrane will be facilitated by the simultaneous inbound surge of magnesium ions (of the same molecular charge) entering the matrix to facilitate ATP molecular stabilization. As this is occurring, FADH and NADH will be delivering a surplus of hydrogen ions to the inner membrane cytochromes that will help fuel electron transfer while also supporting the maintenance of the inner membrane's voltage gradient. They will eventually be "pumped" back into the mitochondrial matrix through cytochrome V to process the synthesis of large volumes of ATP that will be used for immune active transport processes through the capillary cell's continuous outer membrane to facilitate the removal of interstitial space inflammatory breach.

In this manner, calcium, magnesium and hydrogen ions will seamlessly process through the mitochondrial inner membrane, without the use of energy, to support the dance step execution of anti-inflammatory multipurpose as they facilitate the permeability operations of the capillary cell's continuous outer membrane specifically and the outer membrane complex generally. All of this happens as the mitochondrial inner membrane does not compromise the integrity of its potent voltage gradient. The surging of calcium ions to the capillary cell's continuous outer membrane will facilitate the consolidation of permeability enhancements that allow for immune funneling expression into the interstitial space. As they interfere with the continuous outer membrane's sodium-potassium pump, the voltage gradient of this membrane decreases allowing for a more liberal interpretation of facilitated diffusion mechanics of molecules from the blood plasma to be processed into the interstitial space. In addition, the calcium ion facilitated actin-myosin fibril contraction will make the cell's outer membrane complex more oval, thereby biasing an increased pace of interstitial space immune funneling as the functional prerogatives of its abluminal basement membrane preferentially embrace mesenchymal cell messaging rather than those of the nearby end organ cell. As the anti-inflammatory interstitial space immune response executes inflammatory breach removal, capillary cell immune active transport mechanics are often called upon to process the complete reduction of vascular inflammatory free radicals. This could require the active transport immune funneling of T cells, monocytes and immunoglobulins into the interstitial space to complete the reduction processes.

When this interstitial space immune "mop op" operation is occurring, the mesenchymal cell will begin to elicit the cytokine inhibitory "all clear" signal. This message, when received by the capillary cell's basement membrane, becomes an *all-point bulletin* to the continuous outer membrane to stop processing cAMP with its transmembrane accumulation chain reacting infrastructure switch operations that reduce its permeability towards further immune funneling into the interstitial space. When this occurs, calcium ions (and ATP0 will no longer be membrane utilized, will accumulate and form concentration gradients that will lead them back to the mitochondrial inner membrane where they will signal loop a swing in combustion to nitric oxide whereby causing the next dance step to be operationally in full swing.

In summary, the capillary cell's pivot and swing dance step rhythm and its counterbalanced and quality assured anti-inflammatory signal, metabolic and functional countenance will involve:

- A pulsed transmembrane cAMP adjusted concentration gradient which in turn will chain react continuous outer membrane switch operatives that permutate its infrastructure to shift permeability prerogatives as immune funneling mechanics are increased or decreased from the activation/inactivation of luminal adhesion receptors, the gap junction complex, pores, vesicles and transport channels.
- The ebb and flow of calcium, magnesium and ATP to and from the capillary cell's mitochondrial matrix and capillary cell outer membrane complex which will hinge the execution of precision permeability immune funneling mechanics of the dance step rhythm.
- The processing of calcium ions through the mitochondrial inner membrane where they will matrix reaccumulate will in turn cause them to be not just stored but *repurposed* as cofactors in the synthesis of various proteins, heme and antioxidants within the matrix.
- In a similar fashion, exiting mitochondrial matrix magnesium ions will find a similar purpose repackaging within the cytoplasm as they also become cofactors to dance step derived purpose that is occurring during the nitric oxide combustion cycle before it is once again called upon

to stabilize newly minted ATP in the mitochondrial matrix derived from an activated energy combustion cycle.

- The pulsed movements of calcium, magnesium and hydrogen mitochondrial inner membrane exchanges become intimately dance step interactive and multipurposed based on the metrics of the dance step anti-inflammatory purpose fulfillment[6,7].

The Capillary Cell's Dance Step Counterbalanced *Metabolism* and How it Supports Anti-Inflammatory Fulfillment

With a capillary cell dance step pivot and swing, its outer membrane complex and mitochondria will collaborate rhythms that shift metabolic chain reactions within the cell that support the execution of the dance step. That is, with each dance step there will be a refresh shuffling of metabolic chain reactions that will facilitate the derived anti-inflammatory dance step outcome[7]. The capillary cell is uniquely positioned to provide the necessary leadership to these fluxing metabolic transitions due to its unique and functionally sophisticated outer membrane complex constitution. The bullets below highlight a few of the capillary cell dance step derived metabolic loops:

- The facilitation of fluxing capillary cell anaerobic fermentation from glycolysis (nitric oxide combustion) to (gluconeogenesis (energy combustion), whose counterbalancing expressions will chain react pulsed metabolic distribution of pyruvate and fatty acids that will be subsequently utilized by mitochondria for the production of acetyl CoA which in turn will be harnessed for either energy or nitric oxide combustion.
- The distribution of pyruvate or glucose from fermentation is counterbalanced by the dance step rhythm which will also signal facilitate a similar functional resolve within liposomes as they lipolyze or induce lipogenesis on fatty acid chains to prepare them for mitochondrial *beta oxidation* (and acetyl Co A production) or for *lipoprotein synthesis* in nearby ribosomes.
- When pyruvate is fermented from glycolysis it will be preferentially processed to acetyl CoA in the mitochondrial matrix and utilized for nitric oxide combustion. During energy combustion gluconeogenesis will produce glucose from pyruvate thereby reducing pyruvate concentrations within the cytoplasm. This will free up beta oxidized fatty acid reduction of longer chained carbons to become the predominant purveyor of acetyl CoA production as capillary cell mitochondrial combust energy.
- The activation of the capillary cell's mitochondrial *beta* oxidation cycle in the production of acetyl co A will favor the subsequent reduction of the molecule in the Krebs cycle whereby its reduction will generate plentiful hydrogen ions for FAD and NAD transport to inner membrane cytochromes to facilitate energy production. During the nitric oxide combustion cycle, newly minted acetyl CoA will be shuttled to mitochondrial *ribosomes* where they will engage the protein synthesis process aimed at refurbishment infrastructure proteins.
- During mitochondrial energy combustion, longer chained fatty acids will be liposomal lipolyzed to smaller fatty acid carbon chains (15 carbons or less) and fed to the mitochondrial matrix for beta oxidation. With the nitric oxide combustion cycle, liposomes will lipogenesis longer chained fatty acids to become attachment pieces for lipoprotein synthesis.
- With chronic interstitial space inflammation, this metabolic counterbalance gets disrupted to favor persistent increases in capillary cell outer membrane complex permeability gradients

to funnled immune arsenal into the interstitial space that are feedback loop linked with mitochondrial energy combustion.

- The metabolic consequences will cascade chain reactions within the capillary cell that will favor further infrastructure disintegration and loss of multipurpose anti-inflammatory efficacy. In this scenario, gluconeogenesis is persistently favored over glycolysis and mitochondrial beta oxidation and fatty acid utilization is preferred over pyruvate in the production of acetyl CoA. In addition, liposomes will lipolyze more fatty acids into mitochondria rather than facilitate lipogenesis.

- These persistent capillary cell transcellular metabolic perturbations will chain react other metabolic dysrhythmias that will ruminate through the capillary cell's outer membrane complex where they will invoke maladjusted imbalances to interstitial space pH, oncotic and hydrostatic pressure gradients, insulin resistance and oxygen tensions[7]

The Persistently Widened Capillary Cell Gap Junction Orifice and Channel: A Blatant Breach towards Anti-Inflammatory Interstitial Space Immune Funneling

With increasing chronic inflammatory interstitial space resilience, a broad spectrum of proinflammatory capillary cell signaling and metabolic rhythms will evolve that will deter the capacity of the outer membrane complex to anti-inflammatory immune choregraph. As the outer membrane complex pseudocapillarizes its adhesion receptors, pores, vesicles, and voltage gradients, the gap junction orifice and channel also lose their capacity to gate the rate and type of immune arsenal being funneled into the interstitial space [4,5,6,7]. The ladder is compounded by the outer membrane complex configured "tweener effect" whereby the capillary cell lacks the capacity to completely flatten out or become ovoid. Instead, it's configuration limps into a "tweener" which makes the gap junction orifice and channel between capillary cells incapable of effective immune pacing or gating into the interstitial space. This gap junction complex immune funneling disparity will also enable the proclivity for maladjusted metabolic rhythms within the interstitial space that curtail balanced pH, osmolar, fluid, glucose and oxygen/carbon dioxide tensions.

When the gap junction complex becomes pseudocapillarized, its infrastructure consisting of connexins, receptors and junctional proteins lose functional efficacy making them less capable of immune precision choreograph through the channel. This will cause immune funneling errors into the interstitial space that can be signal turned by preexisting chronic inflammatory signaling crescendos to add further momentum to chronic inflammatory outcomes[6,7](Figure 17, appendix).

The gap junction complex "tweener effect" will negatively impact capillary cell metabolic support to the end organ cell as outer membrane to membrane surface area contact between the cells persistently diminishesl[7] Instead the "tweener effect" will improvise:

- ➢ A persistently diminished anti-inflammatory interstitial space immune funneling rhythm that will conjure risk for their conversion to chronic inflammatory purposed alignment.
- ➢ An increasing voracity of chronic inflammatory interstitial space signaling rhythms that will disrupt the mesenchymal cell's capacity to elicit the purpose clarifying "all clear" and "all hands-on deck" signaling streams.

> ➢ A greater likelihood for chronic inflammatory interstitial space signaling rhythms to virilize intentionality and pirate intent from the capillary cell's outer membrane complex.
> ➢ The capillary cell's outer membrane complex "tweener effect" will facilitate sufficient proinflammatory momentum to where they become an active participant towards chronic inflammatory interstitial space intent and subsequent disease purpose fulfillment (Figures 13-17, appendix) [5,6,7].

The capillary cell's decline in its gap junction complex perfunctory role as anti-inflammatory immune gatekeeper and pacemaker into the interstitial space becomes a chronic inflammatory outlier that will enable its increasing intentional rhythms to virilize intent [6,7]. The chronic inflammatory interstitial space resolve will paint the end organ cell into a functional corner as it compiles rhythms that mosaic disease outcomes involving fibrous or amyloid scarring, cancer growths, infectious diseases, coagulopathies/thrombosis and increasingly virile autoimmune complexes[6,7].

The Loss of Interstitial Space Anti-Inflammatory Rhythms that Formulate a Chronic Inflammatory Precipice that will Coincide with End Organ Cell Decay

To the extent that the interstitial space loses anti-inflammatory signaling and metabolic rhythms and subsequent multipurpose fulfillment is to the extent that chronic inflammatory rhythms will have consigned their own brand of consolidated disease consorts [5,6,7]. In this interstitial space outcome, chronic inflammatory signaling and metabolic rhythms will repurpose the landscape to their own advantage. With their interstitial space consolidation, disease consorts will become the dominant signaling and metabolic influencer as their rhythms become increasingly interstitial space intentional and their backwash anti-inflammatory immune suppressive. This will make subsequent immune funneling even more responsive to chronic inflammatory interstitial space directives[5,6,7].

The key disrupter to capillary and downstream endothelial cell dance step mechanics is the inability to timely remove vascular inflammatory free radical interstitial space impediments. When this occurs, the capillary cell dance steps lose signaling and metabolic counterbalance, the cell's infrastructure its functional fortitude and the interstitial space its quality controls for sanitation management[5,6,7]. When this occurs, the interstitial space will manifest disease outcomes as the end organ cell's functional utility diminishes. The capillary cell's outer membrane complex becomes increasingly anti-inflammatory unresponsive, which enables immune contingent funneling errors into the interstitial space. Tis auto perpetuated process becomes a win-win for chronic interstitial space inflammation as it will utilize the decaying capillary cell as its purpose consolidator as it signaling rhythms to the disabled capillary cell's basement membrane become purpose intentional. Within the interstitial space mesenchymal and previously funneled helper T cells signal convert to become chronic inflammatory collaborators. When this occurs, the disabled capillary cell's outer membrane complex will have become a chronic inflammatory facilitator as it divorces itself from end organ cell functional intimacy.

The Proinflammatory "Switch Effect" of Unbalanced Capillary Cell Mitochondrial ROS/RNS Exhaust

Within the context of a counterbalanced capillary cell dance step rhythm, *ROS* (reactive oxygen species (superoxide, hydrogen peroxide)) combustion exhaust from an overly exuberant mitochondrial energy production cycle and *RNS* (reactive nitrogen species (peroxynitrite et al) exhaust from an underperforming nitric oxide combustion cycle), become unhinged *anti-inflammatory membrane switches*. With increasingly aberrant ROS membrane attachments, switch chain reactions are elicited through the membrane attachment that prodrome chronic inflammatory interstitial space prerogatives. Rather than facilitating the removal of vascular inflammatory free radical interstitial space impediments, the aberrant ROS membrane attachments, produce signaled chain reactions that do the opposite meaning they will facilitate an immune pester and fester effect towards the free radical that will increase chronic inflammatory rhythms within the interstitial space rather than reducing the free radical and setting the signaling and metabolic stage for the next dance step. With regards to the diminished functional RNS membrane attachments, their loss will further marginalize switch chain reactions that would occur during the nitric oxide combustion cycle that will further propagate transcellular restitution.

When ROS or RNS mitochondrial exhaust is produced *within the context of the capillary cell's dance step rhythm*, they will enhance the rhythms functional outcomes by processing specific-time limited transmembrane attachments that will facilitate switch chain reactions that support and even magnify the anti-inflammatory effects of dance step multipurpose. In this context, when ROS/RNS exhaust is subsequently reduced to carbon dioxide, water and in the case of RNS-nitrogen, the corresponding metabolic rhythm that it displays (with the subtle interstitial space tweaking of pH and osmolality gradients) will facilitate the signaling of the next dance step. Their membrane attachment therefore augments the anti-inflammatory functional outcome of the coinciding dance step while their antioxidant degradation becomes the metabolic stepping stone towards the next dance step[6,7]. In this manner the capillary cell's mitochondrial exhaust becomes integral to the larger anti-inflammatory dance step processing of precision multipurposed performance.

Implied in the ROS/RNS counterbalanced dance step equation is the multilayered manner in which ROS/RNS exhaust chain reacts intent. From the specific membrane attachment they procure to their timely antioxidant reduction and subsequent metabolic outcomes that ruminate within the capillary cell, their cycling rhythms becomes an integral part of the dance step process and anti-inflammatory multipurpose fulfillment[5,6,7]. This combustion exhaust cycles will utilize specific antioxidant contingencies to reduce the ROS/RNS derivatives as they too become part of the counterbalanced "switch" signaling display that is dance step parlayed. In the reverberation of counterbalanced dance step derived mitochondrial ROS/RNS exhaust, their *production, membrane attachment and antioxidant reduction* will facilitate signaling, metabolic and functional loops that both integrate and enrich the anti-inflammatory dance step processing of multipurpose fulfillment.

In the expression of dance step anti-inflammatory intent, the mitochondrial ROS/RNS production, distribution and reduction will facilitate the anti-inflammatory processing of a counterbalanced dance step outcome that creates its own anti-inflammatory momentum that makes future dance step multipurposed fulfillment more likely. Through the timely processing of both ROS and RNS, the capillary cell dance steps cycles become a genuine an enduring functional anti-inflammatory facilitator of interstitial space outcomes[7].

How the Counterbalanced Capillary Cell's Dance Step *Rhythm* Procures Functional Outcomes that are Multipurposed and Anti-inflammatory Quality Assured

The timely (*circadian*) anti-inflammatory multipurposed execution of sequential dance steps become a signaling and metabolic barometer that outcomes a quality assured processing of interstitial space intent.

This means that each dance step's anti-inflammatory execution should rhythm a *signaled and metabolic counterbalance* that facilitates the execution of a precise and timely purpose fulfillment whose outcome lays the signaling and metabolic lattice that *quality assures* or guarantees the success of the next dance step's execution. The integration of these signaled and metabolic dance step cues facilitates the coordination of diverse arrays of endothelial cell signaling and metabolic *strings* that are packaged to execute a dynamic and recurring anti-inflammatory multipurpose.

The dance step quality assurance metric not only lends itself to increased operational efficiency, but with its built-in refurbishment contingency, keeps the dance step rhythm potentially functioning into perpetuity. n this manner dance step anti-inflammatory momentum is conferred as each step signaled, metabolic and functional outcome is parlayed to spring load both future multipurposed fulfillment as it quality assures its processing. In this manner, the execution of capillary cell dance steps will confer a precise and timely anti-inflammatory execution, provide the necessary signaling and metabolic framework to begin processing the next dance step, and provisions a built-in infrastructure refurbishment proviso that quality assures future dance step multipurpose fulfillment. This will provide an interstitial space system wide system of signaled and metabolic checks and balances that will compensate for any dance step miscues while defensively posturing against proinflammatory interstitial space overtures [5,6,7].

Since each pulsed dance two-step rhythm will likely look different than the previous, due to prevailing differences in interstitial space inflammatory breach, the beat-to-beat *timing* of the capillary cell's dance step anti-inflammatory execution will vary as the *intensity and duration* of the cell's permeability pivots and combustion swings responds to variances in vascular inflammatory free radical interstitial space impediments. This beat-to beat dance step compensatory variance of rate and intensity will allow for pivot and swing compensatory maneuvering while still keeping the dance step rhythm counterbalanced and functionally quality assured. Without dance step rhythm compensatory adjustments, fluxing levels of free radical interstitial space impediments will force delays in the pivot and swing rhythm to create a dance step *dysrhythmia* and subsequent decline in functional anti-inflammatory outcomes [6,7]. If this proinflammatory interstitial space momentum persists, chronic inflammatory interstitial space signaling, metabolic and functional outcomes will inevitably occur.

The Expected Systemic Benefits of an Anti-inflammatory Counterbalanced Capillary Cell *Backwash*

When capillary and downstream endothelial cells execute dance step multipurpose, their interstitial spaces will outcome an anti-inflammatory backwash through the capillary cell and into the central circulation. These assemblages of cytokines, enzymes and free radicals will frame the next dance two-step step by metabolically preparing circulating immune arsenal via chemical reparations to their outer membranes that molecularly configure additional anti-inflammatory precision once they are retrieved back into the interstitial space. This will facilitate the framing of next dance two-step purpose execution via a systemic immune enhancement. This dance step backwash effect will keep the capillary cell dance step process anti-inflammatory virilized as it provides circulating immune contingents with a sharper edge for anti-inflammatory interstitial space execution. This added backwash benefit will inflate end organ chronic inflammatory disease prevention while elongating its longevity as it provides insurance for the endothelial cell network to stay true to its anti-inflammatory dance step roots [5,6,7].

The benefit of a reverberating anti-inflammatory capillary and downstream endothelial cell backwash would be to enhance dance step anti-inflammatory outcomes while limiting any proclivity for circulating proinflammatory molecules from gaining access to capillary cell's interstitial space. In this scenario, they would either be signal or metabolically denatured before they come into contact with the capillary cell's outer membrane complex, or if they did get interstitial space access as a vascular inflammatory free radical, would be timely identified and reduced[7]. The end game of the virilized capillary cell anti-inflammatory backwash is to facilitate a functionally youthful capillary and downstream endothelial cell's dance step rhythm that will translate into a free radical cleansed interstitial space and a functionally robust end organ cell that is primed to stay that way for the long haul.

Chaper Five

How and Why Capillary Cell's Outer Membrane Complex Pseudocapillarize and Mitochondria Lose Functional Reserve

The Demise of the Capillary Cell's Dance Step Rhythm

In simplistic terms, the mechanics of capillary cell outer membrane complex pseudocapillarization, the loss of mitochondrial functional reserve, and the increased code silencing of its DNA occurs as a result of the prevailing tenacity of signaling and metabolic chronic inflammatory interstitial space rhythms (Figure 15, appendix)[5,6,7]. The fusion and subsequent purpose virulence of chronic inflammatory crosstalk within the interstitial space increases its intentionality as its signaling and metabolic rhythms contrive to disassemble the capillary cell's dance step anti-inflammatory processes. When chronic inflammatory interstitial space rhythms conspire at this level against the capillary cell, they will decapitate the cell's functional capacity by blocking its dance step counterbalancing rhythm to cause a decline in its mitochondrial nitric oxide combustion cycle. The capillary cell's disintegration translates into an increasingly inept anti-inflammatory multipurposed execution that enables vascular inflammatory free radicals to propagate within the interstitial space while simultaneously preventing funneled and error prone immune arsenal from eliminating them. The interstitial space *transitioning process* becomes a functional haven for an evolving chronic inflammatory interstitial space emancipation of disease consorts.

As chronic inflammatory interstitial space rhythms consolidate intentionality, the capillary and downstream endothelial cell lose infrastructure cred that would ordinarily provide seamless execution of anti-inflammatory multipurpose. The transitioning is accompanied by an increasing anti-inflammatory resistance from circulating and *proinflammatory reconfigured* immune contingents which are biased to adhere to increasingly dysfunctional capillary cell adhesion receptors, funnel unabated into the interstitial space via an unregulated gap junction complex, and once in the interstitial space signal convert and conform to chronic inflammatory initiatives (Figures 15,16 and 17, appendix) [5,6,7]. As the capillary cell outer membrane complex becomes functionally obsolete, it will no longer provide a sufficient anti-inflammatory resolve to choreograph incoming immune arsenal into the interstitial space in order to execute a precision purposed outcome. As a result, the incoming interstitial space immune contingents are not only preprogramed to fail anti-inflammatory directives, but will easily signal convert to process chronic inflammatory directives.

The interstitial space *transitioning process* not only allows chronic inflammatory signaling and metabolic rhythms to prosper but will nurture their assimilation into an new order that will intention outcomes that work against interstitial space sanitation and end organ cell functional utility as they simultaneously block the capillary-endothelial cell's dance step rhythm[5,6,7]. When interstitial space immune contingents signal convert, they output cytokines, enzymes, free radicals and electromagnetic wavelets that will cater to a chronic inflammatory interstitial space *cadence* that over time will signal pirate intent from the blood plasma through the increasingly disabled capillary cell outer membrane complex. As this chronic inflammatory interstitial space trajectory increases it self-fulfills outcomes that project disease consorts (Figures 17 and 18, appendix) that simultaneously collaborate against the capillary cell's anti-inflammatory dance step rhythm [7].

The Mechanics of *Pseudocapillarization*

The emerging synchronicity of the chronic inflammatory interstitial space signaling and metabolic cadence becomes a potent destabilizing influence to the capillary cell's dance steps. Chief among the capillary cell's increasing detachment from its capacity to anti-inflammatory perform is the declining multilateral function of its outer membrane complex[5,6,7]. The loss of the capillary cell's outer membrane complex to precision choreograph anti-inflammatory purpose into the interstitial space becomes the underlying mechanic that will subsequently cascade signaling and metabolic chain reactions that breaks the cell's capacity to execute multipurpose as its counterbalance is disrupted and functional quality assurance unravels. These proinflammatory outcomes are imprinted by the loss of the capillary cell's mitochondrial nitric oxide combustion cycle which prevents the cell from rejuvenating its worn-out infrastructure thereby allowing its functionally intricate outer membrane complex to fall into increasing disrepair and eventual functional insolvency. Adhesion receptors, pores, vesicles, and gap junction complex functional deprecation will couple with suboptimal regulation of voltage gradients that will in aggregate contribute to a host of immune funneling errors, interstitial space signaling misreads and an increasing proinflammatory prodrome [5,6,7,8,9]. The functional diminution of the capillary cell's outer membrane complex will produce increasing disparities of anti-inflammatory interstitial space outcomes that in themselves will chain react signaling and metabolic rhythms that further reduce the efficacy of the dance step rhythm.

The capillary cell's increasing inability to execute anti-inflammatory multipurpose becomes the gain for budding and invasive proinflammatory signaling vestiges (Figure 13, appendix)[7]. This will eventually create a chronic inflammatory interstitial space opportunity to birth, expand, consolidate and virilize its own brand of intentionality. This rebranding of this chronic inflammatory interstitial space signaling and metabolic hierarchy is transitioned chiefly through the disabled capillary cell's outer membrane complex. In this scenario, the combination of interstitial space misreads and immune funneling errors make haste towards an amalgam of chronic inflammatory converted purpose [6,7].

The Pseudocapillarized Capillary Cell Outer Membrane Complex becomes a Chronic Inflammatory Functional Arbiter that includes the Functionally Compromised Mesenchymal Cell

As the capillary-endothelial cell's outer membrane complex pseudocapillarizes, interstitial space anti-inflammatory signaling and metabolic rhythms lose functional significance [5,6,7]. The increasing interstitial space disparity between a dwindling anti-inflammatory rhythm and a virilizing and intentional proinflammatory signaling and metabolic fortress, will buttress a bevy of willful chronic inflammatory purposed *expressions*. These signaling rhythms will block mesenchymal cell anti-inflammatory functional utility to malign signaling cues to the capillary cell's basement membrane that disrupts the dance step clarifying "all clear" and "all hands-on deck" anti-inflammatory confirmations. Instead, these messages become garbled to where their mesenchymal cell cadence will cater a chronic inflammatory interstitial space outcome [7].

This reverberation of chronic inflammatory interstitial space signal and metabolic transitioning is what drives their consolidation to disease venues and end organ cell failure[7]. In this manner this interstitial space transitioning will accentuate the loss of capillary cell's dance step fortitude to thereby negate its anti-inflammatory multipurposed outcomes. The proinflammatory mechanics of disrupted capillary cell dance steps will always involve plentiful vascular inflammatory free radical interstitial space impingements, a betrayal of funneled immune arsenal and mesenchymal cells to remove them and an increasingly pseudocapillarized capillary cell outer membrane complex that becomes functionally incapable of doing anything about it (Figures 16 and 17, appendix) [7].

The Pseudocapillarization Effect on the Mechanics of a Diminished Capillary Cell Mitochondrial Combustion Reserve

As the choreograph corrupted capillary cell outer membrane complex enables an increasing anti-inflammatory multipurposed misalignment, the capillary cell's dance step cadence gets blocked thereby fixing its permeability gradient towards a persistent immune funneling process as its feedback-loops to nearby mitochondrial signal ongoing energy combustion requirements. This block in capillary cell functional dance step counterbalance becomes a potent chronic inflammatory interstitial space signaling and metabolic inducer as the continued funneling of immune arsenal into the interstitial space will not allow the capillary cell to dance step cycle an infrastructure refresh that would include the overhaul of worn-out outer membrane complex infrastructure that would otherwise contribute to anti-inflammatory precise immune choreography. This dance step block will also keep the cell's mitochondrial combustion in its energy combustion cycle meaning it too will burn through its infrastructure to cause a collapse in mitochondrial volumes, mass, size and functional reserve. The loss of capillary cell mitochondrial functional efficacy coupled with the pseudocapillarized and increasing permeability incompetent outer membrane complex set the interstitial space table for a perfect chronic inflammatory storm that enables an increasingly virulent confluence of disease consorts[7].

When coupled with increasing mesenchymal cell interstitial space vascular inflammatory free radical misreads, the anti-inflammatory pulsing of the capillary cell's continuous outer membrane permeability dance steps becomes increasingly unbalanced and ineffectual which in turn keeps mitochondrial combustion stuck in energy production. The frozen capillary cell dance steps become self-mutilating as its infrastructure, which includes both outer membrane complex and mitochondrial combustion capacity shrink from lack of a nitric oxide combustion cycle. Within mitochondria, the lost reserve reduces combustion capacity of both nitric oxide and energy[5,6,7,8,9]. The decreasing anti-inflammatory interstitial space efficacy to remove inflammatory breach becomes a self-fulfilling chronic inflammatory tool that blocks capillary cell anti-inflammatory multipurpose as its outer membrane complex, mitochondria and nuclear chromatin become increasingly incapable of functional performance.

As interstitial space immune arsenal gets increasingly purpose reassigned to conform to a chronic inflammatory identity, the capillary cell and its mitochondria becomes facilitators to this interstitial space transitioning. The increased and unbalanced mitochondrial energy combustion cycle will couple with increased fission and autophagy to cascade:

> ➤ A persistent increase in ROS exhaust *(superoxide, hydrogen peroxide)* which will excessively membrane attach to *overextend* its damaging effects to capillary cell infrastructure to include increased DNA cross linkages.
>
> ➤ Will nurture increases in immune funneling errors that will incentivize further chronic inflammatory interstitial space signaling virulence and purpose identity.
>
> ➤ Will also create chronic inflammatory interstitial space *metabolic momentum* through accentuating insulin resistance, reduced oxygen tensions, acidic pH and anti-inflammatory misaligned osmotic and osmolarity pressure gradients.
>
> ➤ Will unbalance capillary cell infrastructure metabolism favoring excessive fermenting of sugars (gluconeogenesis) from pyruvate, the mitochondrial beta oxidation of fatty acids to acetyl CoA, and liposomal lipolysis of longer chained fatty acids in preparation for beta oxidation.
>
> ➤ The chronic inflammatory interstitial space signaling and metabolic nuance will signal loop nearby end organ cells to increase nitric oxide combustion rhythms which over time will force excessive RNS combustion exhaust to crosslink and code silence its nuclear chromatin. When coupled with an increased predilection for cellular replication will fuel a risk for *oncogenesis* (Figure 14, appendix) [6,7]

This persistent loss of capillary cell mitochondrial combustion counterbalance will facilitate the cascading of signaling and metabolic rhythms that favor additional chronic inflammatory interstitial space outcomes which in turn will portend poorly on the capacity of the capillary cell to convey anti-inflammatory multipurpose execution as dance step imbalances continue to cannibalizes the cell's infrastructure. As a persistent capillary cell mitochondrial energy combustion cannibalizes its infrastructure, the fission, autophagy and loss of functional reserve will be outsourced, along with its pseudocapillarized outer membrane complex towards facilitating chronic inflammatory interstitial space rhythms that will mastermind disease outcomes[6,7].

Chapter Six

The Ebb and Flow of Interstitial Space Vascular Inflammatory Free Radicals and How They Pulse Anti or Proinflammatory Rhythms to the Interstitial Space

Vascular Inflammatory Free Radicals and How They Nuance Chronic inflammatory Interstitial Space Outcomes

Vascular inflammatory free radicals are ubiquitous interstitial space contingents that can perpetuate either a pro or anti-inflammatory interstitial space signaling and metabolic prodrome depending on how their identification and subsequent reduction becomes homeostatic with the circadian capillary cell's dance step rhythm. If their identification or reduction is somehow delayed, the capillary cell dance step rhythm will get disrupted with persistent delays unbecoming of the cell's capacity to compensate for them. With persistence, these unbalanced capillary cell dance step rhythms will enable the authentication of a chronic inflammatory signaling and metabolic interstitial space roadmap that will transition anti-organ outcomes.

Vascular inflammatory free radicals may enter an interstitial space passively (diffusion or facilitated diffusion) or actively transported (typically as a molecular bystander as an attachment to albumen or other proteins) either extrinsically through end organ epithelial cells or from the blood plasma and endothelial cell endocytosis mechanics. The free radical can be in a gas, solid or liquid form and can harbor various molecular configurations, sizes and shapes that in aggregate contribute to their solubility characteristics, membrane connectivity and ease of molecular identification and reduction. Their interstitial space volumes and rate of inclusion as well as their predilection for certain membrane attachments or organelle integration makes them more or less anti-inflammatory immune identifiable and hence capable of inciting a dance step identification or reduction miscalculation. In this respect, if processing their identification and removal on can be timely and comprehensive, their interstitial space presence will fit into the anti-inflammatory schema of the capillary cell's dance step rhythm. If not, they become a *processing tool* for the potential expression of chronic inflammatory interstitial space outcomes[5,6,7].

Vascular inflammatory free radicals can typically be very adept at facilitating interstitial space membrane infringements via attachment or integrating within the membrane's infrastructure. In other instances, their molecular properties allow them to establish concentrations gradients and diffuse *through* membranes without attaching to them thereby affecting infrastructure on the other side of the membrane such as intracellular organelles (that include mitochondria) and other cytoplasmic infrastructure. The external environment may allow vascular inflammatory free radicals to arrive into interstitial spaces via end organs that include the eyes, mucous membranes of the throat, nose, sinuses, skin, lungs, gums, digestive or genitourinary tracts. They can also arrive from the blood or lymph plasma via endocytosis through the capillary and downstream endothelial cell as residues from leaky gut or metabolic/ catabolic processes that involve the digestive tract, abdominal adipose, liver, kidneys, pancreas and lung. Their potential to fuel chronic interstitial space inflammation will depend upon many different moving pieces that could cause or effect anti-inflammatory rhythms generated from the capillary cell dance step rhythm. When the capillary and downstream endothelial cell dance step rhythm is operationally adept, vascular inflammatory free radicals will more likely be interstitial space identified and timely reduced to thereby becoming an integral part of the anti-inflammatory multipurposed self-fulfillment of a successful dance step rhythm.

On the other hand, when vascular inflammatory free radicals within interstitial spaces cannot be timely removed, they will nuisance the capillary cell dance step rhythm non-compliance where they become facilitators to an increasingly functional chronic inflammatory interstitial space precipice. The list of vascular inflammatory free radicals is expanding as awareness spreads and the science supports the understanding of environmental toxicities on the one hand and how endogenous free radicals adversely affect transcellular infrastructure on the other. A synopsis of potential vascular inflammatory free radical interstitial space displays can be found in my previous books *Hazing Aging*, *Rejuvenation!* and *Rejuvenation2.0.*

How Vascular Inflammatory Free Radicals Transition to Become Interstitial Space Malevolent

Within the context of any given end organ's interstitial space, the presence of vascular inflammatory free radical displays *may not* in themselves *necessarily* be harmful if and when:

- they can be timely identified, reduced and eliminated
- their reduced molecular elements can contribute to the next dance step's foundation as an anti-inflammatory *metabolic modifier*
- the so-called metabolic modifier effect can be signal interpreted by mesenchymal cells as an anti-inflammatory means to an end that clarifies the all-important "all clear" signal
- the rhythms that result from their interstitial space removal can be neatly packaged into a finely tuned and dance step counterbalanced anti-inflammatory reverberation (Figure 9, appendix) [7].

Any free radical which pervades an end organ's interstitial space can be classified as a *vascular inflammatory free radical* and can be differentiated forms of interstitial space molecular interactions in that they don't induce a switch or metabolic operative within their membrane attachment that is favorable to membrane function. Instead, their attachment or membrane integration will elicit responses from other cells and molecules that are *extrinsic to* or *other directed* to and from the membrane's interface [4,5,6,7,8,9,10,11]. When free radicals membrane attach within the interstitial space, they should elicit a specific anti-inflammatory message that gets conveyed to nearby mesenchymal cells to expand a specific interstitial space immune presence. This variably expressed "all hands-on deck" message is contingent on the type, rate and volume of free radical interstitial space exposure as it gets outsourced to the capillary-endothelial cell's outer membrane complex. The response should elicit a precision choreographed and meticulously funneled immune response from the blood plasma into the interstitial space for the expressed purpose of a timely removal. Whether this immune response reflects an anti-or proinflammatory bias will become contingent on several factors chief of which are the level of accurate signaling intelligence that is conveyed to the capillary cell from the mesenchymal cell and the capacity of the capillary cell's outer membrane complex and mitochondria to package together the appropriate immune contingents for their timely removal.

When vascular inflammatory free radicals cannot be timely interstitial space removed, the process will place a strain on anti-inflammatory multipurposed mechanics that can compensate for the accumulation of unbalanced signaling and metabolic discrepancies only to a certain point before the dance step rhythm break down. As this occurs, the degree to which the dance step rhythm can retool its cadence becomes proportional to the level of nuclear chromatin *ROS cross linkage* and subsequent code silencing that occurs which precludes a full capacity to restore infrastructure proteins during its resuscitated nitric oxide combustion cycle. In this context, the removal of vascular inflammatory free radicals from the interstitial space becomes increasingly more difficult as outer membrane complex and mitochondrial infrastructure have lost sufficient levels of their respective functional mechanics so as to reduce their outcome efficacy[5,6,7]. The loss of capillary cell nuclear chromatin DNA/RNA coding capacity becomes an critically important operational loophole for chronic interstitial space processes to gain functional stature particularly when vascular inflammatory free radical interstitial space infringements are pestering and festering.

In the setting of an increasingly senescent and functionally compromised dance steps, the capillary and downstream endothelial cell become prone to becoming chronic inflammatory hijacked. To prevent this, anti-inflammatory *lifestyle* modification and rhythms must be intentionally deployed so further limit the chronic interstitial space inflammatory advantage. Daily anti-inflammatory routines and rhythms become mandatory towards allowing a less than robust capillary cell dance rhythms to keep its functional relevance that would include the timely elimination and reduction of vascular inflammatory free radical interstitial space impingements. In this context, daily circadian anti-inflammatory rhythms involving morning interval training type exercise, consistent sleep hygiene, stress management, and dietary selections and eating times will provide for a sufficient signaling and metabolic cadence that keeps the capillary cell's dance steps and multipurposed anti-inflammatory alignment intact[4,5,6,7,21,24,27,30].

As capillary cells age, the increasing inability to timely eliminate vascular inflammatory free radical interstitial space impingements will only make chronic inflammatory outcomes more likely. The chronic inflammatory push will affect all aspects of anti-inflammatory dance step multipurpose from the elicited pace, stem, and ricochet interstitial space effects to the subsequent systemic circulation backwash from the back end of the dance step process. Included in these rhythms will be the subversion of mesenchymal cell anti-inflammatory "all clear and all hands-on deck" signaling expressions that are tied to dance step interstitial space purpose execution as well as the fluxing of functional rhythms from nearby end organ cells (Figures 11 and 12, appendix)[7]. As the capillary cell's infrastructure increasingly fails to reconstitute from increasing dance step misalignment and ineffectual protein synthesis, its purpose weakened outer membrane complex and mitochondria become increasingly frail and anti-inflammatory incapable of dance step interstitial space and end organ cell outcomes. When this occurs, smaller numbers of vascular inflammatory free radical interstitial space impingements can foster harm to the dance step rhythm and subsequent interstitial space outcomes [4,5,6,7].

How do Vascular Inflammatory Free Radicals Fit into an Anti-inflammatory Capillary Cell Dance Step Rhythm?

The Interstitial space streaming of vascular inflammatory free radicals, if timely eliminated by the capillary cell's dance step rhythm, becomes part of an optimal anti-inflammatory capillary cell dance step recycling operation of multipurposed execution. The impact of vascular inflammatory free radical interstitial space displays can place stresses on the dance step rhythm over time as their capacity to inflict imbalances in the timing and outcomes of the dance steps will increase as the capillary cells and their downstream endothelial cell brethren become functionally less capable. In a perfect dance step mechanic, interstitial space free radicals will be timely identified, eliminated and reduced so as to not unbalance the timing of the capillary cell's dance step rhythm[7]. In this "elimination in rhythm" dance step scenario, the capillary cell's capacity to stage and execute the elimination of an interstitial space free radical will become a moving target based on the degree to which the cell has become functionally senescent. vs the capillary cell ages and its functional apparatus self-limits from lack of infrastructure refurbishment, the capacity to remove free radicals or respond to end organ cell functional requirements will diminish. This implies that with capillary cell aging bias, the volume, rate and diversity of free radical interstitial space impingements must get reduced to enable the capillary cell to remain dance step capable.

The processing of vascular inflammatory free radical impingements within the interstitial space, that will include their reduction into basic molecular constituents (water, carbon dioxide, nitrogen etc.) becomes part of the circadian dance step rhythm as the reduced constituents they become *integrative* towards processing the mesenchymal "all clear" signal and the initiation of the next dance step. In a similar fashion, the retooling of pulsed metabolic interstitial space prerequisites that occurs with the re accumulation of free radical impingements, will trigger signaling and metabolic cascades that will elicit a mesenchymal cell cytokine stimulatory "all hands-on deck" signal to the capillary cell's basement membrane that will expand immune funneling into the interstitial space to cover the removal of inflammatory breach. Even in the context of a functionally senescent capillary cell, the processing of a more limited supply of vascular inflammatory interstitial space free radicals can still enable the continuation of a counterbalanced and purpose effective dance step rhythm.

The Dance Step Processing of Interstitial Space Vascular Inflammatory Free Radicals: Anti-Inflammatory Friend or Foe

Vascular inflammatory free radical interstitial space impingements at any given moment can be complex admixtures of inorganic, organic, simple or complex molecules or gases of varying sizes, shapes and solubilities. Their intrusion into interstitial spaces can be from either an epithelial or endothelial cell direction, from the external environment or as circulating byproducts from multi end organ functional cause or effects. In terms the ladder, examples include circulating inflammatory proteins, adipokines, AGEs, small particle LDL cholesterol, non-HDL cholesterols, triglycerides, homocysteine, lipo(a), and angiotensin II among others[5,6,7].

Circulating vascular inflammatory free radicals, whether originating from end organ cause or effects or from the external environment, will utilize a variety of different mechanics to enter interstitial spaces or to integrate within transcellular outer membranes or its other organelle infrastructure. Their interstitial space invasiveness will be based primarily on their size, shape and solubility and how stealth they have become to being recognized as they seamlessly integrate and passively mobilize into the interstitial space by following solubility, oncotic and osmolality pressure gradients. If the free radical is a gas, their capacity to penetrate through membranes by following concentration gradients as well as how they can pare with transmembrane oxygen, carbon dioxide and nitric oxide exchanges and gradients will also be important. In some instances, free radicals may enter interstitial spaces as passive bystanders by ligand attaching to larger molecules such as albumen and then be actively transported into the interstitial space. Once they have arrived, they can detach and find a membrane surface or some other interstitial space vehicle to attach to induce an inflammatory response. In other situations, circulating "free radicals" may do their proinflammatory damage before they enter interstitial spaces. Circulating adipokines, for example, can molecularly interact with circulating immunoglobulins or albumen to tweak their molecular configurations thereby making them prone to adjust their purposes and become chronic inflammatory interstitial space facilitators. Sometimes circulating and less proinflammatory virile free radicals can be liver or kidney reduced to where their molecular byproduct is more-free radical toxic that its non-reduced predecessor. No matter how free radicals aggregate within interstitial spaces, their presence could cause the capillary cell's dance step rhythm to become desynchronized. This dance step divergence will create opportunity for emerging chronic inflammatory interstitial space signaling and metabolic rhythms to process consolidation [4,5,6,7,30].

The Mechanics of Different Vascular Inflammatory Free Radical Transmembrane Interactivities

When a free radical attaches to an interstitial space membrane surface, it will change the membrane's configuration as well as its capacity to execute purpose while typically without requiring energy, the utilization of enzymes or specialized bonding techniques. Their attachment is considered a *foreign interference* to membrane functioning and will draw the ire from corresponding anti-inflammatory funneled immune displays that will dance step attach to the free radical to begin the opsonization and reduction processes that will being the membrane back to its original functional and molecular configuration [5,6,7]. Reversing the cause and effects of the attached free radical becomes important as the membrane's purpose to the cells signaling and metabolic hierarchy will diminish as long as the free radical attachment is pestering the membrane's surface or effecting its infrastructure. The persistence of this affected membrane to function normally will lead to less *interactive efficacy* with affiliated membranes.

In the capillary cell, a persistent basement membrane free radical attachment, or its assimilation into the continuous outer membrane infrastructure, will eventually trigger a critical level of activated switch imbalances and subsequent dysfunction that will make the basement membrane's interconnectivity with the mesenchymal, end organ cell or with its contiguous continuous outer membrane less purpose effective. This same type of endothelial cell basement membrane free radical malingering is likely occurring throughout the arterial tree thereby making interstitial space transcellular and assimilation with continuous outer membrane exchanges less purpose efficacious.

A well-publicized example of one type of free radical basement membrane attachment is found with small particle LDL cholesterol. When this basement membrane free radical attachment malingers, the capillary and downstream endothelial cell's dance step rhythm will become predisposed to dysrhythmia with cascading imbalances making funneled immune arsenal less capable of eliminating the attached LDL particle. As the attached basement membrane LDL particle "pesters and festers" to become chronic inflammatory, it's malingering will tether to an increasingly incompetent display of immune contingents that become incapable of removing or reducing the LDL particle. With the passage of time, the basement membrane thickens and in larger bifurcating arterial vessels will mature to become a plaque to narrow the vessel lumen and reduce upstream blood flows. The process of making the interstitial space chronic inflammatory and limiting upstream oxygen delivery becomes a serious no-win dilemma for endothelium whereby chronic inflammatory interstitial space signaling and metabolic rhythms will favor the evolution of disease consorts starting with thrombosis and upstream end organ hypoxia. As upstream oxygen displays wither, disease consorts that prefer anaerobic and insulin resistant conditions, such as scarring, oncogenesis and bacterial/viral infections will find these interstitial space living arrangements much to their liking.

Another example within the circulating lipid family of how free radicals can inflict damage to the endothelial cell outer membrane complex is found in the triglyceride category. These longer typically methyl saturated carbon chains will use their fat solubility characteristics to penetrate the endothelial cell's outer membrane infrastructure and proceed to integrate within its lipoprotein landscape. As it does, it reduces the efficacy of the outer membrane complex to function making it a less reliable permeability partner in the management of the capillary and downstream endothelial cell dance step rhythm. Similar membrane infrastructure subversions that occur within any membrane that will accept their lipid solubility to include those found in other organelles such as mitochondrial membranes. When triglyceride penetration and incorporation occur within the capillary cell's continuous outer membrane, its infrastructure *switch and stereotaxic mechanics,* that enables the membrane to adjust its permeability towards immune funneling by twisting or bending to expose or hide specific luminal adhesion receptors, becomes restricted. Similar permeability snafus will involve the capacity of the gap junction complex to manage the pace or sequencing of immune funneling into the interstitial space. The repetitive dumping of triglycerides into the capillary cell's continuous outer membrane infrastructure will negatively impact its capacity to mediate permeability which in turn lessens anti-inflammatory performance of dance step multipurpose. With auto perpetuation, the dance step rhythm will suffer from cascading outer membrane complex pseudocapillarization with similar mitochondrial losses occurring to its functional reserve.

Vascular inflammatory free radicals may damage capillary cell and interstitial space functional mechanics in still other ways by penetrating membranes via simple concentration, diffusion and facilitated diffusion gradients. When this occurs, the can molecular interact with other molecules within the cell's cytoplasm and organelles to disrupt their signaling and metabolic confluences thereby impacting what would otherwise be the completion of an executed dance step. This type of reverberation will make chronic inflammatory interstitial space rhythms more accessible to fusion, virulence and intentionality. Examples of free radical simple diffusion mechanics include certain gases such as *carbon monoxide* or even the prolonged expression of anesthetic gases. Once in cells, these gases will follow concentration gradients and will enter into mitochondria to adversely impact the signaling and functional counterbalances of oxygen, carbon dioxide and nitric oxide gases. The potential of these gases to disrupt endothelial and capillary cell infrastructure with particular reference to mitochondrial combustion mechanics is significant as they most likely will impact the efficacy of both energy and nitric oxide gas production.

One type of free radical-membrane ATTACHMENT involves the formation of a covalent bond without the use of energy or an enzyme. The attachment does not typically cascade a membrane signaling or metabolic rhythm (unlike dance step derived ROS or RNS membrane attachments) but rather blocks the flow of orderly rhythms that purpose execute membrane intent. These free radical transmembrane impingements are often enabled by other proinflammatory interstitial space signaling and metabolic cues that are derived from chronic inflammatory interstitial space signaling and metabolic momentum and the subsequent activation of proinflammatory cytokines, enzymes, electromagnetic wavelets and other free radicals from other previously signal turned immune remnants. When these aggregates of proinflammatory signaling expressions are coupled with chronic inflammatory derived interstitial space acid-base imbalances, reduced oxygen tensions, discrepant oncotic/hydrostatic pressure gradients and flawed insulin resistance, their collective will favor additional intransigence of vascular inflammatory free radical endothelial cell outer membrane complex attachments and malingering interactions.

Unsuccessful Vascular Inflammatory Interstitial Space Free Radical Removal: A *Functional Transparency* that will Process Chronic Inflammatory Outcomes

With the persistence of vascular inflammatory interstitial space impingements and the subsequent blocking of counterbalanced capillary cell dance steps, chronic inflammatory interstitial space signaling and metabolic rhythms will coalesce to virilize purpose. The processing of these transitions will produce a progressive anti-inflammatory insolvency with the deterioration of endothelia cell functional competence and an interstitial space that becomes increasingly signal and metabolically prepared for anti-organ disease consortiums (Figure 15, appendix)[7]. The coupling of this chronic inflammatory interstitial space transgression does not bode well for end organ cell functional utility or longevity [5,6,7,15,30,31]. As these chronic inflammatory processes convert the interstitial space to its own transactional slate, the disabled capillary cell becomes a passive distributor towards its rhythms to further its disease expression(s).

The evolving chronic inflammatory interstitial space amalgam will cater to disease growth while for the most part ignoring end organ cell purpose. This transition will be tethered to:

> ➢ abundant and diverse vascular inflammatory free radical interstitial space fuel
> ➢ a disrupted capillary-endothelial cell dance step rhythm of anti-inflammatory signaled and metabolic counterbalance
> ➢ foreclosure of dance step derived anti-inflammatory signaled and executed *pace, stem, ricochet and backwash* effects through the capillary cell, interstitial space and blood plasma
> ➢ the disruption of mesenchymal cell anti-inflammatory signaling clarity involving its "all clear" and "all hands-on deck" respnses
> ➢ the consolidation of the interstitial space of chronic inflammatory rhythms from the signal conversion of funneled immune arsenal
> ➢ the signal pirating of capillary cell's outer membrane complex to construct purpose specific chronic inflammatory intent[5,6,7,22,23].

How End Organ Interstitial Space Chronic Inflammatory Mosaics Enable Vascular Inflammatory Free Radical Expansion

How and why vascular inflammatory free radical interstitial space impingements become chronic inflammatory interstitial space arbiters will depend on how proinflammatory signaling and metabolic rhythms get constructed and are subsequently amplified within the interstitial space. Their capacity to facilitate interstitial space rhythms towards a proinflammatory purpose will be proportionate to:

> ➢ The remaining functional resolve of the capillary and downstream endothelial cell dance step rhythm.
> ➢ To what degree the capillary cell's outer membrane complex has not become pseudocapillarized.
> ➢ The degree to which the end organ cell has not lost functional leverage.

> ➤ The level of which the capillary cell can still refurbish its infrastructure.
> ➤ The level of immune suppression that has occurred as a result of circulating immune arsenal being molecularly tweaked by a persistent proinflammatory endothelial cell backwash.
> ➤ The degree to which lifestyle adjustments have processed either a circadian anti or proinflammatory rhythm (that will increase or decrease insulin resistance, oxygen reserves, hypertension, dyslipidemia and other metabolic dysrhythmias[1,2,4,5,6,7,14,16,30].

Each of these determinants will process signaling momentum that will favor either a chronic inflammatory or anti-inflammatory interstitial space prodrome that will increase or decrease disease consorts and that will be tethered to the capacity of the capillary and downstream endothelial cell to dance step rhythm fulfill. The interactivity of the capillary cell dance step rhythm and their capacity to anti-inflammatory fulfill multipurposed outcomes will become interdependent on many moving parts that include its capacity to maintain dance step functional counterbalance as it simultaneously refreshes its infrastructure[4,5,6,7].

The Vascular Inflammatory Free Radical *Multiplier Effect*

Vascular inflammatory free radicals become very chronic inflammatory dangerous when they mobilize into end organ interstitial spaces *en-bloc* when they arrive in recurring and unrelentless waves so as to overwhelm or exhaust prevailing anti-inflammatory resources that are derived from the pulsing of capillary cell dance steps[5,6,7]. The vascular inflammatory free radical interstitial space windfall towards chronic inflammatory outcomes will become dependent on how elimination resistant they have become. Their subsequent interstitial space "pester and fester" effect will increase immune funneling mistakes with their subsequent assimilation into chronic inflammatory signaling rhythms, virilizing intent. The pester and fester effect becomes contingent on the volume, pace of interstitial space arrival, diversity, size, molecular solubility and physical properties (solid, liquid or gas) of invading vascular inflammatory interstitial space free radicals and how they influence the decline of capillary and downstream endothelial cell dance steps.

Their persistent and robust interstitial space pummeling can initially produce something akin to a "shock and awe" effect towards interstitial space anti-inflammatory rhythms as their volumes and diversity become disruptive to anti-inflammatory signaling rhythms. Mesenchymal cells also become reactive to the proinflammatory vascular inflammatory free radical surge by impulsing cytokine stimulatory "all hands-on deck" signals that over or underestimating the free radical inflammatory breach to cause outcomes that lend themselves towards an immune funneling crescendo through the capillary cell's outer membrane complex that precludes additional chronic inflammatory interstitial space momentum. The loss of mesenchymal cell signaling clarity regarding the quality and quantity of specific immune funneling requirements will spawn potential chain reactions that snafu appropriate immune contingents that would otherwise eliminate the interstitial space inflammatory breach. As the capacity of the capillary cell's continuous outer membrane to choreograph interstitial space immune funneling becomes less anti-inflammatory reliable, the processing of immune funneled contingents into the interstitial space to remove the vascular inflammatory free radical inflammatory breach becomes less capable. This places a continuous drag on anti-inflammatory interstitial space rhythms and their subsequent outcomes which in turn reduces dance step rhythm efficiency which enhances chronic inflammatory signaling and metabolic convergence towards a conceptualizing disease consort.

This increasing divergence of the dance step rhythm will eventually predict its dysfunction and senescence, as dance step derived anti-inflammatory pace, stem, ricochet and backwash effects fade into the interstitial space and blood plasma background as the capillary cell's outer membrane complex pseudocapillarizes, mitochondrial reserve shrinks and nuclear chromosomal DNA code silences. The chronic inflammatory matrix and then anti-organ assume the signaling and metabolic mantle of the interstitial space as they virilize proinflammatory outcomes via signal pirating their intent through the disabled capillary and downstream endothelial cell outer membrane and infrastructure[6,7]. The proinflammatory interstitial space signaling and metabolic chain reactions that occur from vascular inflammatory free radical interstitial space proliferation is known as the chronic inflammatory *multiplier effect* [5,6,7].

The *pool* of vascular inflammatory free radical interstitial space impingements will expand as their *persistence, diversity and volume* within end organ interstitial space escalates and as they become elimination refractory from an increasingly incapable array of anti-inflammatory funneled immune contingents. The growing compilation of what a vascular inflammatory free radical interstitial space impingement is will include:

- **Externally Inhaled, skin absorbed or mucous membrane attached exposures of various particulates, noxious gases, hydrocarbons, solvents or certain "allergic" contacts with various dusts or foreign proteins.**
- **Ingested or end organ metabolically produced small particle LDL cholesterol, the non-HDL cholesterols, lipo(a), homocysteine, advanced glycation end products (AGEs), adipokines.**
- **The excessive ingestion of heavy metals such as arsenic, lead and mercury or the excessive intake of other "trace" minerals (manganese, copper, cobalt, selenium, zinc).**
- **All intestinal "leaky gut" free radical *derivatives* that get backwashed through the capillary endothelium into the portal circulation to become toxic residues to upstream liver and pancreatic capillary cells and their interstitial spaces.**
- **Their aggregate metabolic outcomes, instead of ushering in the next anti-inflammatory dance step, do the opposite as they further intensify a chronic inflammatory signaling rhythm that increases further leaky gut, fatty liver transitioning, increasing insulin resistance and the subsequent systemic backwash to a host of additional toxic intermediates that foment immune suppression and proinflammatory chain reactions.**
- **The recurring ingestion, inhalation or injection of certain drugs (prescribed or elicit) and/ or their metabolized byproducts that will act as additional free radical contingents that will antagonize capillary cell dance steps and facilitate the interstitial space conversion to accelerated chronic inflammatory outcomes.**
- **The drug list not only includes ingested alcohol derivatives but also ingested, inhaled or injected amphetamines, barbiturates, opioids, anxiolytics and sleeping pills. The proinflammatory drug list also includes the *longer-term* use of *prescription* proton pump inhibitors (acid blockers), steroids, antibiotics, anticholinergics, certain antidepressants or other psychoactive medications.**
- **The repeated exposures to certain food "allergens" that are not just composed of gluten or lactose but may also contain other proteins and additives that are found in highly processed foods, eggs, red meats, peanuts or shellfish [4,5].**

Their aggregates of these free radical impingements within end organ interstitial spaces, not only make chronic inflammatory interstitial space transitioning more likely, but will accelerate the transitioning process towards disease consorts (Figures 15,16 and 17, appendix) [7].

The Effect of Sleep Deprivation, Stress, Abnormal Ghrelin/Leptin Ratios and Increased Adrenal Corticosteroids to Vascular Inflammatory Free Radical Interstitial Space Mobilization

Accelerated adverse outcomes to a systemic multi-end organ chronic interstitial space inflammatory prodrome will often coincide with the overproduction of stress hormones (cortisol, epinephrine, norepinephrine, dopamine)) that are triggered from environmental and secondary stressors as well the different causes of sleep deprivation. The combination of environmental exposures and behavior decisions either as a cause or effect to environmental stressors, become chronic inflammatory problematic when they bias signaling cascades that involve increased insulin resistance, blood pressure, various dyslipidemias, weight gain and imbalances in the production and systemic distribution of various hormones that include angiotensin II, cortisol, epinephrine, norepinephrine dopamine and the gastric production of ghrelin and leptin among others. In the case of the ladder, increased ghrelin activity will increase hunger and food cravings with particular reference to sugars and refined grains that will cause weight gain, abdominal adipose enlargement and metabolic syndrome. At the same time, stress triggers that increase circulating cortisol, will contribute to ghrelin activation and comfort food craving as it also biases an increase in sleep deprivation, insomnia, disturbed sleep hygiene, obstructive sleep apnea and predisposition to use anxiolytics, sleep aids and alcohol to self-medicate the stress and sleep deficiencies. As stress hormones remain unbalanced within the central circulation, ghrelin as well as other hormones will also stay over produced as the hormone leptin has little opportunity to counterbalance the ghrelin effects.

As food cravings persist, so does increases in BMI, insulin resistance, as well as circulating small particle LDL cholesterol, non-HDL cholesterol and triglycerides. When the stress-sleep deprivation is not mitigated, the angiotensin II, ghrelin cortisol imbalances persist which become harbingers to losses in capillary and downstream endothelial cell dance step rhythms, as proliferating vascular inflammatory free radicals are not mitigated and interstitial space immune arsenal signal convert to respond to proinflammatory rhythms. As this occurs, endothelial arterial vessel basement membranes thicken as they lose functional intimacy with their smooth muscle end organ cellular partners and subsequent tensile plasticity to expand or contract their lumens to support upstream pulsed end organ cell oxygen delivery. The reverberating chronic inflammatory processes throughout the arterial tree will bias persistent chronic inflammatory resolve as metabolic syndrome, adult diabetes, hypertension, dyslipidemia and predispositions to numerous polychemical drug and alcohol abuses occur. Secondary behavioral outcomes will mosaic that will manifest as chronic anxiety and bipolar depression to include schizophrenia as well as lower the threshold for PTSD and suicide ideation[4,5,7,21,27]. If chronic inflammatory signaling and metabolic momentum is left unchecked, the development of multi-end organ disease venues will occur that tie into the stress, sleep deprivation, abnormal hormone triad which include the onset of out of control cancer growth, infections that would otherwise not occur, the onset of aggressive amyloid and fibrous scar proliferation, and a proclivity towards various autoimmune complexes, not to mention the chronic inflammatory elephant in the room, the development of coagulopathies and upstream end organ hypoxia and ischemia[15,23]. As the chronic inflammatory neck noose tightens, other hormone imbalances will invariably occur that include but are not limited to reductions in growth, thyroid and sex hormones[7,16,17].

Robert L Buckingham, MD, FACP

Anti-Organ *Disease Consortiums* will Stamp an Irreversible Interstitial Space Signaling and Metabolic Concordance

When vascular inflammatory free radical interstitial space impingements have harnessed a sufficient level of chronic inflammatory immune conversion within the interstitial space, the signaling and metabolic rhythms they generate can irreversibly solidify the *growth, maturation and intentionality* of anti-organ related outcomes that preclude capillary and downstream endothelial cell anti-inflammatory salvage operations. The functional rhythms of the true upstream end organ cell become increasingly ignored which can result in their atrophy and eventual functional insignificance. The capillary cell's status also changes from anti-inflammatory signal leader to passive bystander and facilitator to chronic inflammatory interstitial space intent. The transitioning of the interstitial space will induce a decided bias towards a proinflammatory signaling and metabolic counterculture that will systemically and irreversibly displace anti-inflammatory interstitial space rhythms rhythms[7].

As disease consortiums seed, organize, manipulate and consolidate interstitial space signaling rhythms and resources, the inevitably develop their own signaling and metabolic cadence at the expense of the increasingly alienated end organ cell. Because their functional rhythms are typically much more adaptable to oxygen deficits and insulin resistance, the chronic inflammatory disease consorts become the preferred singled and metabolic rhythms of the interstitial spacel[5,6,7]. As these interstitial space transitions are occurring, the capillary and downstream endothelial cell dance steps are fumbling their rhythms which in turn further shrinks their anti-inflammatory functional resolve. This coinciding proinflammatory momentum to and from the capillary cell into the interstitial space and blood plasma will enhance chronic inflammatory outcomes as it schisms the true end organ cell's functional utility (Figures 16 and 17 appendix)[6,7].

An Outcome Summary of Vascular Inflammatory Free Radical Interstitial Space Multi End Organ Impingements and a Systemic Capillary and Downstream Endothelial Cell Dance Step Misalignment

Figures 11-18 in the appendix provides a step-by step detail of the signaling and metabolic pathways that process capillary cell dance step rhythm misalignment. The pivot and swing degeneration begins with the inability of one of its two dance steps to timely remove vascular inflammatory free racial interstitial space impingements, which in turn delays the reverberation of the capillary and downstream endothelial cell's next dance step. If these dance step delays persist and cannot be compensated for, the capillary and downstream endothelial cell will lose dance step multipurpose capacity to anti-inflammatory fulfill. This will provide signaling and metabolic loopholes within the interstitial space that incentivize proinflammatory chain reactions. As this is occurring, the capillary cell and its downstream endothelial cell brethren will lose their nitric oxide combustion cycle and subsequent capacity to retool its infrastructure or support increased upstream oxygen delivery that will support end organ cell combustion demands. This combination will make the endothelium age more quickly as its infrastructure fails to support tanti-inflammatory purposes and the interstitial space caves to chronic inflammatory outcomes. With the increasing loss of anti-inflammatory resolve, the interstitial space will quicken its pace towards chronic inflammatory outcomes and true end organ cell failure. Capillary cell dance demise occurs as proinflammatory interstitial space signaling streams and metabolic rhythms fuse to posture increasing intentionality and disease consorts (Figures 11 and 12, appendix),[5,6,7].

In a perfectly calibrated capillary and downstream endothelial cell dance step rhythm, the timing, depth and breadth of each step will accurately calibrate the outer membrane complex permeability pivot and mitochondrial combustion swing to timely purpose fulfill a purpose precise dance step outcome that in turn will lay the signaling and metabolic foundation for the execution of the next dance step fulfillment. In this anti-inflammatory configured dance step algorithm, precision-multipurposed outcomes will occur with their signaling and metabolic features biasing the fulfillment of the next dance step. In this manner, each capillary cell dance step will arc an outer membrane complex permeability gradient and mitochondrial combustion swing that will cause and effect both its purposed execution and that of the next dance step.

In this context a well-toned and purposed counterbalanced dance step rhythm becomes a potent multipronged anti-inflammatory effort that ties its effects to the capacity of precision funneled and purpose focused immune arsenal that timely perform their tasks within the interstitial space and which is coordinated by the signaling output from nearby mesenchymal cells. Whereas each dance step's pivot and swing rhythm may have a different velocity and duration to accomplish its anti-inflammatory directives, the signaling and metabolic framework it elicits should always frame a similarly pitched next pivot and swing dance step that will keep the dance step rhythm functionally counterbalanced and purpose quality assured. The capillary cell's dance step rhythm produces outcomes that are dynamically interlocked to the functional outcome of the next dance step making its rhythm a *twostep pivot and swing process*. The multipurposed execution of the two-step process counterbalances and quality assures transcellular restitution and interstitial space hygiene while optimizing end organ cell functional utility. This dance step blueprint implies that there will be beat to beat variability on the basis of what it might take to fulfill its multipurpose but that will be compensated by two step fluxes in the velocity and duration of each of its steps.

From this discussion, it could be assumed that anti-inflammatory dance step rhythms could lose functional counterbalance as one dance step predominates over the next. When this occurs, the dance step can provide a signaling and metabolic salvo that can compensate the rhythm and outcome of the next dance step. At the same time, the next dance step will respond to the previous step's signaling and metabolic salvo by accentuating its velocity, duration or both in order to purpose execute fulfillment that will be functionally compensatory to the previous dance step. The dance step rhythm fulfillment relies on many different signaling and metabolic chain reactions that are formulated from several different cells which could provide fodder for outcome slippages and subsequent dance step dysrhythmias. It is in this scenario, where both the complexity of the capillary cells outer membrane complex infrastructure and its intricate arrays of transmembrane switches, receptors and transport mechanics, can work together to compensate for these transgressions in order to reestablish a dance step signaling, metabolic and functional counterbalance that will quality assure successive next step outcomes.

When the preponderance of vascular inflammatory free radical interstitial space impingements produces a sufficient dance step dysrhythmia such that it cannot be signal or metabolically compensated, the cell and its downstream brethren will begin to its capacity to anti-inflammatory multipurpose perform (Figures 13 and 14, appendix). As the capillary cell's dance step rhythm flounders, its interstitial space domain, mesenchymal and end organ cells that are linked to it also become vulnerable to becoming signal converted to proinflammatory rhythms (Figures 15 and 16, appendix). With persistence, the chronic inflammatory interstitial space matrix and anti-organ become increasingly more purpose intentional as they leverage the interstitial space signaling and metabolic rhythms towards increasing intentionality. The birthing of disease consorts will eventually produce their own brand of consolidated interstitial space rhythms that will intention purpose as they pirate and cytokine backwash through the disabled capillary cell's outer membrane complex signaling streams that augment their interstitial space fulfillment as they incite a systemic anti-inflammatory immune suppressive effect (Figures 17 and 18, appendix).

Robert L Buckingham, MD, FACP

How Capillary Cells Vet the Processing of Anti-Inflammatory Rhythms

When the capillary cell's outer membrane complex pulses anti-inflammatory precise functional rhythms, multipurpose fulfillment is achieved as its two-step *endocytic and exocytic* ruminations interlock functional execution of the interstitial space and circulating blood plasma immune constituents. The dance step exocytic backwash, that occurs during its nitric oxide combustion cycle, enables circulating inflammatory mediators to be *anti-inflammatory prepared* as providers for a precision purposed anti-inflammatory outcome when precision funneled into the interstitial space. The exocytic backwash that prepares circulating immune arsenal for this task is based on the working order of the anti-inflammatory dance step rhythm and the crosslinked messages that help facilitate the dance step's purpose fulfillment from nearby mesenchymal cells. The endo and exocytic resources that flow through the capillary cell as part of its two-step dance step fulfillment, become dependent on the capacity of its outer membrane complex to adjust its permeability gradients to accurately reflect on these signals. This requires that its continuous outer membrane accurately receive the correct messaging from the interstitial space mesenchymal and immune contingents in order to process shifts in master switch cAMP that will in turn pulse a permeability gradient that facilitates the correct proportion of luminal adhesion receptor exposures, gap junction complex receptivity and pore, vesicle and transcellular transport mechanics that will process increases or decreases in transcapillary and endothelial cell endo or exocytic mobilizations.

A well-preserved luminal capillary cell glycocalyx will add to anti-inflammatory immune funneling precision as it collaborates with the continuous outer membrane to affix circulating immune contingents in preparation for continuous outer membrane adhesion receptor attachment or vesicle/pore transcellular endocytic mobilization. In this manner, the capillary cell's outer membrane complex will funnel specific compilations of immune contingents into the interstitial space composed of polymorphonuclear, B and T leukocytes, clotting factors, complement, immunoglobulins, platelets, monocytes, albumen and inflammatory proteins based on the type and quantity of inflammatory breach. These purpose precise inflammatory mediators will carry out anti-inflammatory directives that will circadian remove the inflammatory breach and then procure signaling and metabolic outcomes that facilitate entry of the next dance step (Figures1-5, appendix) [5,6,7]. The in-rhythm result will multipurpose interstitial space sanitation, refurbishment of transcellular infrastructure and increase end organ cell functional reserve. The capacity to incentivize dance step purpose fulfillment is anti-inflammatory immune *enhancing* and chronic inflammatory interstitial space *inhibitory*.

The dance step rhythm can be thought of as a series of interdependent and purpose fulfilling signaling and metabolic chain reactions that are elicited from the cytokine, enzyme, electromagnetic and free radical output of precision choreographed inflammatory mediators. These rhythms pulse expressions that purpose execute dance step anti-inflammatory fulfillment while at the same time outcome signaling derivatives that frame the next dance step. This recurring rhythm compels transcapillary endo and exocytic streams to and from the interstitial space and blood plasma to be *anti-inflammatory inclusive* while at the same time expressing inhibition for the potential of *chronic inflammatory* signaling and metabolic rhtyhms [6,7,22,23].

Within the confluence of the anti-inflammatory dance steps, vetting of anti-inflammatory funneled and purpose precise immune agents through the capillary cell's outer membrane complex is robust as its infrastructure has been nurtured through dance step refurbishment to accommodate and quality assure the multipurposed outcomes of the circadian rhythms it elicits. The endo and exocytic flows through the capillary and downstream endothelial cell support anti-inflammatory multipurpose fulfillment while at the same time refresh the cell's infrastructure that in turn will bias a rhythmic pace, stem, ricochet and backwashed execution of dance step multipurpose. As long as its nuclear chromosomal DNA can sufficiently code for protein synthesis and that its nitric oxide combustion cycle remains robust, the infrastructure refurbishment will remain intact which will keep the dance step rhythm anti-inflammatory inclusive as it simultaneously outperforms chronic inflammatory interstitial space signaling and metabolic overtures. Dance step interstitial space immune vetting is further refined by:

- The capacity of the mesenchymal cell to send and receive intelligence regarding the interstitial space inflammatory breach and then pass this on to the capillary cell's basement membrane as an "all hands-on deck" or "all clear" signal.
- The capacity of the capillary cell's basement membrane to correctly translate and relay the conveyed mesenchymal messages to and from the continuous outer membrane.
- The gathered luminal capacity of the capillary cell's continuous outer membrane to target the required immune responses from the signaling cues it was provided that will y push transmembrane cAMP adjustments and open up its luminal infrastructure towards specific immune funneling.
- The cAMP fluxes will enable the processing of infrastructure switch chain react that will facilitate specific immune funneling as luminal adhesion receptors are exposed to the glycocalyx.
- The fluxing trans continuous outer membrane *cAMP expressions* will also transfigure *metabolic adjustments* within the interstitial space that will pulse pH, osmolality, transluminal glucose/fatty acid gradients and ratios and oxygen carbon dioxide tensions.
- The adjustment in continuous outer membrane permeability mechanics will also pulse the luminal glycocalyx to increase or decrease its *stickiness* that will enhance adhesion receptor attachment of specific circulating immune arsenal.
- The permeability mechanics of funneled immune arsenal into the interstitial space will be increased or restricted by the capacity of nearby mitochondria to combust surges of dance step pulsed energy or nitric oxide which in turn become part of the feedback loop chain reactions that process dance step outcomes.
- These fluxing dance step hyperbolas will facilitate the transfiguration of its outer membrane complex from oval (responsive to the interstitial space mesenchymal cell) or flat (responsive to the interstitial space end organ cell outer membranes) to increase or decrease its responsiveness to either cell based on dance step purpose (Figures 5,6,7,9,10, appendix)[6,7].

Fluxing dance step rhythms will vary their intensity of response and duration based on what is required to dance step fulfill and the intensity and rate of the previous dance step response. For whatever reason, when these dance steps become desynchronized dance rhythms lose capacity to compensate anti-inflammatory purposed outcomes or coordinate completely with the previous dance step's execution. Inevitably with a disjointed dance two step, dance step functional miscues will increase, immune funneling will lose capacity to generate precision outcomes, and anti-inflammatory purpose reconciliation of the interstitial space will be less than satisfactory[5,6,7,25]. The loss of capillary cell dance step endo and exocytic anti-inflammatory functional resilience becomes the chronic inflammatory towards enhanced interstitial space inflammation, as immune funneling errors will transfer their signaling allegiance to increasing chronic inflammatory rhythms (Figures 17 and 18, appendix) [7].

Robert L Buckingham, MD, FACP

When Anti-Inflammatory Dance Step Purpose Fulfillment is *too Little* or *too Late*

The successful reverberation of a capillary cell pivot and swing dance step rhythm requires many mutually inclusive and interlocking signal and metabolic chain reactions from different cells that help facilitate momentum towards its counterbalanced and multipurposed anti-inflammatory fulfillment of *transcellular restitution, interstitial space hygiene and enduring end organ cell functional reserve* (Figures 10 and 20, appendix) [5,6,7]. The mechanics of these consecutive multicellular coordinated dance step reverberations when robust will have a baked-in *signaling and metabolic resilience* that biases its own rhythm counterbalance and anti-inflammatory multipurposed quality assurance. The dance step fulfilled anti-inflammatory momentum will enable the capillary and downstream endothelial cell to seamlessly *auto adjust* its beat-to-beat dance steps to accommodate variability of different levels of interstitial space inflammatory breach or end organ cell functional output. The timely processing of each dance step becomes dependent upon how and when the previous dance step was purpose fulfilled with its outcome success or lack thereof becoming part of the signaled and metabolic processing of the next dance step.

The implication within the context of dance step fulfillment is that the maintenance of end organ cell functional reserve, the optimal sanitation of interstitial space and the completed infrastructure restitution of the capillary cell and its interstitial space allies becomes co and interdependent on the timely and comprehensive outcomes to its consecutive dance steps. The counterbalanced endo and exocytic transcapillary flows of cytokine, enzyme, free radical and electromagnetic cues become the existential rhythms that preclude anti-inflammatory dance step purposed fulfillment. It is the continued egress of these dance step rhythms that prevent the capillary cell dance steps from becoming "too little or too late" in their resolve to execute multipurpose [7,24].

End organ, adjacent capillary and nearby interstitial space mesenchymal cells live in a continuous processing of a pulsed signaling and metabolic microenvironment where the capillary cell facilitates endo and exocytic rhythms that enact anti-inflammatory multipurposed fulfillment to and from the interstitial space and blood/lymph plasma. These executed outcomes will then provide a metabolic and signaling framework that incentivizes the next dance step shift in purpose fulfillment as its outer membrane complex permeability gradient and mitochondrial combustion output adjusts to accommodate this shift. The dance step process, whereby multipurpose is fulfilled becomes the circadian mechanic that facilitates dance step functional endurance (Figures 10 and 20, appendix).

The facilitation of a functionally counterbalanced dance step rhythm implies a multipurposed anti-inflammatory fulfilled circadian "sweet spot" that requires precise and facile adjustments within each signal and metabolically coordinated dance step as each two-step will have some level of functional variability compared to the previous two step. process. This implies that each functionally counterbalanced pivot and swing two-step process will arc a slightly different set of signaling and metabolic prerogatives that fulfill anti-inflammatory multipurpose with each consecutive step contiguous with and interdependent upon the previous dance step's functional execution. The capacity to formulate adaptive anti-inflammatory beat to beat dance step functional performance becomes dependent on the capillary cell's ability to restore or replace worn out infrastructure which become codependent on the cell's capacity to generate a nitric oxide combustion cycle whereby its nuclear chromatin has not been code silenced to process at capacity protein synthesis [7]. The capillary cell's capacity to dance step flex its beat-to beat functional reserve keeps its rhythm's anti-inflammatory multipurposed performance intact. Doing so delays transcellular obsolescence that enables anti-inflammatory rhythms to maintain interstitial space preeminence thereby preventing the "too little, too late" functional outcome that enables a chronic inflammatory interstitial space adjudication.

Chapter Seven

The Mechanics of the Anti-Inflammatory Capillary Cell Dance Step: The *"Pace and Stem"* Effect

The Pulsed Anti-Inflammatory Capillary Cell's Dance Step *Pace and Stem* Effect

The capacity for capillary endothelial cells to *signal lead* anti-inflammatory outcomes that timely remove interstitial space inflammatory breach while optimizing its sanitation in one dance step while procuring transcellular restoration and increasing end organ cell functional reserve in the next step defines the pivot and swing *pace and stem effect* (Figure 10, appendix) [5,6,7]. It is achieved through the pulsed capillary cell's fluxing of signaling and metabolic interstitial space transitions that facilitate the pulsing of purpose specific anti-inflammatory outcomes into the interstitial space that are dance step multi transactional. The process requires signaled input and purpose coordination with nearby mesenchymal and end organ cells that together with the anti-inflammatory compilation of purpose specific immune cells and other interstitial space coordinates become integrative to the capillary cell's pace and stem effect. These mechanics are dance step conveyed through the pulsed fluxing and purpose fulfillment that emanates endo and exocytic signaling and metabolic dance step rhythms through its highly evolved outer membrane complex.

The functionally sophisticated outer membrane complex will pulse shift its permeability to conform to dance step functional prerogatives that procure these outcomes into the interstitial space and allied cellular partners as the pace and stem effect and also to the central circulation as the backwash effect which will be discussed in a separate chapter. The pace and stem effect features an immune recipe that will obliterate inflammatory breach to sanitize the interstitial space. When it does this, it opens the door for optimal engagement and functional intimacy between the outer membranes of the capillary and end organ cell as the next dance step ushers into the interstitial space increasing flows of nutrient and oxygen delivery. The capillary cell sequential dance step pivot and swing adjustments in outer membrane permeability and mitochondrial combustion output will message their pace and stem effects to adjacent capillary cells via gap junction connexins as well as to downstream arterial endothelium.

This interstitial space orchestrated multipurposed anti-inflammatory outcomes work best when the dance step rhythm is counterbalanced which in turn will functionally quality assure its outcomes as each step postures optimal outcomes while securing signaling and metabolic thresholds that foundation fulfillment of next step purpose. The dance step "in rhythm" pace and stem effect will provide impetus for the mesenchymal cell to message its pulsed "all clear" and "all hands-on deck" signals, which pave the way for capillary cell dance step pivot and swing transitioning. This capillary cell outer membrane permeability sequence will also be conveyed to its end organ cell partner as its basement membrane exchanges surface intimacies between the end organ and mesenchymal cells outer membranes when the cell reconfigures its morphology from oval to flat. In this manner the signaling and metabolic rhythms that in turn produce anti-inflammatory functional outcomes within the context of the capillary cell's dance steps become the interstitial space pace and stem *executioners* as they share to and from pulsed feedback loops with funneled interstitial space immune arsenal and allied mesenchymal and end organ cells. The capillary cell's dance steps become the **functional *pacemaker*** that optimizes the functional rhythms of its allied cellular interstitial space partners. The capillary-endothelial cell's *pivot and swing* dance steps, and its *reverberating anti-inflammatory pace and stem outcomes,* become the preferred method by which allied cells within its interstitial space domain manage and integrate their functional homeostasis.

The capillary cell dance step rhythm pace and stem effect will directly tie into the functional utility of the capillary cell's entire organelle infrastructure and their purpose fulfillment as well as of its interstitial space network and downstream endothelial cell brethren. This in turn will get signal and metabolically crosslinked with other more distant endothelium, capillary cells and end organ cells. In this manner the dance step multipurposed pace and stem anti-inflammatory fulfillment, becomes an interstitial space institutional effect that is co shared with immune, mesenchymal and end organ cells[6,7,29]. In doing so, the capillary cell dance step pace and stem process produces anti-inflammatory interstitial space rhythms and outcomes that provide signaling and metabolic thresholds that interloop the capillary cell anti-inflammatory multipurpose to the functional reserve and outcomes of all its allied interstitial space cells[5,6,7]. Without a viable capillary cell dance step interstitial space pace and stem effect all other cells within its domain including the end organ cell become less functionally capable with the interstitial space becoming increasingly more vulnerable to chronic inflammatory signaling and metabolic rhythms.

When the capillary cell dance step rhythm is functionally counterbalanced and quality assured, the interstitial space pace stem effect is anti-inflammatory enhanced. The interstitial space signaling and metabolic collective between the capillary, mesenchymal and end organ cells will cantilever an interstitial space anti-inflammatory *ricochet effect*[7]. Hence the pulsed dance step rhythm will pace, stem and ricochet an anti-inflammatory interstitial space reverberation of enhanced anti-inflammatory multipurposed fulfillment that becomes a powerful inhibitory adjunct that purges chronic inflammatory rhythms. When the capillary cell dance step rhythm maintains its functional composure, it will not only transmit a potent *anti-inflammatory* context into its interstitial space domain, but its signaling and metabolic output will also denature any pretext of a proinflammatory signaling or metabolic context (Figure 10 and 20, appendix).[7]

The Mechanics of the *Pace and Stem* Effect

The streaming of a pulsed pace-stem anti-inflammatory signaling rhythm requires a counterbalanced capillary cell pivot and swing dance step process whereby its functional capacity to timely remove vascular inflammatory free radical interstitial space impediments remains robust. The interstitial space inflammatory breach removal becomes an integral part of the dance step signaling and metabolic rhythm that triggers its pace and stem to its allied cellular partners and signaling domain. Within the functional context of the mesenchymal cell, the purpose fulfillment of the dance step will include feedback loop rhythms to and from the mesenchymal cell that "signal and metabolically gate" the anti-inflammatory interstitial space outcome as its outer membrane that is now contiguous with the capillary cell's basement membrane tracks with immune processes that are removing the inflammatory breach. As the process gets completed, the capillary cell outer membrane complex will transition to become flatter, moving its surface are away from the mesenchymal cell to become contiguous with its end organ cell partner as the cells next dance step become intentional to its functional needs. In this manner the dance step rhythm becomes a *fluxing and rotating outer membrane triangular arrangement* between the capillary, mesenchymal and end organ cell that is interdependent on the pace and stem anti-inflammatory outcomes that are processed through the capillary cell dance steps. Based on these reverberated signaled and metabolic compilations, the capillary cell's continuous outer membrane will pulse its dance step permeability by fluxing master switch continuous outer membrane cAMP levels, that in turn will create functional intimacies with the mesenchymal cell, when free radicals are being interstitial space cleared, or the end organ cell, when the interstitial space is sanitized and its functional utility is being maximized. The capillary cell's continuous outer membrane cAMP response will in large part adjust based on signaled exchanges with the mesenchymal cell's "all clear" cytokine inhibitory or expansionary "all hands-on deck" signaling streams. It is within the context of the capillary cell continuous outer membrane's master switch cAMP that the capillary cell's outer membrane complex will increase or decrease its permeability gradients to subsequently swing mitochondrial combustion towards energy or nitric oxide to accommodate a shift in dance step purpose.

As continuous outer membrane permeability to inflammatory mediator funneling decreases, transcapillary cAMP levels increase which in turn reduces the outer membrane complex need for calcium ions and ATP which are no longer required to support the immune funneling processes. Their subsequent accumulation within the capillary cell's cytoplasm will form concentration gradients that will penetrate the porous mitochondrial outer membrane, enter the intermembrane space and begin processing signal and metabolic exchanges with the voltage potent mitochondrial inner membrane. The dynamics of these exchanges will feedback loop inhibition of ATP synthase at cytochrome V while causing the activation of nitric oxide synthase within the mitochondrial matrix to stimulate production of nitric oxide gas. As the same time, the capillary cell's outer membrane complex will have reduced its permeability to funneled inflammatory mediators into the interstitial space as the outer membrane complex has shifted its purpose to pace and stem effect signals and metabolic rhythms that enhance end organ cell functional utility as the capillary and nearby mesenchymal cell also process infrastructure restoration. When in a reverberating dance step rhythm, the mechanics of the pivot and swing pace and stem effect will be circadian timely, signal and metabolically counterbalanced, functionally quality assured and multipurpose anti-inflammatory fulfilled (Figures1-5, appendix)[5,6,7].

The sequential dance steps will not likely carry the exact same pivot and swing permeability and combustion footprint. This means the fluxed pace and stem messages to the interstitial space serve as a dynamic reminder that the interstitial space, capillary and accompanying allied cells represent a dynamic and pulsed continuum of functional adjustments based on a compilation of many interlocked signaling, metabolic and functional rhythms. The beat-to beat variability of the dance step's pace and stem effect will functionally threshold through:

- The pulsed intensity and duration of the capillary cell continuous outer membrane's cAMP gradient as it engages switch infrastructure that includes the activation or inhibition of different protein and tyrosine kinases that both gate and activate chain reactions that effect membrane permeability.
- These switch activations/deactivations will facilitate trans capillary outer membrane complex adjusted permeability gradients that enhance or inhibit the funneling of interstitial space inflammatory mediators from blood or lymph plasma.
- One outcome of many to shifting outer membrane complex permeability will be the fluxing of the continuous outer membrane's *voltage gradients* to align with its permeability immune

funneling maneuvers. The fluxing voltage gradient is mediated by the transmembrane infusion of mitochondrial released calcium which becomes a potent inhibitor to the sodium and potassium voltage "pump".

- The calcium ion infusion to the capillary cell's continuous outer membrane will be in sync with surging mitochondrial combustion of ATP that will in turn be released to the outer membrane complex for the active transport of certain types of immune arsenal into the interstitial space via transport vesicles or transcellular transport channels as these transport vehicles require energy to work against osmotic or hydrostatic pressure gradients.
- The calcium ion effect will lower the continuous outer membrane's voltage gradient which in turn will allow for the increase mobilization of transmembrane gases and smaller inflammatory mediators from the blood and lymph plasma via diffusion and facilitated diffusion.
- The dance step mitochondrial infusion of calcium to the continuous outer membrane will also bring about a transfiguration of the capillary cell's outer membrane complex to become oval, thereby withdrawing its basement membrane away from the end organ cell to become more intimate with the outer membrane of the nearby mesenchymal cell[5,6,7].

Capillary Cell Infrastructure Feedback Loops and Shifting Mitochondria Combustion

The capillary cell dance step rhythm, and the functional interstitial space dance step pace and stem effect it enables, is initiated by outer membrane complex permeability shifts that push a variety of operational switch mechanics within its infrastructure. The execution of outer membrane complex permeability adjustments requires both signaling and metabolic clarity from the interstitial space mesenchymal and end organ cells as well as inter looped engagement with its mitochondrial combustion apparatus as it swings energy and nitric oxide production that conform to permeability adjustments[6,7]. This back-and forth capillary cell outer membrane complex permeability rhythm is mitochondrial combustion facilitated to become a potent functional multipurposed anti-inflammatory rhythm as it paces and stems the intent of adjusted purpose to its interstitial space cellular allies. The dance step implications to swinging capillary cell mitochondrial combustion are:

- Rhythm codependent on the timely mesenchymal cell "all clear" or "all hands-on deck" signal that clarifies dance step intentionality and the subsequent capillary cell mitochondrial combustion cycle.
- When continuous outer membrane cAMP concentrations flux to increase or decrease outer membrane complex permeability on the basis of the mesenchymal cell signal, the fluxes in transmembrane calcium and energy become powerful feedback loops to the mitochondrial inner membrane to signal adjustments in combustion output.
- The capillary cell's fluxing outer membrane complex permeability gradients become the primary arbiter of mitochondrial combustion mechanics.
- The production and pulsed release of dance step mitochondrial derived ATP, nitric oxide, calcium and magnesium will facilitate anti-inflammatory functional outcomes that become integral to the capillary cell's pace and stem effect.
- The reverberation of the capillary cell's dance step mitochondrial energy and nitric oxide combustion cycles become integrative to a counterbalanced cytoplasmic glycolysis/gluconeogenesis fermentation rhythm as well as inducing a similar stimulus towards liposomal lysis and lipogenesis. The dance step processing will also counterbalance

- mitochondrial pyruvate and fatty acid oxidation towards the production of acetyl co A as well as its distribution to ribosomes or the Krebs cycle.
- In this parabolic back and forth fluxing of outer membrane complex permeability and mitochondrial combustion, will cause the remainder of the capillary cell's infrastructure to functionally conform to its functional outcomes.
- Within mitochondria itself the fluxing of its combustion apparatus will chain react signaling and metabolic rhythms that increase or decrease the production or degradation of heme, antioxidants and other of its infrastructure derivatives as well as incentivizing its fission/fusion, autophagy (pore suicide)/replication cycles (Figures 8 and 9 appendix)[6,7].

The capillary cell's outer membrane complex permeability *push* will facilitate either mitochondrial nitric oxide or energy combustion which in turn will chain react the execution of *completely different* sets of capillary cell signaling and metabolic rhythms that execute anti-inflammatory multipurpose which both *counterbalance and quality assure* the execution of each pivot and swing dance step. The back-and forth dance step process will get conveyed to the interstitial space and allied cells as a rhythmic pace and stem effect which keeps its allied cells within its domain on the same functional page.

The Capillary Cell's Mitochondrial Combustion Shift Facilitates Execution of the Pace and Stem Effect

When the capillary cell dance step rhythm stalls out, so does its pace and stem effect to its interstitial space allied cells. The loss of the capillary cell's dance step rhythm and subsequent diminishment of its nitric oxide mitochondrial combustion cycle produces rhythm *dyssynchrony,* which nullifies dance step signaling and metabolic counterbalance, restricts anti-inflammatory multipurpose and predisposes to chronic inflammatory interstitial space signaling and metabolic reverberations from signal converted immune arsenal. To summarize, a nullified capillary cell mitochondrial nitric oxide combustion cycle will cause:

- The reduction of capillary and mesenchymal cell infrastructure refurbishment with specific reference to loss of mitochondrial fusion/replication cycle.
- A reduction in *telomerase* activation as nuclear telomeres shorten to expose nuclear chromatin to ROS cross linkage.
- The reduction of all capillary and mesenchymal cell infrastructure repair to include the mitochondrial refurbishment of *heme, antioxidants and combustion infrastructure.*
- The reduced refurbishment of the capillary cells outer membrane complex that includes its mosaics of pores, receptors, switches, gates, vesicles and infrastructure proteins.
- The reduction of all the ancillary functional benefits derived from nitric oxide that involve fluxing and counterbalanced metabolic rhythms that improve upstream oxygen delivery to enable optimal end organ cell function [,6,7].

The *Pace and Stem* Effect Optimizes Interstitial Space Allied Cell Functional Reserve and Longevity

The capillary cell's dance step-pace and stem effect will utilize counterbalancing signal and metabolic exchanges to functionally outcome anti-inflammatory multipurpose which in turn will benefit the functional rhythms of its allied cellular interstitial space partners[6,7]. In this context, the pace and stem effect will pulse multiple streams of interlocking signaled and metabolic rhythms that project inclusive anti-inflammatory interstitial space outcomes that optimizes mesenchymal and end organ cell functional attributes. The efficient recycling of in rhythm dance step anti-inflammatory multipurpose through its pace and stem effect will incentivize the allied cell residing within the interstitial space towards improved functional longevity.

Built into the pace and stem effect is a reverberating anti-inflammatory *multipurpose refresh* as each dance step's executed fulfillment becomes the signaling and metabolic lattice for the next dance step's execution. These rhythms get messaged to the interstitial space and allied cells as streams of activated cytokines, enzymes, free radicals and electromagnetic wavelets that in turn chain react purpose execution. The capacity of the pace and stem effect to reverberate interstitial space anti-inflammatory multipurpose will incentivize its allied cellular partners to optimize their purpose fulfillment as each cellular entity integrates its functional rhythms to dance step outcomes. In this manner the dance step's pace and stem effect becomes collaborative to the functional fulfillment of all allied interstitial space cells. At the same time, its reverberation substantiates a robust anti-inflammatory signaling and metabolic nomenclature that prevents chronic inflammatory interstitial space rhythms from finding any intentionality (Figure 10, appendix). When capillary-endothelial cells are permutating anti-inflammatory dance step rhythms, its pace-stem effect will collectively *refurbish, quality assure and functionally optimize* the interstitial space and its allied cells within its domain[6,7]. This makes the capillary cell's pivot and swing dance step rhythm a pace and stem multipurposed anti-inflammatory interstitial space powerhouse whose functional aptitude is only limited by the degree to which its nuclear chromosomal DNA can code process protein synthesis infrastructure refurbishment[5,6,7].

Chapter Eight

The *"Ricochet and Backwash"* Effects of the Dance Step Rhythm

The Anti-Inflammatory Signaling and Metabolic Dance Step Rhythm will Pace and Stem Effect a Complementary *Ricochet and Backwash Effect*

With the timely removal of end organ interstitial space vascular inflammatory free radical impingements, the mesenchymal cell "all clear" cytokine *inhibitory* signal will salvo to the capillary cell's basement membrane messages that restrict further immune interstitial space funneling from blood and lymph plasma (Figures 6 and 7, appendix)[5,6,7] The signal will cause the capillary cell's outer membrane complex to transition its permeability whereby numerous infrastructure mechanics are put into place that limit immune funneling into the interstitial space. The outer membrane complex permeability adjustment is facilitated primarily by master switch cAMP which facilitates the necessary infrastructure chain reactions to adjust permeability. The permeability shift will invoke a host of signaling and metabolic influences within the capillary cell that will also process a powerful shift in mitochondrial combustion.

When the capillary and downstream endothelial cell pivot and swing dance step rhythm is properly *paced and counterbalanced it will invoke a quality assured multipurposed anti-inflammatory set of outcomes* that are mutually beneficial to the capillary and allied cells as well as its interstitial space domain. The anti-inflammatory reverberation of the capillary cell's dance steps to its interstitial space domain is known as the *ricochet effect* and is facilitated by pulsed and precision purposed cytokines, enzymes, electromagnetic wavelets and free radical streams from various transcellular membranes that in unison rhythm an orchestrated multipurpose.

The dance step *ricochet effect* becomes an existential component to dance step anti-inflammatory purpose fulfillment. When coupled with the pace and stem effect, the combined rhythms will outcome a tsunami of anti-inflammatory *special effects* that optimize interstitial space sanitation that becomes additive to its operational homeostasis. As it conveys its anti-inflammatory verve, the signaling and metabolic special effects invoke a powerful immune rhythm that firmly antagonizes pro and chronic inflammatory interstitial space seeds to deny their efforts to stream expression. The anti-inflammatory signaling and metabolic ricochets as they achieve functional success will in turn produce rhythm streams towards the capillary cell's basement membrane (that synergize with the mesenchymal cell's 'all clear" signal) that will dance step induce an exocytic push through the capillary cell as an anti-inflammatory backwash into the blood or lymph plasma. This *backwash effect* of anti-inflammatory molecular streams will fuse with other similar anti-inflammatory streams within the blood plasma to collectively process a systemic immune enhancement by molecularly tweaking circulating immune arsenal outer membranes to prepare them for purpose fulfillment once dance step funneled into the interstitial space. This anti-inflammatory backwash through the capillary cell becomes a mitochondrial combustion nitric oxide *facilitator* as their exocytic push should enable a systemic anti-inflammatory immune enhancement as released capillary cell nitric oxide induces increases in upstream oxygen delivery. The combination of capillary cell dance step interstitial space anti-inflammatory *ricochet* effect (from increased outer membrane complex permeability to funneled inflammatory mediators) followed by the two step blood and lymph plasma *backwash* (facilitated by the dance step's nitric oxide combustion cycle) will stream and rhythm a host of anti-inflammatory metabolic rhythms as well as streams of cytokines, enzymes, free radicals and electromagnetic wavelets which support a systemic authentication of anti-inflammatory end organ interstitial space outcomes(Figure 10, appendix)[7].

The capillary cell's reverberating and pulsed outer membrane permeability pivot and mitochondrial combustion swing in order to be fully operational will require both the interstitial space ricochet and systemic backwash effects to occur in a counterbalanced two step dance tandem. The outcome success of Its rhythm will momentum the reverberation of powerful anti-inflammatory rhythms that message intent and purpose execution through the capillary cell's dance steps *in both* interstitial space (ricochet effect) and blood plasma (backwash effect) directions. In this manner the capillary cell outer membrane complex facilitates pulsed chain reactions that communicate and execute multipurpose through the rhythm of its dance steps that include all immune performing elements on both luminal and abluminal membrane surfaces in both endo and counterbalanced exocytic directions [5,6,7]. The back and forth dance step rhythms that invoke a robust anti-inflammatory *pace, stem, ricochet and backwash* will signal and metabolically counterbalance an "in rhythm" multi-purpose execution whose conveyance through the capillary cell requires bidirectionality.

Ricochet and Backwash Malignment

If the capillary-endothelial cell pivot and swing dance step rhythm becomes anti-inflammatory misaligned, the permeability pivots of the capillary cell's outer membrane complex will become unbalanced and desynchronized[5,6,7]. This permeability and combustion block will cascade chain reactions of adverse signaling and metabolic rhythms within the capillary cell that eventually cannot be compensated for which in turn inhibits the dance steps from executing an interstitial space or blood plasma anti-inflammatory resolve. The loss of dance step rhythm counterbalance becomes the signaling and metabolic loophole that is utilized by budded proinflammatory interstitial space seeds to find a chronic inflammatory foothold. With maturation to a certain signaling and metabolic threshold, the interstitial space and blood plasma will sync their purpose alignment that reduced the anti-inflammatory pace, stem, ricochet and backwash effects as its rhythms becomes increasingly intentional towards disease consort advocacy.

The anti-inflammatory success of each pivot and swing dance step depends on the timely counterbalancing ebb and flow of its *in-rhythm* signaling and metabolic effects. The execution of these rhythms, which pulse and stream from purpose precise anti-inflammatory coordinated immune, mesenchymal and end organ cells functional outcomes, will correspondingly elicit waves of interlocking cytokines, free radicals, enzymes and electromagnetic wavelets that drive dance step multipurpose fulfillment (Figure 9, appendix) [6,7]. In aggregate, these rhythms execute anti-inflammatory purpose while at the same time fending off rhythms that might conspire against them. The to-and-fro interstitial space ricochet and backwash reverberations through the capillary cell will crosstalk a potent anti-inflammatory language that facilitates clarity to purpose execution that will include an optimized interstitial space sanitation and allied cell infrastructure restitution as it enables and enduring end organ cell functional reserve.

When interstitial space components are in an anti-inflammatory *signaling and metabolic consensus and in rhythm* with the capillary cell pivot and swing dance steps, they facilitate a recurring multipurpose fulfillment (Figure 10, appendix) [5,6,7], whereby the ricochet and backwash effects become a **rhythmic signaling and metabolic shield** of reverberating and interlocking chain reactions that signal loop anti-inflammatory fulfillment. These interlocking anti-inflammatory chain reactions are accomplished by:

- The signaled clarity from the interstitial space mesenchymal cell of the "all clear" and "all hands-on deck" cytokine salvos to the endothelial and capillary cell's basement membrane.
- The precision of the capillary cell's outer membrane complex to facilitate an appropriate luminal permeability response from those signals.
- The capacity of capillary cell mitochondria to deliver optimal combustion outcomes to the outer membrane complex permeability pivots.
- The capacity of each dance two-step to have *"rhythm plasticity"* whereby each dance step can vary its intensity and duration to accomplish anti-inflammatory purpose execution.
- The purpose transparency of anti-inflammatory ricochet and backwashed signaled and metabolic rhythms.
- The dance step's capacity to outcome purpose ready interstitial space sanitation, transcellular restitution, end organ cell functional resolve and blood plasma immune optimization (Figure 10, appendix) [7].

How the Capillary Cell's Dance Step Anti-Inflammatory Backwash Effect Works

The dance step anti-inflammatory backwash into the blood and lymph plasma of cytokines, enzymes and free radicals becomes a potent molecular anti-inflammatory inducer of circulating immune constituents as they support their molecular reconfigurations towards the enhancement of anti-inflammatory interstitial space outcomes. These enhancements will facilitate an anti-inflammatory *reverberation* as each dance two-step will induce a backwash that will continue the molecular transfiguration of circulating immune constituents towards an anti-inflammatory interstitial space purpose fulfillment. The consignment of these anti-inflammatory bidirectional dance step mechanics will involve:

- Pulsed capillary cell *fermentation rhythms* of gluconeogenesis (during interstitial space immune funneling interstitial space ricochet) and glycolysis (during the blood plasma backwash).
- The anti-inflammatory capillary cell fermentation shifts will be intimately linked to its mitochondrial combustion practices of how it utilizes pyruvate and fatty acids to produce acetyl co A and where acetyl co A gets shuttled once it is produced. The same hold true for liposomal lipolysis and lipogenesis of longer chained fatty acids.
- A transcapillary dance step shift of purpose that is signaled to all of its organelles to conform to the purpose identity.
- The capillary cell two step effect that counterbalances mitochondrial energy and nitric oxide combustion to the ricochet and backwash rhythm and anti-inflammatory outcomes.
- The backwash effect is also linked to capillary cell infrastructure restitution that includes the entirety of its outer membrane complex, mitochondrial combustion apparatus and the nuclear DNA protective telomere caps.

> ➢ Keeping ROS and RNS combustion exhausts counterbalanced thereby preventing their untimely binding to membrane and nuclear chromatin surfaces (Figures 9 and 10 appendix) [5,6,7]

An End Organ Example of How the Anti-Inflammatory Backwash Integrates with Functional Multicellular Rhythms

A significant benefit to a reverberating anti-inflammatory trans-endothelial cell backwash is to reduce circulating immune contingent vulnerability of being interstitial space signal converted to express a proinflammatory rhythm [6,7]. The power of the anti-inflammatory backwash effect becomes attached to the integrity of future capillary and downstream endothelial cell dance step fulfillment as it empowers circulating immune arsenal to become purpose prepared for next step interstitial space inflammatory breach removal. The dance step amplification of end organ interstitial space sanitation becomes integral to the fulfillment of the second step of the dance rhythm as it supplies the necessary signaling and metabolic framework for transcellular restitution that is buttressed with increased upstream oxygen delivery.

With the context of each end organ's interstitial space there will be a different anti-inflammatory template due to the functionality of the end organ cell, its outer membrane relationship to the capillary cell's basement membrane, and its relationship to the nearby mesenchymal and pericyte cells. This extends to how the capillary cell's dance steps pace, stem, ricochet and backwash each end organ cell based on its functional attributes. In these functionally diverse end organ scenarios, the anti-inflammatory backwash effect will reflect how these different interstitial space transcellular outer membrane exchanges outcome their respective purposes in the context of the pivot and swing dance steps. Regardless of how these mechanics are facilitated, when in dance step anti-inflammatory rhythm, the backwash through the capillary cell will incentivize anti-inflammatory blood plasma immune initiatives that will enhance future dance inflammatory breach removal[6,7].

Within the context of the liver hepatocyte, the cell is flanked within its sinusoid by the capillary cell's very porous basement membrane as well as by nearby Kupffer and pericyte cells in the Space of Disse. The interactivity of these cells in the dance step executed removal of space of Disse inflammatory breach (vascular inflammatory free radical) will induce an exocytic backwash back through the capillary cell consisting of cytokines and free radicals that will be anti-inflammatory intensive towards preparing (by molecularly tweaking their outer membrane configurations) circulating immune contingents within the portal circulation towards becoming anti-inflammatory responsive to next dance step space of Disse inflammatory breach removal. When anti-inflammatory inclusive, the space of Disse manages its sanitation to where the hepatocyte becomes more functionally astute as it reconciles sizeable metabolic rhythms to output complex multipurpose fulfillment of proteins, cholesterols, clotting factors and other byproducts that become institutional to the functional homeostasis of multiple other end organ cells. In this context the capillary cell's anti-inflammatory dance step rhythm integrates purpose fulfillment with multiple cells within its space of Disse domain that will also include the functional rhythms of the mesenchymal and pericyte cells. It is the combination of these signaling, metabolic and functional maneuvers within the pace and stem of the capillary cells pivot and swing rhythm that facilitates anti-inflammatory interstitial space outcomes whereby each cell's functional derivative within the dance step's domain will be optimized. This in turn will enable a potent anti-inflammatory backwash into the portal circulation. The immune enhancements that are collectively gathered from this backwash will provide for a future anti-inflammatory bias when the next dance step processes the removal of vascular inflammatory free radical breach within the space of Disse.

The back and forth of the capillary cell's pivot and swing dance step rhythm will allow for execution of dance step purpose fulfillment as each two step interstitial space ricochets and blood plasma backwashes anti-inflammatory rhythms, which in the liver sinusoid, occurs between the space of Disse and portal circulation. The back-and forth capillary cell's dance step anti-inflammatory rhythm and multipurpose fulfillment will create a signaling and metabolic counterbalance that incentivizes all the cells within its domain to optimize their performance which in turn also prevents these cells from transitioning into darker domains such as hepatocyte fatty liver transformation. It should also block the unnecessary distribution of hepatocyte derived proinflammatory sugars, small particle LDL cholesterol, other inflammatory proteins, triglycerides, adipokines and AGEs.

When the capillary cells within the liver sinusoid are dance step fulfilled and transcellular integrative, space of Disse vascular inflammatory free radical clearance is enhanced, the functional integrity of the cells within the capillary cell's domain are optimized, and the capacity for chronic inflammatory interstitial space rhythms to occur within its domain are greatly diminished. This means that cancer cells are effectively neutralized or isolated, infectious seeds are contained, autoimmune mishaps are deterred and scarring or thrombosis mistakes are diminished.

The backwash expression within from the capillary cells of the liver sinusoid will interlink with backwash from other liver sinusoids or even from more distant end organ cells to produce an optimized immune compilation of anti-inflammatory enhanced contingents that are capable of removing vascular inflammatory free radical interstitial space breach which in turn further intensifies the capillary cell's capacity to execute its dance step process (Figures 10 and 20, appendix)[7]. The capillary cell's dance step rhythm will produce a counterbalanced ricochet and backwash that will keep all the allied cells within its domain in a finely tuned anti-inflammatory arc of multipurpose fulfillment. This will ensure that vascular inflammatory free radicals are timely interstitial space removed and chronic inflammatory interstitial space seeds are aborted or isolated before they become virilized[7].

Chapter Nine

When End Organ Interstitial Spaces Lose Their Signaling Way: The Path Towards Chronic Inflammatory Intent

The Menace of Persistent Proinflammatory Interstitial Space Signaling and Metabolic Noise

The proinflammatory dysrhythmia within end organ interstitial spaces is provoked by persistent, abundant and diverse arrays of vascular inflammatory free radical impingements that occur as a result of maladaptive lifestyle choices involving ingestion or inhalation of sugars, salt, alcohol, drugs and tobacco. The capillary and downstream endothelial cell dance steps cannot suitably remove them which unbalances its dance step rhythm with the loss of signaling and metabolic counterbalance producing cracks in the integrity of its multipurposed outcomes. As funneled immune arsenal become increasing incapable of eliminating the interstitial space inflammatory breach, dance steps become increasing incapable of delivering a quality assured multipurpose thereby enabling chronic inflammatory interstitial space signaling and metabolic rhythms a chance to fill the interstitial space void. This chronic inflammatory interstitial space snag will further subvert the circadian dance step rhythm as pace, stem, ricochet and backwash rhythms anti-inflammatory desynchronize thereby enabling an auto perpetuating and increasingly intentional proinflammatory interstitial space signaling and metabolic amalgam that will birth disease venues.

The primary interstitial space mechanic that abets this transition is the loss of dance step *signal and metabolic counterbalance* which then dissipates its functional quality assurance of multipurposed outcomes. As anti-inflammatory in-rhythm signals and their corresponding metabolic chain reactions become disrupted, flaws in dance step outcomes increase to where they lose functional credibility. The anti-inflammatory dissonance will incentivize chronic inflammatory interstitial space transitioning as funneled anti-inflammatory purpose neutral immune arsenal signal convert to become the agents of choice towards the concocting of chronic inflammatory intent. The process will transition virilize chronic inflammatory intent as the pseudocapillarized capillary cell's outer membrane complex becomes the funneling conduit of a chronic inflammatory immune cell wish list (Figures 11 and 12, appendix) [5,6,7].

The primary funneling mechanic toward this chronic inflammatory interstitial space transitioning is how their increasingly intentional signaling rhythms can *pirate* immune intent from the blood plasma through the pseudocapillarized capillary cell outer membrane complex that will facilitate the buildout of a disease consort. This enables the maturing chronic inflammatory signaling rhythms (the chronic inflammatory matrix and anti-organ)) to have increasing input into what immune type and how much of it is being funneled into the interstitial that can be signal turned and then reassigned to a specific chronic inflammatory task involving the disease consort build out. The capacity for chronic inflammatory interstitial space rhythms to outgun anti-inflammatory varieties will become dependent on the degree to which chronic inflammatory rhythms have virilized intentionality, the amount of capillary cell outer membrane complex pseudocapillarization, and the degree to which circulating immune remnants have been molecularly tweaked by proinflammatory backwash to conform to chronic inflammatory intent once interstitial space funneled and purpose converted (Figure 16, appendix) [6,7].

The chronic inflammatory signal pirating of the capillary cell's outer membrane complex will enable specific entrees of immune arsenal into the interstitial space that will run contrary to anti-inflammatory purposes while being biased to signal conform to chronic inflammatory intent as previous backwash has made them anti-inflammatory immune suppressive. In this manner funneled immune contingents will be anti-inflammatory purpose inept as they become proinflammatory purpose consigned to become part of an organizing chronic inflammatory amalgam of virilized intent. The auto perpetuated block of the capillary cell's dance step rhythm will make their increasingly pseudocapillarized outer membrane complex a worthy purveyor towards assisting the buildout of these chronic inflammatory interstitial space machinations[6,7].

The following bullets highlight how interstitial space chronic inflammatory signaling and metabolic rhythms transition:

- Vascular inflammatory free radical impingements pester and fester within interstitial spaces to facilitate the loss of capillary and downstream endothelial cell dance step rhythm.
- The disruption will eventually decrease anti-inflammatory interstitial space capacity to multipurpose perform reliable outcomes.
- As immune funneling miscues into the interstitial space escalate, they become anti-inflammatory purpose ineffectual and chronic inflammatory purpose useful.
- The increasing chronic inflammatory interstitial space signaling and metabolic purveyance coupled with capillary cell outer membrane complex pseudocapillarization, will enable signal pirating of immune content to and from the disabled capillary cell's outer membrane complex to bias the processing of a chronic inflammatory anti-organ build out.
- The chronic inflammatory *pirating* effect will be consummated by an auto perpetuating chronic inflammatory interstitial space *backwash* whose cytokine signaling rhythms will molecularly tweak circulating immune arsenal such that they are prepared to conform to chronic inflammatory interstitial space purposes (Figures 15 and 16, appendix)[6,7].

Inherent in the Potential Poisoning of Capillary Cell Dance Steps is that Rhythms Emanating from Them Can be Either Anti or Proinflammatory

One key mechanic towards the organization of a chronic inflammatory interstitial space intent is how their signaling rhythms that backwash intent through the capillary cell and into the blood plasma can prepare circulating immune contingents for their chronic inflammatory purpose once interstitial space funneled. This speed of this immune "transitioning" is based on several interstitial space signaling confluences that also involve the degree to which the capillary cell outer membrane complex has ben pseudocapillarized and the interstitial space mesenchymal cell has been signal coopted to favor a chronic inflammatory purveyance. As proinflammatory interstitial space rhythm control consolidates, the capillary cell dance step rhythm will

Robert L Buckingham, MD, FACP

multipurpose unhinge as its outer membrane complex and infrastructure transitions toward the chronic inflammatory pirating mechanic[6,7].

As funneled immune arsenal signal convert and chronic inflame purpose conform, their transmitted cytokines, enzymes, free radicals and electromagnetic wavelets express a chronic inflammatory purpose that will couple with increasing proinflammatory metabolic dysrhythmias to further frame intent. It is within this reverberating chronic inflammatory context where signal pirating of the capillary cell's outer membrane complex will increasingly virilize intent. The transitioning will process a plethora of potential anti-organ outcomes that will signature chronic inflammatory rhythms that will mosaic a confluence of disease consort buildouts (Figure15, appendix) [5,6,7].

The Chronic Inflammatory Interstitial Space Anti-Inflammatory *Desynchrony Effect*

The cascading chronic inflammatory consolidation of signaling and metabolic rhythms within the interstitial space will paralyze the capillary cell's anti-inflammatory dance steps and their functional outcomes in what can be termed the dance step rhythm *desynchrony effect*. Desynchrony will occur when anti-inflammatory capillary cell dance step rhythms become so weakened that they can no longer facilitate a reliable multipurpose. The implication being that invasive chronic inflammatory interstitial space signaling and metabolic rhythms have developed a trajectory whereby they have made the fledgling and increasingly diminished anti-inflammatory landscape inconsequential. The chronic inflammatory desynchrony effect implies that disease consorts will eminently manifest within the interstitial space. This transition requires that persistent vascular inflammatory free radical interstitial space impediments are mediating a chronic inflammatory interstitial space expansion that is being led by the interstitial space infusion of signal turned and purpose virilized immune arsenal. In addition, interstitial space mesenchymal cells will have been sufficiently signal converted to further conspire against the capillary cell's anti-inflammatory dance step rhythm.

The interstitial space chronic inflammatory desynchrony effect will increase the functional virulence of the emerging chronic inflammatory matrix and anti-organ[6,7]. This interstitial space proinflammatory transitioning will further *cannibalize* the capillary cell's infrastructure and the posturing of its anti-inflammatory dance steps to instead become a signaling and metabolic conduit of chronic inflammatory outcomes[7]. As the interstitial space desynchrony effect progresses, the capillary cell dance steps disintegrate as the cell becomes less of an anti-inflammatory beacon and more of an anti-organ enabler[7]. The signaling and metabolic cascades elicited will not only bias interstitial space diseases but will cripple what remains of end organ cell functional reserve.

The Interstitial Space Chronic Inflammatory *Multiplier Effect*

With persistent penetration into end organ interstitial spaces, vascular inflammatory free radical displays will antagonize the capillary cell's capacity to immune funnel sufficient and precise assets for their timely removal[6,7]. When this disparity smolders it births the chronic inflammatory interstitial space *multiplier effect*, which cascades sufficient proinflammatory interstitial space signaling and metabolic momentum so as to render the capillary cell dance steps anti-inflammatory ineffectual. Factors that directly or indirectly contribute to the chronic inflammatory multiplier effect include:

✓ The inability for the capillary and downstream endothelial cell's dance steps to timely remove vascular inflammatory free radical interstitial space displays.

✓ The degree to which immune funneling mistakes increase into the interstitial space have proliferated.

✓ The degree to which the capillary cell's dance step signaling and metabolic rhythm becomes signal and metabolically unbalanced.

✓ The degree to which the ricochet and backwash effects have functionally transitioned towards a chronic inflammatory purpose.

✓ The degree to which the capillary cell's infrastructure has becomes functionally obsolete[5,6,7].

The chronic inflammatory interstitial space multiplier effect will hinge on loss of dance step counterbalance, a diminished nitric oxide combustion cycle and the subsequent loss of infrastructure refurbishment. The process will make the capillary cell's disabled outer membrane complex ripe for chronic inflammatory interstitial space signaling inducements that will facilitate an exchange in purpose identity [5,6,7].

Linked to the chronic inflammatory multiplier effect is a proportional capillary and downstream endothelial cell *aging effect* that reduces its capacity to anti-inflammatory multipurpose dance step perform which in turn will increase chronic inflammatory willfulness towards intentional interstitial space disease consorts[6,7]. The implication from these two proinflammatory projections is that chronic inflammatory transitioning of the interstitial space will meet up with less anti-inflammatory resistance due to a deteriorating capillary cell capacity to perform. This will make the interstitial space even more vulnerable to proinflammatory rhythms as it will require *fewer* vascular inflammatory free radical interstitial space impingements to stall out the capillary cell's dance steps thereby making the space more chronic inflammatory conducive[4,5,6,7,16,24,30]. The chronic inflammatory interstitial space multiplier when coupled with the capillary cell senescence will likely produce lethal disease outcomes which become predictable outcomes beginning in midlife. In this scenario, lifestyle decisions, which lessen vascular inflammatory free radical interstitial space risk, become critical adjuvants as to whether or not this occurs. In this manner the capillary cell's aging effect will increase the chronic inflammatory multiplier effect and visa-versa.

The Signaling and Metabolic Synergies of the Chronic Inflammatory Multiplier and *Pirating Effects*

The combination of the anti-inflammatory interstitial space signaling and metabolic desynchronization and the increasing momentum of the chronic inflammatory multiplier effect will contribute to an increasingly virile capillary and downstream endothelial cell *aging effect*. The gathering of this signaling and metabolic interstitial space amalgam will increase capillary cell functional disability as the outer membrane complex, mitochondrial reserve and nuclear chromosomal DNA becomes increasingly anti-inflammatory inept. The encapsulation of capillary cell infrastructure decay will allow chronic inflammatory rhythms within the interstitial space to begin monopolizing functional willfulness as they begin to signal their own purposes to the mesenchymal cell outer membrane and capillary cell's basement membrane. This will transition the signal pirating effect as interstitial space backwashed proinflammatory intentional cytokines, enzymes and free radicals push through the capillary cell into the central circulation where they will tweak the molecular nomenclature of circulating immune arsenal in preparation for their redirected proinflammatory purpose once funneled into the interstitial space. These rhythms become anti-inflammatory immune suppressive as they speak to the signaling language of intentional chronic inflammatory interstitial space rhythms and their evolving disease consorts [5,6,7]. As increasingly numbers of funneled immune contingents convert and disperse intentional chronic inflammatory rhythms, their collective arbitrage will increase a proinflammatory willfulness to the interstitial space as the ricochet and backwash effects through the capillary cell become chronic inflammatory elicited (Figure 16, appendix).

The chronic inflammatory *pirating effect* on the capillary and downstream endothelial cell's basement membrane will also include the anti-inflammatory signal uncoupling of interstitial space mesenchymal cells which in turn will scramble their capacity to signal clarify "all clear" and "all hands-on deck" circadian signaling rhythms[6,7]. The transition from anti-inflammatory to chronic inflammatory interstitial space rhythms will involve the conversion of multiple streams of interlocked signaling and metabolic feedback loops which will be predicated on the degree to which the capillary cell's outer membrane complex will enable the interstitial space pirating effect.

The maturing of the chronic inflammatory interstitial space pirating effect on the capillary cells outer membrane complex to enable the expression of intentional proinflammatory signaling content to the blood plasma is known as the *chronic inflammatory matrix* [5,6,7]. As a result of this signaling transition, chronic inflammatory interstitial space funneled white blood cells, platelets, inflammatory proteins, immunoglobulins, complement and clotting factors, will become chronic inflammatory facilitators as they consign their released cytokines, enzymes and free radical chain reactions towards a chronic inflammatory interstitial space purposed identity. These increasingly virilized rhythms will impinge on the capillary cell's outer membrane complex to express and backwash an increasingly intentional momentum of chronic inflammatory purpose that will elicit disease consorts in a process known as the *chronic inflammatory anti-organ* [5,6,7].

How Persistent Vascular Inflammatory Free Radicals Transition the Interstitial Space Signaling, Metabolic and Functional Platform

Interstitial space vascular inflammatory free radicals can potentially disrupt interstitial space anti-inflammatory rhythms in several different ways [5,6,7]. When they do, their interstitial space pester and fester effect will interrupt the capillary cell's dance step rhythm counterbalance, increase interstitial space immune funneling mistakes, decay its infrastructure and predispose the interstitial space to convert to a chronic inflammatory signaling and metabolic platform. Vascular inflammatory free radical interstitial space impingements may enter the interstitial space *bidirectionally* which means they can mobilize from either the blood plasma or from the external environment through end organ's epithelial cell. This process of chronic bidirectional interstitial space poisoning will process immune funneling mishaps by the type of free radical, volume of entry and how it attaches or interacts with the different cell's outer membrane surfaces and infrastructure. Examples of these free radical-nascent cellular membrane mechanics include:

❖ How a specific free radical interacts with the nascent cellular membrane that would include attachment, diffusion through or malevolent assimilation within its infrastructure
❖ Utilizing the capillary and downstream endothelial cell's outer membrane complex active transport mechanics that mobilize albumen or other inflammatory proteins into the interstitial space whereby the circulating free radical will ligand attach to become a vagabond passive passenger into the interstitial space, after which it can detach from the transported protein to become an openly expressive free radical.

- ❖ By erroneously attaching to an exposed luminal continuous outer membrane adhesion receptor, they can camouflage admittance to the interstitial space via the gap junction complex assuming a false identity.
- ❖ By utilizing their unique size, shape and solubility characteristics they can capillary cell transmembrane diffuse through its continuous outer membrane to become involved with capillary cell infrastructure that can antagonize organelle function such as mitochondrial combustion mechanics
- ❖ A similar transcellular infrastructure *heckling effect* can occur in other cells within the interstitial space as well las the end organ cell itself. (Figure 9, appendix) [6,7].

When interstitial space vascular inflammatory free radicals cannot be timely dance step identified and removed, they will enable proinflammatory signaling and metabolic chain reactions that will desynchronize or uncouple the counterbalance of the cyclic anti-inflammatory rhythms that conform to the capillary cell dance steps. This will lead to an increasing disparity between anti-inflammatory and proinflammatory interstitial space chain reactions that will increase chronic inflammatory outcomes [5,6,7,8,9].

A Lethal Outcome to the Chronic Inflammatory Interstitial Space Battleground: Increasing Insulin Resistance

The chronically inflamed interstitial spaces *gateway* compilations of proinflammatory metabolic mechanics their outcomes will increase insulin resistance (Figure 15, appendix) [7]. Within the crucible of the disabled capillary cell dance step rhythm, increasing chronic inflammatory interstitial space signaling and metabolic momentum will cause the endothelial cell to lose fermentation counterbalance and bias additional *gluconeogenesis*. This will increase transcapillary and endothelial cell glucose concentration gradients which will bidirectionally diffuse through its outer membrane complex to affect the central circulation *and* interstitial space. The persistent increase in circulating blood sugars will have adverse metabolic ramifications in all end organs with particular reference to the manufacturing and distribution mechanics of the liver, pancreas and abdominal adipose. In these end organs the systemic blood sugar misalignment will contribute to infrastructure chain reactions that increase lipogenesis as the opposite occurs within the endothelial cytoplasm. In the liver and adipose cells, persistent blood sugar elevations predispose to the increased production/ distribution of LDL cholesterol, non-HDL cholesterol, triglycerides, advanced glycation end products and assorted inflammatory proteins. Within end organ interstitial spaces, persistently increased glucose levels and malevolent lipids will increase dysfunction of all cellular lines, including the capillary cell's basement membrane, as various other mesenchymal, pericyte, immune and end organ cell outer membrane surfaces and infrastructure are afflicted. The attachment interactions will increase dysfunction of membrane mechanics which will spread to involve the cell's infrastructure and their capacity to perform the cell's purpose. These types of metabolic and transcellular functional derangements will mature chronic inflammatory outcomes that biases the distribution and replication of infectious agents or the proliferation of interstitial space cancer cells.

The persistence of capillary and downstream endothelial cell insulin resistance will trigger a counterproductive cascade of interstitial space metabolic rhythms that will diminish the capacity of the anti-inflammatory capillary cell dance step rhythms to execute purpose while simultaneously biasing the accelerated maturation of chronic inflammatory interstitial space disease outcomes that could be end organ lethal. As insulin resistance escalates, the liver, pancreas and abdominal adipose will increase the production and circulation of malignant cholesterols, homocysteine, triglycerides, advanced glycation end products, proinflammatory adipokines and other inflammatory proteins that will multi-end organ interstitial space disseminate to further propagate and virilize a chronic inflammatory resolve[7].

This chronic and persistent fomenting of insulin resistance will produce a virilized chronic inflammatory multi-end organ interstitial space intent that will simultaneously thwart anti-inflammatory immune directives (Figure 18, appendix) [6,7]. The insulin resistance will nuance a continuous and abundant supply of metabolic vascular inflammatory free radicals that will relentlessly disrupt outer membrane capillary and endothelial cell surfaces but will also assimilate into its infrastructure as well as within other cells connected to its interstitial space domain to inflict a maligned transcellular functional dysrhythmia. As this occurs, the capillary cell dance step rhythm and associated anti-inflammatory outcomes will diminish as insulin resistance fuels a continuous flow of proinflammatory free radical distractions that will dysregulate and functionally unbalance transcellular fermentation, liposomal lipogenesis/lipolysis and mitochondrial combustion mechanics. The evolving chronic inflammatory metabolic rhythms triggered by insulin resistance will assimilate into an interstitial space that becomes a protagonist towards the chronic inflammatory anti-organ. As disease consorts consolidate the interstitial space signaling venue, the backwash cytokine and free radical expression they emit into the systemic circulation will be anti-inflammatory immune suppressive and proinflammatory immune enhanced (Figures 17 and 18, appendix) [6,7].

The Chronic Inflammatory Vascular Free Radical *"Allergen"* Affect

A clump of external (environmental) vascular inflammatory free radical interstitial space impingements can incite an acute, subacute or chronic immune response towards their arrival and will differ from other free radical impingements due to the type of immune response it will attract towards their interstitial space attachment. When identified and opsonized the type of immune response it generates is classified as an *allergic reaction or response* [6,7]. External environmentally expressed "allergens" are not typically thought of as a vascular inflammatory free radical, but in the broadest sense, their potential to membrane attach or penetrate without necessarily requiring an enzyme or molecular ligand and their potential to incite a chronic inflammatory interstitial space response, places them in the category of a vascular inflammatory free radical.

The capillary cell dance step derived immune response to an interstitial space allergen will elicit a different constellation of funneled and sequenced immune participants form the blood plasma as well as adjusted signaling arms from nearby mesenchymal cells. It will also sequence different types of "B cell" responses that involve different types of immunoglobulins (IgD and IgE) compared to other immunoglobulin responses. In spite of these immune funneling differences, their trajectory into end organ vulnerable interstitial space and their subsequent membrane attachment and immune response elicited could be considered a type of "antigen-antibody" reaction and classified in the broadest sense as a vascular inflammatory free radical.

When an allergen (typically an inhaled or ingested foreign particle or molecule) is not timely interstitial space opsonized by a sequenced and precise immune response, it may trigger a broad spectrum of variable "allergic immune responses" that can be classified as chronic inflammatory. Just as in other chronic inflammatory interstitial space situations, when this occurs the capillary cell's dance step rhythm will likely become dysrhythmic, lose functional counterbalance, and begin making immune funneling mistakes that increase or exaggerate the immune response towards the interstitial space allergen making it less effective in removing the allergen. As immune mistakes proliferate their released cytokines, enzymes and free radicals create chain reactions that feed off of each other to further exaggerate the allergic immune response. With reverberation a chronic interstitial space inflammatory response will occur that will continue to fuel proinflammatory chain reactions that will override anti-inflammatory rhythms or the effects of the unbalanced capillary cell's dance steps. As the allergic response becomes increasingly chronic, the capillary cell dance step rhythm will desynchronize and just like with other types of vascular inflammatory y free radical input, will virilize chronic inflammatory intent to unmask the processing of disease consorts. In this manner, a well-placed and persistent display of mucosal or intestinal "allergen(s)" free radicals can trigger a chronic inflammatory interstitial space response that will transition signaling and metabolic rhythms towards disease venues that include vasculitis, tumors, infections, scarring or autoimmune mishaps.

The initial "acute" allergic immune response funneled into the interstitial space is typically very interstitial space reactive as entering cytokines and acute phase reactants process an urgent immune expansion towards the allergen attachment. This initial phase will likely involve the influx and activation of acute phase reactants such as histamines, kinins and other cytokines that are very *vasoactive* implying they will substantially increase capillary cell outer membrane complex permeability towards additional inflammatory mediators into the interstitial space. The immune funneling process and subsequent inflammatory outcome can vary from something very subtle yet effective in the antigen removal to something very inflammatory mediator escalating whereby the response gets out of hand with subsequent interstitil space edema that is associated with end organ failure and hypotension (anaphylactic shock). In this setting, chain reactions within the interstitial space will force dramatic sets of proinflammatory signaling and metabolic shifts, the ladder of which will cause fluid shifts into the interstitial space, pH acidification, hypoxia, large shifts in osmotic and hydrostatic pressure gradients, insulin resistance and a complete loss of interstitial space anti-inflammatory counterbalance as effective interaction between capillary, mesenchymal and end organ cell goes into functional free fall. The inflammatory mediator interstitial space surge is led by inflows of IgE, basophils and eosinophils whose activated cytokines posture a potent vasoactive purpose that shifts large flows of blood towards the affected mucosal or intestinal interface. The processing of the "allergic response" will also involve at some level the interstitial space activation of immunoglobulins IgA, IgD and mast cells. When anti-inflammatory appropriate, the capillary cell dance step rhythm will stay in charge of the immune response and will package an immune compilation into the interstitial space that will quality control the allergen removal without disintegration into an overly exaggerated acute response or an ineffectual one that would lead to a chronic inflammatory interstitial space residual that becomes a set-up to a disease consort.

When the immune response to the allergen degenerates to a chronic inflammatory delivery, precision purposed immune funneling into the interstitial space becomes uneven and purpose reckless with their subsequent release of cytokines and enzymes supporting additional chronic inflammatory interstitial space disintegration [6,7]. In this setting, the interstitial spaces become prone towards an intentional chronic inflammatory consolidation that will prosper disease outcomes. The interstitial space immune arrays become disgruntled and purpose misaligned sets of eosinophils, basophils, mast cells, B and T leukocytes, and immunoglobulins that collectively have become persona non grata to the diminished anti-inflammatory capillary cell dance steps.

The Mechanics of an Allergic Interstitial Space Chronic Inflammatory Conversion

Within the context of a mucosal or intestinal allergic membrane attachment, the brisk anti-inflammatory response should timely opsonize its elimination and degrade its molecular components to trigger the mesenchymal cell's "all clear "signa and subsequent shift in dance step purpose[7]. Within this context the capillary cell outer membrane complex will choreograph a purpose precise immune carousel that sequentially targets the allergen to opsonize and reduce it to nitrogen, water and carbon dioxide. The dance step's anti-inflammatory rhythm will activate appropriately sequenced cytokines, histamines, kinins, IgE, eosinophils, basophils and macrophages that will sequentially posture the opsonization and reduction of the allergen as part of the two-step dance rhythm. In this context the capillary cell dance steps will process anti-inflammatory interstitial space signal and metabolic chain reactions that pulse the timely execution of purpose[7]. The chain reactions and their outcomes become part of the capillary cell's dance step rhythm as the facilitate the signaling and metabolic turnover for the next dance step.

Depending on the allergen interstitial space circumstances, when in the context of a dance step precise immune response, the processing of their removal will not stray form the dance step rhythm as more purpose precise immune arsenal are brought into the interstitial pace to handle the allergen load [6,7]. The timing of their opsonization and reduction becomes important to dance step success as delays will create an unbalanced rhythm with subsequent degeneration of dance step purpose fulfillment. When this occurs, subsequent immune dispersals into the interstitial space become increasingly purpose confused and prone to a chronic inflammatory purpose conversion. As this chronic inflammatory interstitial space transitioning process unfolds, the capillary cell dance steps and accompanying anti-inflammatory rhythms it elicits, will predictably decline to eventually chain react decay in the capillary cells outer membrane complex and infrastructure. This makes the cell a chronic inflammatory target for immune pirating through its dysfunctional outer membrane complex to further support chronic inflammatory interstitial space outcomes that extend beyond the chronic inflammatory responses to the allergen. In this chronic inflammatory interstitial space setting, allergens become the free radical fuel that will springboard the maturation of cancers, infections, scarring, vasculitis, thrombosis and autoimmune complexes (Figures 16-18, appendix).

The Interstitial Space Diffusion of Noxious Gases and How they Increase the Potential for Chronic Inflammation

The repetitive inhalation of carbon monoxide (CO) (from inhaled tobacco or hydrocarbons) or other noxious gases, can act as another type of vascular inflammatory free radical that can disrupt the capillary cell dance steps that involve combustion and metabolic feedback loops that involve other gases such as oxygen, carbon dioxide and nitric oxide. Unlike other free radicals, noxious gases can easily penetrate through membranes via simple diffusion as they follow concentration gradients from one side of the membrane to the other without the need to be actively transported or attachment facilitated. Within mitochondria, CO could disrupt combustion feedback loops within the matrix involving oxygen, carbon dioxide, nitric oxide and their byproducts to reduce combustion efficacy of either energy or nitric oxide production. In this setting, CO could disrupt oxygen, carbon dioxide and nitric oxide signaling ratios within the combustion apparatus as oxygen delivery to the interstitial space becomes an increasingly scarce commodity[7]. This increasing interstitial space oxygen-carbon monoxide gas disparity, if persistent, will favor a persistent shift in the capillary cell towards an unbalanced dance step rhythm that will favor increased energy combustion, gluconeogenesis and lipolysis as carbon monoxide gas blocks red blood cell delivery of oxygen into multi-end organ interstitial spaces.

When a sufficient volume of carbon monoxide gas penetrates the capillary cell's mitochondrial matrix, it will posture a "combustion adjustment" that will increase energy combustion and loss of dance step functional counterbalance. This carbon monoxide effect on the capillary cell's dance step rhythm will predispose to a proinflammatory interstitial space prodrome that will include a persistent interstitial space hypoxemia that will favor metabolic chain reactions that bias acidic pH and insulin resistance.

Within the mitochondrial matrix, carbon monoxide will also block cytochrome electron transfer energy combustion further straining an already deficient energy production. The blocking mechanic will involve the carbon monoxide affinity to the cytochrome iron ring which is pivotal to electron transfer. Given a sufficient volume of carbon monoxide gas, its mitochondrial presence becomes combustion paralyzing whether it is occurring in endothelium or epithelium.

The carbon monoxide effect, within the context of the anti-inflammatory capillary cell dance steps, will severely impact the multipurposed and functionally counterbalanced processing of interstitial space homeostasis. This would include both sides of the two step dance process as the energy combustion cycle increases but is less effective and the nitric oxide combustion cycle becomes increasingly extinct[6,7]. When persistent carbon monoxide poisoning is coupled with other vascular inflammatory free radical interstitial space displays, it will further accelerate chronic inflammatory outcomes[6,7]. In these instances the carbon monoxide effect on mitochondrial combustion mechanics within the capillary cell will couple with other vascular inflammatory free radical interstitial space impingements accelerate declines in capillary cell dance step drive anti-inflammatory multipurpose execution thereby setting up the interstitial space for a virilized chronic inflammatory expression.

In review, the carbon monoxide gas effect will enable the confluence of multiple proinflammatory chain reactions that will allow for:

- Preferential heme binding (as compared to oxygen) with the circulating red blood cell reducing oxygen delivery to capillaries to produce a relative hypoxemic effect.
- Within endothelial and epithelial cell mitochondria, energy combustion deteriorates due to blocked electron cytochrome transfers.
- Within capillary cell mitochondrial combustion counterbalance of if further reduced as CO interferes with oxygen, carbon dioxide and nitric oxide gas tensions.
- CO will block mitochondrial inner membrane *cytochrome C oxidase located in the mitochondrial inner membrane*, which becomes the rate limiting linchpin towards cytochrome electron transfer and efficient energy production (Figure 15, appendix)[5,6,7].

The Persistent Vascular Inflammatory Free Radical Interstitial Space Presence Becomes Chronic Inflammatory Fuel that Processes a Compelling Disruption to the Capillary Cell's Dance Steps

The chronic inflammatory interstitial space signal and metabolic transitioning relies on a steady supply of vascular inflammatory free radical interstitial space impingements to keep the capillary cell's dance step rhythm disjointed. The subsequent dance step overreach to remove them will eventually create such a dance step imbalance so as to degrade the capillary cell's infrastructure which then incentivizes immune funneling mistakes to make the interstitial space a breeding ground for chronic inflammatory rhythms [5,6,7]. Eventually these chronic inflammatory rhythms will coalesce to increase intentionality as they simultaneously marginalize anti-inflammatory purpose [5,6,7]. As the capillary cell's dance step rhythm dissipates, it loses anti-inflammatory signaling and metabolic liquidity as its own infrastructure collapses from the loss of its nitric oxide combustion cycle.

As vascular inflammatory free radical interstitial spaces impingements pester and fester, their capacity to fuel a chronic inflammatory expression will be proportional to the level they can disrupt the timing of their anti-inflammatory opsonization and reduction to water, carbon dioxide and nitrogen (Figure 15, appendix)[7]. How they unbalance the capillary cell's dance step rhythm will determine in large part how the interstitial space becomes chronic inflammatory vilified. As the interstitial space signaling and metabolic rhythms cede purpose to chronic inflammatory intent, disease consorts will find these rhythms to their liking. With progression, the capillary cell will surrender control of its outer membrane complex and infrastructure to these rhythms and with it the functional purpose of its interstitial space domain (Figure 16, appendix).

Chapter Ten

The Sequential Maturing of a Chronic Inflammatory Interstitial Space Signaling Proforma: Morphing into the *Inflammatory Matrix*

Mastering the Chronic Inflammatory Interstitial Space Signaling Proforma

The process whereby an interstitial space matures to a virilized chronic inflammatory disease venue can be compared to a road map whereby the destination goal has veered off into a different (and darker) reference point. The processes of how chronic inflammatory rhythms veer the interstitial space away from end organ cell functional nurturing can have many signaling and metabolic twists and turns whose machinations also involve how they interact with and purpose perform with declining anti-inflammatory rhythms. This is similar to the chronic inflammatory road map whereby the new and darker destination (disease venue) utilizes roads (signaling and metabolic rhythms) that may not be paved (uneven signaling), with potholes (signaling glitches) that are darkly lit (metabolic dead ends) and not clearly marked (rhythms could easily drift into a different direction) in order to arrive at a destination that is possibly different yet similar to what was expected (one or more disease venues).

When the chronic inflammatory road map evolves, and disease coordinates come into view, its signaling and metabolic collective will conspire against the capillary cell's dance steps to weave an operational process that will utilize what is left of the senescent cell to change the purposed identity of the interstitial space form nurturing end organ cell function to processing disease consorts(Figure 13, appendix)[6,7]. Depending on which roads (signaling and metabolic rhythms) the chronic inflammatory interstitial space process utilizes will in large part determine what destination (disease venue) will occur.

The chronic inflammatory interstitial space consolidation will outcome disease consorts from persistent vascular inflammatory free radical processes that will at its core outcome hypertension, insulin resistance (adult diabetes), dyslipidemia as well as a myriad of other free radical residues that are triggered by combination of inherited or acquired genetic vulnerabilities and assorted environmental exposures. The pathway that consolidates chronic inflammatory intent will involve a series of signaled and metabolic conversions that channel rhythms away from an anti-inflammatory interstitial space resolve to instead abnd mitochomembrane complex to funnel immune agents that will signal confirm to their purpose identity. When this occurs, chronic interstitial space inflammation will extract from the blood plasma immune agents that are "anti-inflammatory immune suppressed" as their outer membranes have been reprogramed via molecular tweaking to bias conforming to a chronic inflammatory purposed identity. When this occurs, the interstitial space transitions towards a different identity as the end organ cell's functional exuberance wanes (Figure 16, appendix)[5,6,7].

Achieving this chronic inflammatory interstitial space milestone involves will require a reorganization of interstitial space signaling and metabolic priorities. The process will fundamentally shift away from the timely removal of vascular inflammatory free radicals and optimizing the interstitial space to enable end organ cell functional optimization and towards disease expression. In this manner, as dance steps become less anti-inflammatory capable, its functionally deficient outer membrane complex will increasingly cater to a chronic inflammatory interstitial space signaling and metabolic apocalypse of disease consorts (Figures 8 and 14, appendix) [7,13].

The Loss of Anti-inflammatory Interstitial Space Operational *Plasticity* from an Atrophied Capillary Cell Outer Membrane Complex and Infrastructure

With progressive increases in chronic inflammatory interstitial space signaling and metabolic virilization, the evolving rhythms will punish the capillary cell's anti-inflammatory dance step rhythm, foreclose on its nitric oxide combustion cycle, and eclipse the capacity of its outer membrane complex to choreograph anti-inflammatory immune funneling relief into the interstitial space to process its hygiene and enable end organ cells to function at full throttle. Included in this dance step decay is the inability to process transcellular *restitution* which in terms of the capillary cell, is critical towards the retooling of its elaborate outer membrane complex and mitochondrial functional reserve[6,7]. The inability to timely eliminate vascular inflammatory free radicals from the interstitial space will eventually produce enough contrarian signaling and metabolic chain reactions to enable chronic inflammatory interstitial space rhythms to degrade the space for its own purposes. The capillary and downstream endothelial cell's dance steps become so anti-inflammatory compromised that they can no longer cater to anti-inflammatory outcomes.

The capillary cell's outer membrane complex pseudocapillarization effect will enable the interstitial space transitioning of chronic inflammatory intentionality. The process will transition chronic inflammatory virilization of the interstitial space by a backwash that signal pirates its proposed purpose to circulating immune constituents that have been molecularly tweaked to conform to chronic inflammatory purposes. The transitioning of the interstitial space from anti to proinflammatory intent can have false starts but can pick of processing speed as chronic inflammatory rhythms virilize intent. When this occurs, lingering interstitial space vascular inflammatory free radicals become fuel that feeds the chronic inflammatory fire that in turn will ignite a host of chronic inflammatory interstitial space expressions. The increased bungling of funneled anti-inflammatory immune arsenal into the interstitial space by the disabled capillary and downstream endothelial cell becomes a treasure trove of signaling and metabolic benefit to prevailing chronic inflammatory rhythms (Figure 9, appendix)[6,7]. When this occurs, unbalanced interstitial space metabolism will cater to a predilection of disease consorts via increased pH acidification, hypoosmolality gradients , insulin resistance and reduced oxygen tensions.

How the Pseudocapillarization Effect Diminishes Capillary Cell Anti-Inflammatory Interstitial Space Resolve

The loss of the capillary cell's outer membrane complex anti-inflammatory functional reserve means that it can be signal manipulated by chronic inflammatory interstitial space rhythms. The transitioning process will lend its disabled outer membrane complex to purpose align with chronic inflammatory outcomes. The mechanics of this outer membrane complex transition include:

> A persistent diminution of continuous outer membrane master switch cAMP levels.
> The persistent reduction (volume and diversity) of functionally viable luminal adhesion receptors, pores, budded vesicles and transcellular transport channels.
> A reduction in voltage capacity of the continuous outer membrane.
> A reduction in the capacity to expand or contract the aperture and width of the gap junction complex.
> A persistent thinning of the luminal glycocalyx mesh while the abluminal basement membrane thickens[6,7].

It is in this pseudocapillarized context that chronic inflammatory interstitial space rhythms will be poised to steer the capillary cell's disabled outer membrane complex into a different functional direction[7]. The transition will cater to the processing of chronic inflammatory interstitial space signaling efforts to mature disease consorts[5,6,7].

The Maturing of Chronic Inflammatory Interstitial Space Signaling and Metabolic Rhythms Transition from Being Merely Anti-Inflammatory *Disruptive* to Becoming Chronic Inflammatory *Purpose Intentional*

As proinflammatory end organ interstitial space rhythms consolidate interstitial space intent, they begin to intentionally send and receive their own signaling broadband to the capillary cell's outer membrane complex [6,7]. Whereas optimizing end organ cell functional requirements require capillary cell dance step *pulsed* and interstitial space adjusted pH, oxygen tensions, osmolality gradients as well as precisely tuned fluxing of glucose and fatty acid concentrations, the processing of interstitial space chronic inflammatory disease consorts can make do and even thrive with these metabolic derangements. With increasing dance step rhythm decay and less subsequent anti-inflammatory metabolic pulsing within the interstitial space, disease outcomes will use these metabolic shortfalls to their own advantage to express their growth and signaling preeminence.

The virilization of chronic inflammatory interstitial space signaling and metabolic rhythms reaches a tipping point when interstitial space funneled immune agents no longer cater to anti-inflammatory outcomes but prefer signal conforming to a chronic inflammatory purpose. This capacity hinges on the signal and metabolic proinflammatory transitioning of the interstitial space that coincides with the loss of the capillary cell's anti-inflammatory dance step pace, stem, ricochet and backwash effects. The implication is that increasing chronic inflammatory interstitial space *intentionality* will become capable of controlling how and where funneled blood plasma resources are utilized[7]. As these rhythms virilize proinflammatory intent, the metabolic interstitial space overlay they create will increasingly cater their chronic inflammatory outcomes making their interstitial space transitioning a-fait de accompli.

In contrast to end organ cells that are functionally dependent on the anti-inflammatory capillary cell dance steps, chronic inflammatory disease consorts find renewable exuberance from the signaling and metabolic rhythms that are misaligned to anti-inflammatory causes [7,25,32]. These rhythms will instead find functional value in interstitial space conditions where the metabolic outcomes are hostile to the functional viability of the end organ cell such as those purporting reduced oxygen tensions of increased insulin resistance. The metabolic interstitial space transitioning will include:

> A persistent expansion of vascular inflammatory free radical interstitial space fuel.
> The funneling of anti-inflammatory resistant immune contingents into the interstitial space.
> A static metabolic interstitial space proforma of persistent reductions in oxygen tensions, increased insulin resistance, acidic pH and aberrant fluid, electrolyte, osmotic and hydrostatic pressure gradients.
> The increasing capacity for chronic inflammatory signaling rhythms to coopt signaling intent form the capillary cell's outer membrane complex[7].

How Chronic Inflammatory Interstitial Space Signaling Prerogatives Exploit the Capillary Cell's Outer Membrane Complex

An important foundation piece of virilizing chronic inflammatory interstitial space intent is determined by its capacity to pirate the flow of immune contingents into the interstitial space that will conform to its purposed identity[7]. This mechanic will require the capacity to signal manipulate what is left of the disintegrating capillary cell's outer membrane complex to process an immune funneling that will prefer to respond to chronic inflammatory outcomes. As the interstitial space functionally transitions, the capillary cell's pseudocapillarized outer membrane complex becomes its organizing facilitator. The outer membrane complex mechanics of this transition include:

- The *tweener effect*, whereby the gap junction orifice and channel's width cannot sufficiently expand or contract which in turn limits its capacity to elicit an anti-inflammatory immune funneling payload which predisposes to interstitial space immune funneling errors.
- With the loss of gap junction orifice *adhesion* and *cadherin* receptors, the processing of anti-inflammatory immune funneling through its complex loses capacity to anti-inflammatory choreograph precise purpose.
- Instead, what is more likely to be gap junction processed into the interstitial space from blood plasma are anti-inflammatory purpose misaligned immune contingents that can be signal extorted to a proinflammatory conforming purpose.
- The pseudocapillarization process will cause the capillary cell's gap junction complex to lose *connexins and receptor proteins* that include AJ and TJ receptors. This will portend a *loosey-goosey effect* on funneled immune contingents through the gap junction complex. This occurs as the gap junction complex processes funneled white blood cells into the interstitial space from the blood plasma.
- The subsequent gap junction complex proinflammatory bottleneck effect will cause its protein infrastructure <u>to become less effective towards gating a precision purposed anti-inflammatory immune contingency into the interstitial space.</u>

- The reduced capacity to anti-inflammatory immune choreograph interstitial space purpose will inherently make the gathered immune contingents more likely signal stray towards a chronic inflammatory rhythm and purpose [6,7].

The Chronic Inflammatory "Smokescreen Effect"

An early and anti-inflammatory disruptive chronic inflammatory interstitial space signaling feature can be described as the *smokescreen or camouflage effect* [6,7]. This occurs persistent interstitial space vascular inflammatory free radical impingements couple with funneled and increasingly purpose misaligned immune contingents that subsequently elicit cytokines, enzymes and free radicals that further confuse or smokescreen immune contingents that are processing anti-inflammatory outcomes. When these immune contingents confuse anti-inflammatory intent their signaling rhythms will spread false information about the free radical interstitial space impingements that misleads mesenchymal, pericyte and anti-inflammatory paces immune cells. The smokescreen effect will cause anti-inflammatory gathered cells to stream messages to the capillary cell's basement membrane that are misconstrued or lack purpose clarity towards interstitial space anti-inflammatory outcomes. The effect will make inflammatory breach removal less effective and more time consuming thereby delaying the capillary and downstream endothelial cell's two step dance rhythm. This process if dance step sequential will progressively increase anti-inflammatory immune ineptness to where the dance step process eventually stalls out.

With progression of the camouflage effect, chronic inflammatory interstitial space signaling rhythms will mature to virilize purpose intentionality[7]. In this scenario, the increasing chronic inflammatory signaling prosperity will aggressively recruit and signal convert interstitial space immune contingents and mesenchymal cells towards their purpose identity as they denude anti-inflammatory interstitial space rhythms. The smokescreen effect will be harnessed to the emerging and purpose intentional *chronic inflammatory matrix* whose mission will be to initiate signal pirating of the capillary cell's outer membrane complex to enable specific proinflammatory immune funneling detail into the interstitial space.

The maturing of the chronic inflammatory interstitial space smokescreen effect will eventually enable the processing of interstitial space disease venues as the signaling apparatus gets revamped to express a chronic inflammatory rhythm. The subsequent backwash it expresses through the capillary cell and into the blood plasma will incentivize an anti-inflammatory immune suppression through cytokine and enzyme induced molecular reconfiguration of their membrane surfaces. These chronic inflammatory signaling and metabolic rhythms to and from the pseudocapillarized capillary cell outer membrane complex will:

- Continue to auto perpetuate rogue immune funneling attributes into the interstitial space.
- Virilize and consolidate intentional chronic inflammatory interstitial space signaling and metabolic purposed identity.
- Provides a signaling and metabolic interstitial space template that biases immune, mesenchymal and pericyte cell proinflammatory conversion.
- Provides backwash detail towards a circulating anti-inflammatory immune suppression.
- Further enhances chronic inflammatory interstitial space signaling rhythms via the reverberation of activated proinflammatory cytokines, enzymes, inflammatory proteins, free radicals and electromagnetic wavelets.
- Maneuvers increased chronic inflammatory interstitial space intentionality via the proinflammatory manipulation of osmotic, hydrostatic and pH gradients as well as with the

reduction of upstream oxygen tensions and increased insulin resistance (Figure 18, appendix) [6,7].

The chronic inflammatory smokescreen effect evokes an interstitial space signaling rhythm that becomes anti-inflammatory disruptive to eventually becoming a foundation piece towards intentional chronic inflammatory outcomes. When this occurs in full signaling and metabolic bloom, the multi end organ interstitial spaces become a chronic inflammatory reservoir of purposed identity[6,7].

The chronic inflammatory interstitial space smokescreen progression from anti-inflammatory disrupter to disease collaborator will tie in with all endothelia and end organ interstitial spaces as the signaling and metabolic chain reactions they enable incentivizes a backwash that anti-inflammatory immune suppresses[7]. When this occurs, end organ cells by necessity must functionally wither as their collective capacities to perform are negated by the oppressive chronic inflammatory transitioning of their interstitial space's signaling and metabolic rhythms towards a disease venue cadence (Figure 18, appendix).

Chapter Eleven

The Final Chronic Inflammatory Interstitial Space Solution: The *Anti-Organ*

The End Game of Consolidated Chronic Inflammatory Interstitial Space Signaling and Metabolic Rhythms

With the reverberation of chronic inflammatory interstitial space signaling and metabolic rhythms, the stage will be set for the intentional expression of anti-organ disease venues (Figures 16 and 17, appendix)[6,7]. In this chronic inflammatory interstitial space stage, the capillary cell's capacity to signal pace, ricochet and backwash anti-inflammatory signaling and metabolic rhythms has become so marginalized by the emerging chronic inflammatory anti-organ that meaningful anti-inflammatory purpose responsiveness into the interstitial space is no longer possible.

The failure of the capillary cell dance step rhythm to anti-inflammatory resist becomes the gain of chronic inflammatory interstitial space signaling and metabolic momentum[7]. The transitioning of the interstitial space towards darker functional displays becomes self-fulfilling as the interstitial space cellular constituents purpose convert to align with anti-organ signaling rhythms. When this occurs, the anti-organ will hijack intent to stifle what remains of anti-inflammatory purposed rhythms as it stiffens proinflammatory resolve (Figure 17, appendix).

The anti-organ interstitial space emergence will be associated with:

- The severe and often irreversible muting of anti-inflammatory interstitial space signaling and metabolic rhythms.
- The consolidation of interstitial space functional rhythms towards a chronic inflammatory purpose.
- The eclipse of the capillary cell's outer membrane complex to choreograph anti-inflammatory purpose.
- The capacity for merging interstitial space disease venues to brand their own signal and metabolic processes which expand their intent while backwashing an anti-inflammatory immune oppressive outcome within the blood plasma.
- A universal functional reduction of what remains of true end organ cells[6,7].

With the maturing of chronic inflammatory interstitial space anti-organ purpose fulfillment, the interstitial space fundamentally shifts its identity to signal and metabolically cater to disease platforms (Figure 17, appendix)[6,7].

The Evolution of the Interstitial Space *Anti-Organ* will Favor Oncogenesis

A predictable response from a virilized chronic inflammatory interstitial space signaling and metabolic confluence is for the nearby end organ cell to "circle the wagons" and defensively posture its outer membrane permeability gradients to resist the rising tide of interstitial space proinflammatory rhythms. It does this through several outer membrane mechanics that decreases outer membrane permeability towards the penetration of toxic interstitial space metabolic and free radical residues that have collected there and would damage end organ cell infrastructure. In this manner, end organ cell outer membranes are spared calcium ion penetration from nearby mitochondria thereby keeping its voltage gradient elevated and subsequent permeability to interstitial space free radicals diminished. In addition, the endocytic active transport from the interstitial space into its cytoplasm and infrastructure diminishes whereas exocytic rhythms to push previously absorbed toxic residues increase[6,7]. When these permeability rhythms of the end organ cells outer membrane persist, the end organ cell will begin to lose *functional counterbalance* as chronic inflammatory risks within the interstitial space requires that its outer membrane permeability gradients stay persistently increased to prevent free radical penetration into their cytoplasm. With this level of outer membrane defensive posturing, the end organ cell's mitochondria will be biased to combust less energy and more nitric oxide to prevent its infrastructure from being denatured from toxic interstitial space free radical displays.

While this end organ cell outer membrane permeability and mitochondrial combustion imbalance persists, the nearby capillary cell's outer membrane complex and mitochondria are signal and metabolically unbalanced in the opposite direction as its outer membrane complex continues to funnel immune arsenal into the interstitial space ward off chronic inflammatory interstitial space processes. These diametrically opposed signaling and imbalances of capillary and end organ cell outer membranes and mitochondria will cause all involved cells within the capillary cell interstitial space domain to functionally conform to these unbalanced rhythms. The result will be a diminution of the pulsed anti-inflammatory signaling and metabolic rhythms as chronic inflammatory interstitial space rhythms escalate. This will being about an end organ cell's functional fail which will chain react:

- the loss of functional integrity, counterbalance and operational *homeostasis* within its infrastructure
- accelerate its atrophy, senescence and apoptosis
- bias persistent increases in its mitochondrial combustion of nitric oxide gas (and *RNS-reactive nitrogen species exhaust*), which will form lingering concentration gradients within the cell that will unfavorably bind to membrane surfaces or nuclear chromosomal DNA to impair their intended purposes
- will inadvertently produce infrastructure chain reactions that bias the activation of end organ cell *growth factors*, that will ruminate excessive cellular replication, that when coupled with increased RNS-nuclear chromosomal DNA cross linkage, will increase risk for aberrant and recurring cellular division that favors oncogenesis (Figure 17, appendix) [7]

The persistent virilization of chronic inflammatory interstitial space signaling and metabolic rhythms will reduce end organ cell functional reserve as energy combustion is sacrificed for nitric oxide combustion. An unintended outcome will be the posturing of end organ cell oncogenesis from its overstretched mitosis. The persistence of end organ cell nitric oxide combustion will unleash multiple combinations of transcellular growth stimuli that will manifests through unnecessary mitotic replication. When this is coupled with the malignant transformation of its RNS crosslinked nuclear chromatin, the combination will bias unhinged oncogenesis as repeated cellular division occurs with multiple synthesized proteins within its infrastructure, that would ordinarily check and balance functional prerogatives, are either functionally denatured or missing altogether. This makes the newly minted cells not only less amenable to nascent cell functional attributes. but more likely to continue unmitigated cellular replication.

As these chronic inflammatory residuals continue to predispose to end organ cell oncogenesis, diminished anti-inflammatory interstitial space functional reserve will limit capacity to identify and remove them thereby increasing their replicative and autonomous interstitial space expressions. The newly formed "oncogenic cell lines" will have conformed their infrastructure metabolic rhythms to positively respond to interstitial space conditions that increase insulin resistance and reduced oxygen tensions when compared to their nascent cellular brethren which find these conditions more metabolically hostile. By using pyruvate to ferment energy, the mitochondrial combustion of nitric oxide will stay unmitigated thereby favoring unhinged replicative recycling and functional oncogenic demagoguery.

As the growing cancer mass continues to replicate and functionally uncouple from its nascent cellular ancestors, it will invoke its own rebel signaling and metabolic hierarchy that will exclusively cater to mass expansion and transcellular replication. The cancer mass growth roadmap will utilize preexisting chronic inflammatory interstitial space signaling and metabolic rhythms to position the cells within its infrastructure to find metabolic enhancements within this interstitial space environment. In this manner and unlike its nascent cell ancestors, the cells within the expansile mass will find metabolic benefit form an interstitial space that has become pH acidic, relatively oxygen deprived and insulin resistant. The ability of the cancer mass to utilize interstitial space metabolic rhythms that its nascent cell ancestors find hostile, gives them a functional leg up within an interstitial space that will increasingly favor these metabolic rhythms. As the cancer mass functional prerogatives mature to both control and extort interstitial space signaling and functional dynamics, the groundwork will be laid to involve other disease venues as well[6,7].

Eventually the cancer mass will force interstitial space chain reactions that are autonomous from its nascent cell ancestors as they separate their functional prerogatives to become independent contractors towards the usage of interstitial space natural resources. The conversion process is supported, not only by increasingly virilized chronic inflammatory interstitial space signaling and metabolic rhythms, but also by signal converted immune and mesenchymal cells. When these cells go all in towards the enablement of the cancer mass self-expression, cells within the mass will begin to subspecialize purpose fulfillment as its growth will require its own blood supply. Accordingly, angiogenesis within the cancer mass will be fortified with the infrastructure disbursement of numerous *transport tubules* that will further support the growth of its infrastructure from the passage of nutrient and oxygen. As this occurs, a network of infrastructure nerve conduction will evolve to enable transcellular communication and a connective tissue lattice will form to support the weight of its rapidly burgeoning size. This parabolic transformation will require help from signal converted immune, mesenchymal and pericyte cells, who will exchange their functional rhythms from anti to proinflammatory cadences to help process the expansile growth of the mass. As this occurs, the disabled capillary cell has converted its disabled outer membrane complex to become a functional conduit to cancer mass expression[7]. The loss of the capillary cell's dance step anti-inflammatory execution creates a powerful signaling void that can be overturned by the evolving chronic inflammatory matrix, anti-organ and its oncogenic outcomes.

The Anti-Organ *Triple Whammy Effect*

When the end organ's interstitial space becomes chronic inflammatory preoccupied, the signaling, metabolic and functional chain reactions that are elicited will coalesce an anti-organ *triple whammy effect*. As anti-inflammatory interstitial space rhythms retreat, their hibernation coincides with a diminished capillary cell dance step rhythm which in turn will prioritize an increased chronic inflammatory signaling and metabolic cadence that will process signal pirating of the capillary cell's outer membrane complex (Figure 18, appendix)[7]. The subsequent chronic inflammatory interstitial space streaming will conduit an increasingly virilized chronic inflammatory expression as funneled immune cells, immunoglobulins, platelets and clotting factors signal convert to chronic inflammatory outcomes. This chronic inflammatory interstitial space processing becomes part of a multi-end organ seismic shift of converted purpose identity as increasingly proinflammatory signaling and metabolic rhythms pervade and functionally process intent.

The chronic inflammatory signaling and metabolic *triple whammy effect* will involve:

- a pervasive increase of anti-organ intentionality towards disease consorts
- a progressive chronic inflammatory immune pirating effect through the capillary cell's outer membrane complex
- a systemic dance step compromise involving all capillary and endothelial cells
- the ricochet and backwashed converted trans capillary and downstream endothelial cell streaming of virilized chronic inflammatory rhythms that purport multi-end organ disease consortiums
- the rate of this chronic inflammatory interstitial space transitioning will be dependent upon the degree to which the systemic capillary cell population has had its dance step rhythm functionally compromised[5,6,7]

In this manner, the triple whammy of chronic inflammatory interstitial space effect becomes a systemic anti-organ affair that involves all end organs. As the systemic circulation becomes anti-inflammatory immune suppressed, chronic inflammatory multi-end organ interstitial space transitions of anti-organ purpose fulfillment will occur that are directly linked to a pan capillary cell collapse of its dance step rhythm (Figure 18, appendix).

What Constitutes an Anti-Organ *Profile*

The consolidation of an interstitial space *anti-organ signaling and metabolic proforma* will virilize disease consorts. This process will extort and increasingly sophisticated and intentional set of signaling and metabolic maneuvers that utilize signal converted immune arsenal and mesenchymal cells towards its purpose fulfillment. The constitution of the anti-organ interstitial space profile will become dependent upon:

- the nature of vascular inflammatory free radical interstitial space impingements
- the influx rate and type of immune constituents that are sequentially funneled (and signal converted) within the interstitial space
- the nature of what signal converted immune constituents will stream and what chronic inflammatory rhythms they coalesce with
- the chronic inflammatory nuance of its metabolic expression
- the rate and degree of capillary and downstream endothelial cell dance step rhythm degradation

- the functional and genetic detail of the true end organ cell that will predispose to specific anti-organ disease mosaics[5,6,7].

The compilation of anti-organ disease mosaics will engage, adapt to and coalesce with evolving chronic inflammatory signaling and metabolic thresholds within the interstitial space to forward its gathered vested interest of controlling the space's functional dynamics[5,6,7]. The time, rate and sequencing of anti-organ interstitial space disease threads will couple with proinflammatory to mosaic expression. As chronic inflammatory rhythms consolidate purpose, the interstitial space transforms its signaling and metabolic mechanics to cater to the new rhythms. Depending on the end organ, even small amounts of oxygen deficit will induce hypoxia, to end organ cells, reduction in functional rhythms and predisposition towards interstitial space and transluminal thrombosis. Within other end organs, their interstitial spaces will be prone towards producing amyloid or fibrous scar tissue. Regardless of the chronic inflammatory interstitial space signaling and metabolic displays, the end organ cell will suffer functional decay, atrophy and even die as its interstitial space mosaics a compilation of various infections, cancer growths or misaligned autoimmune complexes. Depending on whether the capillary cells basement membrane is inherently porous or not, the anti-organ will funnel interstitial space immune mosaics that will build-out the interstitial space predicated on what the basement membrane will enable. The build out and how is sequences will likely appear much different in liver, pancreas and intestine compared to brain, heart, retina and skeletal muscle (Figure 14, appendix) [5,7].

Through the coalescence and utilization of preexisting and existential proinflammatory interstitial space signaling and metabolic rhythms, the adaptable anti-organ will have a functional leg-up in comparison to the more signal and metabolically purpose confined end organ cell[6,7]. This is due in part to the anti-organ's capacity to *leverage* and *incorporate* evolving interstitial space proinflammatory signaling and metabolic rhythms into its functional proforma. This implies that interstitial space chronic inflammatory signaling and metabolic gradients will coalesce their own intentionality as they simultaneously resist anti-inflammatory rhythms and end organ cell functional requirements.

The anti-organ's capacity to *adapt*, *coexist* and *benefit* from evolving chronic inflammatory interstitial space rhythms makes disease expression more likely to occur[7]. The evolving signal and metabolic momentum of anti-organ fulfillment will also posture resistance towards subsequent anti-inflammatory interventions. As the anti-organ remasters and consolidates interstitial space rhythms, it will begin to control *functional outcomes* as it invokes its own brand of interstitial space homeostasis[6,7]. The signaling and metabolic composite will both monopolize and integrate proinflammatory rhythms to consolidate its ricochet and backwash ebb and flow into and out of the interstitial space and central circulation that will arc its purpose fulfillment. The initial end organ clinical expression within an interstitial space will typically manifest as a single dominant disease venue (such as a cancer, infection or hypoxic ischemic event), but with further maturation will become capable of transitioning multiple disease consorts at the same time.

Consolidating Anti-Organ Interstitial Space Intent

The anti-organ signaling mechanics within a given interstitial space will expand its reach as its rhythms nurture the activation of purpose targeted cytokines, enzymes, free radicals, communicating microtubules, electromagnetic wavelets and other signaling and metabolic caricatures. It will coalesce these rhythms to escalate purpose fulfillment as it simultaneously blunts anti-inflammatory caricatures that would work against these chain reactions [6,7]. The consolidation of chronic inflammatory rhythms will drive anti-organ fulfillment as they simultaneously decapitate signaling resistance against them.

The escalated chronic inflammatory interstitial space signaling and metabolic rhythms are further virilized by signal converted mesenchymal and pericyte cells and the adjacent signaling rhythms that are expressed from the induction of other disease seeds[7]. Their rhythm collectives will clarify anti-organ purpose as they vilify anti-inflammatory interstitial space processes. The anti-organ can retrofit signaling and metabolic prerogatives to coincide with a continuously adaptable purpose realignment. In this manner, the anti-organ will process its own interstitial space signaling and metabolic collective utilizing vascular inflammatory free radicals, the disabled capillary cell's outer membrane complex as it's funneling agent, and purpose converted immune and mesenchymal cells (Figures 17 and 18, appendix).

As anti-organ interstitial space disease venues sub-populate within interstitial spaces, signal turned mesenchymal cells will become important anti-organ functional facilitators as they lend signaling confluence to the propagation of disease consorts while simultaneously blocking signaling streams that support the capillary cell's dance step rhythm. The departure of the mesenchymal cell from an anti-inflammatory interstitial space context will help the anti-organ by:

> being a direct chronic inflammatory interstitial space participant as it produces fibrous scar tissue while signaling immune cells to produce amyloid scar tissue.
> as a cause or effect anti-inflammatory signaling scrambler by delaying or subverting the "all clear" or "all hands-on deck" signal
> directly blocking anti-inflammatory interstitial space dance step derived rhythms

As the anti-organ rhythm consolidates interstitial space purpose, the nearby capillary cell has lost capacity to process anti-inflammatory rhythms. For this to reverse, the capillary cell specifically and endothelium in general must be able to resuscitate their dance steps in a rhythm that approximates their full functionality. A full dance step resurgence will require that capillary cell infrastructure has the capacity to fully recover lost components such that their anti-inflammatory multipurpose recaptures its functional counterbalance (Figure 19, appendix).

A genuine reboot of the dance step rhythm will also involve an anti-inflammatory reconversion of nearby interstitial space mesenchymal cells, meaning they will once again peg anti-inflammatory rhythms that precision clarify the two step dance process[5,6,7]. When this anti-inflammatory interstitial space-pulsed signaling and metabolic conglomerate reemerges, it will posture a robust counter punch to subsequent anti-organ maneuvering that should be sufficient to reverse or block disease propagation (Figure 20, appendix).

Anti-Organ Outcomes will Thrive with the Expression of Darker Interstitial Space Metabolic Paths

One key factor that accelerates the rate of anti-organ interstitial space confluence is how proinflammatory metabolic expressions will improvise its virulence. In contrast to the end organ cell, anti-organ disease expression is most likely enhanced from reduced interstitial space oxygen tensions, increased insulin resistance, acidic pH-anomalies and hypo osmotic pressure gradients[5,6,7]. In these settings, the end organ cell is purpose deflated, while on the other hand, the anti-organ will utilize these metabolic aberrancies to its advantage to process their outcomes. All five major disease groups (*oncogenesis, infectious agents, autoimmune attachments, hypercoagulable* states and *thrombosis,* and *amyloid / fibrous scar deposition*) become anti-organ inducible from these proinflammatory metabolic interstitial space rhythms. They are facilitated by the anti-organ's utilization of:

> *fermentation* (cancer cells, infectious agents) mechanics for energy production that in turn will process excess interstitial space sugars thereby allowing their combustion mechanics to bias nitric oxide (replicative) production
> fermentation to produce energy, cancer and bacteria cells can use limited interstitial space oxygen supplies to propagate nitric oxide combustion and vis-a-vis replication.
> Its signal *pirating effect* on the capillary cell's basement membrane and outer membrane complex to funnel the necessary immune contingents that would further additional proinflammatory metabolic rhythms
> interstitial space signal transitioning that couples with proinflammatory metabolic rhythms to virilize anti-organ expression [6,7]

In this manner, evolving disease consorts will become contingent on escalating proinflammatory metabolic rhythms. The transition does not just confer advantage to cancer cells or infectious agents, but also to chronic inflammatory converted immune and mesenchymal cells as their signaling rhythms will yield further impetus towards chronic inflammatory priorities[5,6,7]. What becomes end organ interstitial space likely is that virilized chronic inflammatory metabolic rhythms will signal enhance anti-organ expression making its disease outcomes more purpose expansile.

The Unwinding of Anti-Organ Infrastructure is Dependent on How Comprehensive its Rhythms have Functionally Integrated with Pervasive Chronic inflammatory Interstitial Space Chain Reactions

The resuscitation of a diminished capillary cell pivot and swing dance step rhythm from an interstitial space dominated anti-organ will require a sharp and sustained reduction of vascular inflammatory free radicals within the interstitial space. When this occurs, weakened but still functionally viable interstitial space anti-inflammatory rhythms will begin to process their elimination as their volumes become easier to manage. As such their removal will provide a signaling consensus that will stream to nearby mesenchymal cells to produce a muted but effective cytokine inhibitory "all clear" signal. This will in turn stream to the capillary cell's basement membrane and then outer membrane complex to initiate a permeability pivot that will place a damper on further immune interstitial space funneling. As cAMP, ATP and calcium ions accumulate within the capillary cell's cytoplasm due to this permeability pivot, concentration gradients and subsequent feedback loops are created towards the mitochondrial inner membrane and cytochromes that swing combustion to nitric oxide. This will initiate the next pivot and swing dance step and the reverberated beginning of anti-inflammatory multipurposed recycling of the dance step rhythm. The rebirth of the counterbalanced capillary cell dance steps will remove the oxidative rust from its infrastructure as the return of the nitric oxide combustion cycle will provide such impetus. Doing so will begin the interstitial space transitioning process whereby signaling influence moves away from the anti-organ and towards anti-inflammatory rhythms. When this occurs, interstitial space metabolic rhythms will transition improved oxygen tensions and reduced insulin resistance as well as the return of more optimal "anti-inflammatory" pulsed osmotic, oncotic and pH gradients[7].

When anti-inflammatory interstitial space signaling and metabolic prerogatives become dance step integrative, the anti-organ's interstitial space control becomes vulnerable as anti-inflammatory purpose precise immune funneling resumes. The reconversion of the Interstitial space purpose to an anti-inflammatory multipurposed dance step rhythm becomes complementary towards expelling anti-organ chronic inflammatory resolve (Figure 20, appendix)[7].

The consolidation of interstitial space anti-inflammatory signal and metabolic rhythms will fortify a multipurposed identity that can eventually thwart anti-organ functional displays. This becomes more likely if and when:

❖ **Anti-inflammatory immune funneling has been sufficiently restored.**
❖ **The interstitial space anti-inflammatory metabolic rhythms have improved their functional countenance.**
❖ **The capillary cell's dance step nitric oxide combustion cycle has been sufficiently transitioned.**
❖ **The capillary and downstream endothelial cell's nuclear chromosomal DNA is still sufficiently code capable to execute protein synthesis infrastructure replacement[6,7].**

When anti-inflammatory interstitial space signaling, metabolic and functional rhythms can find sustenance, their outcomes will effectively compete with previously entrenched anti-organ rhythms (Figures 19 and 20, appendix) [7]. The effect will pulse a net positive anti-inflammatory interstitial space purveyance that will reconvert the direction of interstitial space rhythms as anti-organ rhythms unwind. It does as anti-inflammatory cytokines, enzymes, selected free radicals and electromagnetic wavelets revamp their purposes within the interstitial space[7]. The return of an anti-inflammatory capillary and downstream dance step rhythm will prop up allied cell refurbishment, interstitial space hygiene and end organ cell functional resolve (Figure 20, appendix).

How the Anti-Organ Gateways Disease Mosaics

Any end organ's interstitial space can transition a chronic inflammatory anti-organ given a sufficient rate and volume of persistent proinflammatory signaling and metabolic chain reactions [5,6,7]. Within this context, vascular inflammatory free radical basement membrane impingements among others, typically become so commonplace that they cannot be dance step timely removed thereby creating loss of dance step counterbalance, and the deterioration of dance step anti-inflammatory multipurposed execution. The inability to remove vascular inflammatory free radicals begins the progressive assault of chronic inflammation within all end organ interstitial spaces that culminates in the buildup of basement membrane or other membrane impingements. In larger downstream arterial vessels basement membranes will begin the process of thickening that will yield obstructive plaques in bifurcating vessels which in turn will reduce upstream oxygen delivery. The loss of reliable upstream oxygen to a very combustion dependent end organ cell will chain react decay in its functional rhythms. With persistence and progression, the upstream end organ cell will atrophy from insufficient oxygen delivery as its interstitial space becomes signaling fodder for various chronic inflammatory anti-organ outcomes that will include coagulopathies, thrombosis and other disease venues. The upstream chronic inflammatory path will cause capillary cells to pseudocapillarize their outer membrane complex, shrink their mitochondrial volumes and compromise their nuclear chromatin from increasing ROS cross linkage. The functional decline of the capillary cell becomes the anti-organ's growth vehicle as it transitions functional priorities through the manipulation of the capillary cell's outer membrane complex.

When hypoxia and ischemia has sufficiently marginalized enough functional viability from the upstream end organ, its signaling and metabolic fallout will predispose to other anti-organ disease venues whose mosaics intertwine with the evolving chronic inflammatory interstitial milieu and the specific functional vulnerabilities within any given end organ's interstitial space. The disease mosaic that intervenes will be based on the fortitude and signaling hierarchies of these vulnerabilities within the evolving chronic inflammatory interstitial space hegemony.

Within the context of an upstream chronic inflammatory interstitial space nest, the anti-organ will create a signaling and metabolic monopoly that will initially manifest one dominant disease consort while at the same time predisposing to other secondary disease venues. This occurs as the anti-organ assembles a signaling and metabolic lattice that will nurture secondary disease development. As upstream oxygen tensions diminish, the associated increases in interstitial space insulin resistance and non-pulsed pH and other aberrant pressure gradients will confer a survival and growth advantage to cancer cells and assorted infectious agents[7].

In these chronically persistent anti-organ interstitial space makeovers, signal converted and purpose retooled immune and mesenchymal cells will release cytokines, enzymes and free radicals that nurture chronic inflammatory rhythms that can involve multiple disease fronts that will become increasingly ignored by a diminished anti-inflammatory immune reserve. As these chronic inflammatory interstitial space rhythms consolidate, they will construe virulence towards anti-organ intent that will eventually control the lion's share of the interstitial space signaling and metabolic hierarchy. When this occurs, the interstitial space will transition from being anti-inflammatory multipurposed to becoming chronic inflammatory manipulated. At a certain signaling and metabolic threshold, the process becomes irreversible as the anti-organ will exert too much control over the interstitial space and the capillary and downstream endothelium lack sufficient infrastructure reserves to combat it.

Chapter Twelve

Scarring: One Outcome of Signal Turned Mesenchymal/ Lymphocyte Cell Purposed Conversion from Darker Interstitial Space Signaling Rhythms

The Chronic Inflammatory Escalation of Multi End Organ Interstitial Space Fibrous and/or Amyloid Scar Tissue

The chronic inflammatory production of fibrous or amyloid scar tissue or both occurs when proinflammatory signaling and metabolic chain reactions within a given end organ's interstitial space have consolidated to where mesenchymal or lymphocyte cells have been purpose recalibrated to produce either fibrous or amyloid scar tissue. These secreted residues form an interstitial space lattice that separates the functional continuity between the end organ cell and the functionally disparate capillary cell that will strangulate end organ cell performance [5,6,7]. The secreted proteins will arrange in such a way that makes end organ and capillary cell outer membranes incapable of functional intimacy which predisposes to both cell's loss of functional resolve. The production of amyloid and fibrous scar tissue from signal converted mesenchymal and lymphocytes becomes a manifestation of a maturing chronic inflammatory interstitial space signaling and metabolic lattice.

The secretion of these metabolically inert proteins will form a non-penetrable *"accessory"* membrane like barrier that blocks to and from functional intimacy between interstitial space cells. The chronic expression of scar tissue, regardless of which type, implies that the interstitial space has converted it's signaling impetus to an overriding proinflammatory signaling and metabolic rhythm. The interstitial space scar scaffolding is just one of several potential chronic inflammatory outcomes that will escalate disease conglomerates. The inert interstitial space scar buildout can be described as *embalming* the already functionally compromised end organ cell making even more difficult to function or interact with adjacent cells within the interstitial space.

Within its architecture and by blocking access to anti-inflammatory cells and rhythms, fibrous and amyloid scar tissue can become a respite and seeding magnet for cancer cells, infectious agents or both. By preventing anti-inflammatory immune recognition while facilitating reduced oxygen reserves, amyloid and fibrous scarring will push disease entrees that rely on fermentation and insulin resistance to propagate their growth. In this setting, the scar lattice when coupled with other favorable chronic inflammatory metabolic prerogatives will bellwether additional anti-organ disease expressions.

The formation of scar tissue, regardless of where its produced, will share some unique chronic inflammatory features that include:

> ➤ A functionally inert lattice that can provide a signaling and metabolic cover for other disease consorts.
> ➤ Its processing is favored by chronic inflammatory interstitial space oxygen deficits, insulin resistance and non-pulsed pH and other permeability gradients.
> ➤ The scar lattice makes the interstitial space refractory to anti-inflammatory rhythms or what might be left of capillary cell dance steps.
> ➤ The patterns of which interstitial space scar will process will become dependent on specific chronic inflammatory signaling rhythms within the space and with what cells they can subjugate. In some cases, other disease venues or surreptitious signaling from the end organ cell itself can trigger the production of scar tissue.
> ➤ The interstitial space scar presence will both cause or effect other disease consortiums [6,7].

Scar lethality to the end organ cell is caused primarily by its barrier effect that cuts off functional communication with other cells including its most intimate partner, the capillary cell [5,6,7]. Scar secretion not only suffocates the functional integrity of the end organ cell but also can become a death nail to an already compromised capillary cell dance step process. As such the secretion of these inert polypeptides becomes a reliable marker of a virilized chronic inflammatory interstitial space mosaic that enables the anti-organ further signaling confluence to pirate functional intent through the capillary cell's outer membrane complex.

The Scar Anti-Organ *Gateway* Effect

The propensity for scar tissue to be lattice invasive, and to couple its infrastructure with the propagation of other disease venues, makes its presence a potent co-conspirator towards the anti-organ transitioning of the interstitial space. For this reason, interstitial space fibrous or amyloid scaring will have a *gateway effect* towards the propagation of other disease consorts [6,7]. As such any end organ interstitial space, given the presence of a sufficient scar lattice, will incentivize a sufficient anti-inflammatory immune suppression to consolidate an anti-organ trap that will process additional disease consortiums.

As expected, these chronic inflammatory interstitial space rhythms will progressively decay the capillary cell's anti-inflammatory dance steps. The dance step decline will create sequential immune funneling errors that become self-fulfilling to further support additional scar formation and the propagation of other disease consorts. The interstitial space signaling momentum will lend support for signal converted lymphocytes, monocytes and mesenchymal cells to further produce additional fibrous or amyloid scaffolding which in turn will nidus additional disease conscripts.

As chronic inflammatory interstitial space scarring matures, the inert barrier will block outer membrane relationships between the capillary and end organ cell as the former's outer membrane configuration stays *ovoid* and fails to process either functional intimacy or oxygen delivery to the end organ cell. When scar tissue has sufficiently matured, its reversibility becomes more difficult as its lattice coupled with other proinflammatory signaling and metabolic rhythms, makes the interstitial space an anti-inflammatory outlier and a virilizing instigator of additional disease propagation.

Robert L Buckingham, MD, FACP

The End Organ Interstitial Space Spectrum of Scar Formation will be Based on How Chronic Inflammatory Signaling Rhythms Mature

The processing of either amyloid or fibrous scar tissue within end organ interstitial spaces will depend on how chronic inflammatory signaling reverberations have affected the mesenchymal and lymphocytic cells that process their production[5,6,7]. For example, within the liver sinusoidal space of Disse, the chronic inflammatory toxic broth will chain react signaling and metabolic rhythms that will predispose to various disease mosaics that will include the possible processing of fibrous or amyloid scar production. In the setting where the hepatocyte transitions to become more like a fat cell, mesenchymal cell induced fibrous scarring will more likely occur. If interstitial space chronic inflammatory processes predispose to autoimmune complexes, amyloid scarring within the space of Disse may become preferential. Both fibrous and amyloid scarring are increased when the intestinal leaky gut delivers to the portal circulation recurring salvos of toxic food derivatives and other intermediates to the liver sinusoids that involve the processing of highly refined sugars, food processing intermediates, saturated animal fats, and non-digestible resins. These leaky gut deposits will accelerate space of Disse chronic inflammatory signaling and metabolic rhythms, destabilize the liver sinusoidal capillary cell dance step rhythm and position the interstitial space mesenchymal or lymphocyte cells to produce to either fibrous or amyloid scar tissue.

In other end organs, the mechanics of fibrous or amyloid scar deposition may be induced from different chronic inflammatory interstitial space rhythms. In these situations, scar production may tag with recurrent end organ physical trauma, infections, or ischemia to predispose to either amyloid or fibrous scarring. In these cases, the repeated process of reinjuring the end organ cell in some form by any of these processes will in turn produce chronic inflammatory signaling rhythms that predispose interstitial space monocytes, lymphocytes or mesenchymal cells to secrete fibrous or amyloid scar tissue.

The implication gathered from this discussion is that persistent chronic inflammatory interstitial space signaling dysrhythmias and their metabolic overtures will portend a compilation of disease consorts that will cause or effect scar deposition[6,7]. In all end organs, this chronic inflammatory interstitial space transitioning will always posture the failure of the capillary and downstream endothelial cell's dance step rhythm to maintain its anti-inflammatory functional countenance. The chronic inflammatory rhythms that are generated in turn will composite a predisposition towards end organ disease venues that will include the various types of scarring. When fibrous or amyloid scar deposition occurs, it will *gateway* other disease mosaics by the nature of the interstitial space lattice it creates.

Scar Confluence and their Interaction with the Various *Neurodegenerative Mosaics*

Fibrous or amyloid scarring within the brain is typically chronic inflammatory *integrative* as their processing will often be contiguous with other disease venues, such as hypoxia/ ischemia (TIAs, CVAs), recurrent head trauma (CTEs, concussions), meningeal infections or autoimmune complexes. The scarring *outcome* whether fibrous or amyloid will cause and effect loss of *nerve cell functional continuity and plasticity* while also contributing to its atrophy and death. The scar process, regardless of what cell it is derived from or the type of scar tissue formed, becomes part of a broader chronic inflammatory descriptive of central nervous system decline known *as neurodegeneration* [5,6,7]. With this regard, the progression of chronic cerebral neurodegeneration will almost *always* involve some level of amyloid or fibrous scarring or both. Most cases of neurodegeneration camouflage their early progression with subtle clinical signs or symptoms that can be partially compensated but as loss of nerve cells progresses, clinically over signs and symptoms become more obvious as neurodegeneration becomes less regional and more global.

The chronic inflammatory progression within the cerebral cortex may feature a mosaic of both fibrous or amyloid scarring which on closer inspection will be coupled with other anti-organ disease entities. These chronic inflammatory interstitial space aggregates will posture rhythms and metabolism that puts pressure on the anti-inflammatory functional integrity of the blood brain barrier and the capillary cell's dance step rhythm with the ladder providing the necessary pacing rhythms to keep the aligned cells functioning in aggregate. When the blood brain barrier is self-maintaining anti-inflammatory rhythms, the cerebrospinal fluid within the interstitial space is well sanitized, and corresponding nerve cell function optimal. However, if and when the chronic inflammatory anti-organ signaling and metabolic rhythms within the cerebrospinal fluid find sufficient countenance, scar formation will become likely and will often coincide with the presence of recurrent head trauma, strokes, seizures, infections, autoimmune processes, or intracranial cancers. As scarring and other disease remnants ruminate progression, aggregate brain function becomes less operational and much less integrative. When this occurs, cognitive decline becomes transcendental as the capacity to remember, retain new information or perform executive functioning declines along with loss of motor skills, and sensory processing.

Within this context, chronic inflammatory neurodegenerative scarring is never be an isolated intracerebral event but rather a collective composition of disease consorts that will be connected to *reduced* intracranial blood flows and oxygen delivery, (CVA, TIA, diffuse white matter disease and Parkinson's syndrome), recurrent *traumatic brain injury* (TBI, concussions and CTE), infections (meningeal and encephalitis), tumors (primary and metastatic), autoimmune complexes (multiple sclerosis) and their combinations. Their neurodegenerative reflections within the cerebral cortex will encapsulate a severely compromised intracerebral interstitial space and cerebrospinal bath whereby the blood brain barrier generally and capillary cell dance step rhythm specifically have become so functionally compromised that they have become unable to successfully counter the anti-organ signaling and metabolic onslaught.

Initial neurodegenerative diagnosis and treatment is typically time delayed as signs and symptoms are often vague and overcompensated for by learned behaviors. In addition, staging blood work, CSF, motor neuron and cognitive testing, and imaging displays can be non-specific. What does occur, is typically a mishandling of these early signs or symptoms until they become more functionally disruptive and with less likelihood of their reversal as chronic inflammatory rhythms have seized more control of the interstitial space landscape. Without adequately addressing the early signs of chronic inflammatory invasiveness, neurodegeneration is allowed to progress unabated until it firmly establishes a global signaling and metabolic control of a very functionally compromised brain. Rather than addressing the decline of the blood brain barrier and the capillary cell's dance step rhythm, current treatment preferences either ignore the early stages of neurodegeneration, when interventions would do the most good, or they get distracted to preferentially address interventions that could help decaying nerve cells while not paying sufficient attention to the underlying chronic inflammatory staging processes within the cerebrospinal fluid and interstitial space that are compiling the disease outcomes..

This inability to link chronic inflammation to neurodegeneration will include the formation of both amyloid and fibrous scar tissue. Until the health of the blood brain barrier generally and the capillary cell dance step rhythm specifically is addressed, neurodegeneration cannot be successfully countered as there will be insufficient anti-inflammatory rhythms to the cerebrospinal fluid to counter the incipient progression of chronic inflammatory interstitial space influences that are exercising signaling and metabolic control over the cerebral cortex landscape. Unfortunately, by waiting for signs and symptoms to progress before address chronic inflammatory root causes, the maturation of these rhythms will virilize a central nervous system intent that will become impossible to reverse. As long as treatment options are directed at fortifying nerve cells rather than attacking the origins of chronic interstitial space inflammation, neurodegenerative outcomes will remain refractor to intervention. Instead, treatment paradigms should pay closer attention to the factors that have caused the decline of the blood brain barrier and the anti-inflammatory power it has lost from the inability of its capillary cells to maintain their dance step rhythm. The uncoupling of the blood brain barrier to its anti-inflammatory management of the cerebrospinal fluid and interstitial space should be where the root causes of neurodegeneration will be found and should center on the systemic elimination of vascular inflammatory free radicals and preventing blood brain barrier immune funneling mistakes in irreversibly dance step compromised capillary cells. Doing so should subvert reduce upstream oxygen delivery deficiencies to the very oxygen dependent brain with a special emphasis on blocking the glial and lymphocyte cells that produce further fibrous and amyloid scar tissue deposition.

As neurodegeneration unfolds, regardless of what type of disease venue initially unfolds, the brain's nerve cells will be compromised, lose functional plasticity, and will knee jerk some level of atrophy that could initially be limited to a single brain region but will eventually spread to y become global. Nerve cell atrophy implies that the scope and complexity of their axon and dendrite connectivity will shrink to reduce their capacity to nuance cognition. The loss of interconnectivity will be associated with deficiencies of secreted neurotransmitters (acetylcholine, dopamine, GABA, etc.) and imbalances of nerve and glial cell inhibitory and excitatory signaling rhythms. When these inefficiencies are progressive and sustained, there will elicit incipient cognitive deficits with their rate defined by the degree to which the cerebrospinal fluid and interstitial space has been chronic inflammatory compromised. The cognitive compromise can present as subtle but can also be stuttered, prompt, regional, global and severe. Regardless of the rate, how or what the cognitive decline looks like, the brain becomes increasingly disconnected to itself as its scope of sensory, motor and cognitive acuity diminishes[5,6,7].

In most neurodegeneration, with the passage of time and progression, there is a blurring of the clinical characteristics that might distinguish one type of degeneration from another. This occurs as cerebral atrophy progresses and nerve function declines regardless of whether the underlying primary disease venue it a stroke(s), scar tissue, an autoimmune process or a combination of them. What does matter is that the chronic inflammatory processes within the interstitial space have marginalized the processing of anti-inflammatory rhythms form the blood brain barrier and their pacing from capillary cells. As they diminish, they off little resistance towards the aggressive and increasingly intentional chronic inflammatory precipice. As chronic inflammatory rhythms process the brain's interstitial space, regardless of the processing mechanics, the CSF will degrade in commensurate fashion to show increasing displays of signal converted white blood cells and inflammatory proteins that will cater to chronic inflammatory rhythms. As this occurs, cerebrospinal and imaging analysis will reveal lower concentrations of neurotransmitters as well as various degrees of cortical atrophy. EEGs will show more slow waves, less alpha rhythm and disturbed sleep patterns including less deep and REM sleep. As these processes assimilate chronic inflammatory outcomes, the brain becomes increasingly impaired as different disease processes are added into the processing. This will include regional or global amyloid or fibrous scarring (or both).

The implication of these progressive chronic inflammatory neurodegenerative derivatives is that there is a fundamental breakdown in the anti-inflammatory rhythms emanating from the blood brain barrier which is a reflection of the pace and stem effect of the capillary cell's dance step rhythm. The management and prevention of neurodegeneration would therefore require that the health of this glial, pericyte and capillary cell conglomerate remain pristine. This caricature will require the aggressive management of vascular inflammatory free radical cerebrospinal fluid and interstitial space impingements that will be necessity become more stringent with aging as the rigor of anti-inflammatory rhythms wane form lack of capillary cell dance step capacity. It will also require the aggressive management/prevention of insulin resistance, hypertension, dyslipidemias, obesity and metabolic syndrome as well as the near or complete abstinence from tobacco products and alcohol. It will also require reductions in the long term use/abuse of certain allopathic drugs that are known to produce proinflammatory outcomes that include the use of stimulants and anti-anxiety/sleep medications, antibiotics, steroids, proton pump-acid blockers, anticholinergics and certain antidepressants. It would also require increasing intentionality towards improving sleep hygiene, stress management, regular interval training type exercise and vegetarian based eating.

All neurodegeneration regardless of how it presents or what pathologies are attributed to it, will have at its interstitial space core the following characteristics:

- **the inability to timely remove vascular inflammatory free radical interstitial space impingements from the brain's infrastructure.**
- **the loss of rigor from the counterbalanced and anti-inflammatory multipurposed capillary cell dance step rhythm.**
- **the decay of blood brain barrier (glial, pericyte and capillary cell) functional inter connectiveness.**
- **sequential Increases in immune funneling errors into the CSF (as the capillary cell outer membrane complex becomes pseudocapillarized) such that it becomes less anti-inflammatory capable to neutralize proinflammatory based signaling or metabolic rhythms.**

No matter the neurodegenerative context, it will always progress with the anti-inflammatory dissolution of the blood brain barrier and the capillary cell dance step rhythm as its progression becomes an admixture of various neurodegenerative processes. In a most common example of the progression of vascular dementia, the initial manifestations of forgetfulness and loss of recall will involve the anti-organ derived loss of upstream blood flow and oxygen reserve that will predicate axonal and dendrite nerve atrophy between the brain's cortical gray matter and the midbrain's thalamus and hippocampus. As the brain volume shrinks from accumulated axon, dendrite and brain cell atrophy, the space void it creates is replaced by the inert and functionally void production of amyloid or fibrous scar or a combination of both. In other neurodegenerative settings such as the autoimmune processes of multiple sclerosis, the early clinical manifestations of weakness and loss of visual clarity are connected to imaging results of white mater "skip lesions" and a cerebrospinal fluid showing assorted arrays of chronic inflammatory white blood cells and inflammatory proteins. As multiple sclerosis progresses, it too will affect cognitive function as the brain atrophies, nerve cells disintegrate and die and their void is taken up by fillers such as fibrous or amyloid scar tissue. The final stages of multiple sclerosis, with the generalized weakness, dementia, incontinence and seizures, can look very similar to the end stages of vascular dementia or to other neurodegenerative types. In this clinical setting the early Parkinson Syndrome where the initial clinical manifestation may be resting tremor or unsteady gait, its chronic inflammatory progression will elicit increasing sensory, motor and cognitive declines that appear eerily similar to the end stages of the vascular dementias or to multiple sclerosis. It becomes likely that as these end stages assimilate similar clinical paradigms attributable to advancing neurodegeneration, the chronic inflammatory processing of these outcomes will include the breakdown of the blood brain barrier's functional capacity and the capillary cell's dance step rhythm as well as the likely interstitial space production of amyloid and fibrous scar tissue as fillers to increasing nerve cell atrophy. There may even be some "chronic inflammatory autoimmune enhancements" that involve the denaturing of dopamine and other neurotransmitter receptors within the process. Regardless of which neurodegenerative process has received early clinical recognition, as its progresses to involve global brain infrastructure, other neurodegenerative processes will appear to blend in an end stage clinical commonality.

The various anti-organ neurodegenerative assemblages within the brain's interstitial space that will lead to amyloid and/or fibrous scarring will include:

- The families of the different *Parkinson Diseases* (currently defined as a net loss of dopaminergic receptor responsiveness) will initially involve the midbrain's substantia nigra but will globally extend its reach to include the atrophy of the entire cerebral cortex resulting in a diffuse sensory, motor and cognitive decline.
- The so-called "autoimmune" *Lewy body dementia* (manifesting as precipitins (autoimmune/ viral complexes?) within the prefrontal and frontal lobes and concomitant atrophy. With progression the lewy body precipitins will encompass the entire cerebral cortex that will manifest as a similar end stage severe dementia.
- The various early onset *white matter "ischemic" consortiums* that are typically associated *with loss of memory, information retrieval and learning capacity.* This form of atrophy disconnects the brain's gray matter from its deeper midbrain regions as atrophied axon and dendrite lose inter connectiveness typically from diffuse small vessel vascular disease and reduced oxygen delivery. With progression the brain globally will atrophy, lose volume and become a cognitive wasteland of severe sensory, motor and executive function deficits.
- Another type of white matter process is the *"skip lesions" of multiple sclerosis* thought to be autoimmune in nature. The early clinical manifestations can include memory loss and dementia but typically involve increasing weakness, fatigue, dysesthesias and visual disturbances.
- The various forms of *gray matter atrophy (focal-or regional early or diffuse-late) will involve* both large and small arterial vascular disease and will process a more limited supply of upstream oxygen delivery to the oxygen dependent brain cells to cause and effect a diffuse or focal neuronal dysfunction, atrophy and death from asphyxiation. The clinical outcomes will include TIAs, CVAs and focal seizures associated with insipid or abrupt changes in cognitive function that will foment dementia over time.
- *CTE (chronic traumatic encephalopathy)* atrophy from recurring head trauma (TBIs, concussions) with subsequent loss of brain volume that is associated with inappropriate anger management, suicide, major depression and risks for poly chemical substance abuse. Premature dementia and Parkinson's Disease becomes an expected outcome.
- The classic presentation of Alzheimer's Dementia where chronic and progressive sensory, motor and cognitive deficits correlate with global cerebral atrophy and autopsy results showing amyloid plaques. Since Alzheimer's Disease is commonly linked to advanced age and reduced oxygen supplies to the brain it can be recharacterized as a type of vascular dementia.
- Another autoimmune variant of neurodegeneration with an autosomal dominant genetic predisposition are the various clinical presentations of ALS (amyotrophic lateral sclerosis) which is associated with demyelination of peripheral motor nerve cells whose severe debilitating outcomes of generalized muscle weakness, spasticity, paralysis, dysphagia and loss of airway control become associated with brain hypoxia, ischemia and subsequent dementia.
- The various forms of increased intracranial pressures that will cause and effect *hydrocephalus* whereby the flow of CSF to and from the choroid plexus *gets untethered* to normal pressure

gradients which typically increases intracranial pressures and compresses nearby nerve cells causing their dysfunction and atrophy. The result increases motor, sensory and cognitive abnormalities and predisposes to loss of coordination, incontinence and falls that will eventually progress to a global cerebral atrophy and dementia.

- Expanding cancer masses will not only rob surrounding brain tissue of oxygen but will cause maladjusted intracranial pressure gradients as they dupe the functionally compromised blood brain barrier towards catering to their functional requirements. As the mass grows, it will compress adjacent brain tissue, increase cerebral edema, produce adverse osmotic and hydrostatic pressure gradients to the brain's interstitial space to result in secondary displays of neurodegeneration that include scarring, hypoxia and ischemia (and dementia) and risk for infection.
- The insipid and sometimes abrupt loss of cognitive function from the brain's chronic exposures to heavy metals that include aluminum, lead, mercury or arsenic.
- The aggregate compositions of *metabolic encephalopathies* from other end organ failures that include liver (increased blood plasma ammonia), kidney (increased blood plasma urea nitrogen) or lung (increased blood plasma carbon dioxide and reduced oxygen tensions) as well as the cognitive manifestations associated with septic events from bacteria, fungi, amoeba or viral infections.

The immune dysfunction that manifests the different types of neurodegenerations will stem from a variable chronic inflammatory interstitial space signaling and metabolic profile that is transitioned by a dysfunctional blood brain barrier and compromised capillary cell dance step rhythm. In this setting the initial expression of neurodegeneration may express a clinically unique disease consort that over time and with chronic inflammatory expansion and functional control of the interstitial space and blood brain barrier would produce a global and blended "end stage "outcome of severe sensory, motor and cognitive impairment. This means that regardless of how neurodegeneration presents, (as an ischemic, infectious, traumatic, scarring or autoimmune cascade), the end stages of its expression will likely involve other disease consorts with the cognitive manifestations of the end stage being clinically similar. When and as these chronic inflammatory rhythms coalesce within the brain's interstitial space their virilization and intentionality will be processed by a functionally disabled capillary cell within the blood brain barrier whose diminished anti-inflammatory reserve will enable vascular inflammatory free radicals to pester and fester, funneled immune contingents to become purpose distracted and anti-organ signal converted and nearby glial, pericyte and mesenchymal cells to become enablers of chronic inflammatory fulfillment. In most neurodegenerative disease expression this will include the processing of beta or gamma amyloid or fibrous scar tissue.

How End Organ Interstitial Space Chronic Inflammatory Rhythms Pace Scar Production

Regardless of the end organ or interstitial space involved, the consolidation of chronic inflammatory rhythms into a unified anti-organ purpose that will often include the processing of scar tissue will always coincide with a diminished anti-inflammatory interstitial space reserve and a decline in the capillary cell's dance step rhythm[7]. The chronic inflammatory decline of the capillary cell's rhythm is typically not an isolated event but rather a diffuse and systemic matter that involves all end organs and the entire vascular tree. In this manner, as the capillary cell's dance steps fail, each end organ's interstitial space will become chronical inflammatory compromised. One of several initial chronic inflammatory interstitial space outcomes could be the deposition of amyloid or fibrous scar tissue. The compilation of end organ interstitial space scarring with or without the expressions of other disease venues will become dependent upon:

- The level of capillary and downstream endothelial cell dance step dysrhythmia and how their collective outer membrane complexes have been anti-organ signal coopted.
- The nature of vascular inflammatory free radical interstitial space impingements.
- How funneled immune arsenal have been purpose transitioned.
- How this combination enables the signaling and metabolic threshold towards a chronic inflammatory interstitial space expression.
- How the chronic inflammatory signaling and metabolic processing of disease consorts interacts with the functional rhythms and genetic vulnerabilities of the involved end organ cell 7.

When chronic inflammatory interstitial space immune contingents have signal converted to form anti-organ functional prerogatives, they will process intent by signal pirating the capillary and downstream endothelial cell outer membrane complex to funnel additional immune contingents into the interstitial space that can be signal converted to fulfill specific chronic inflammatory tasks that will enable disease expressions. How this pirating maneuver is carried out is to a large degree based on how the interstitial space will manifest a disease mosaic that will include the production of the scar tissue. Within this context, scarring will blend with other chronic inflammatory anti-organ venues. The subsequent outcome of one disease expression may chronic inflammatory cause and effect other secondary disease consorts, that in conjunction with a diminished anti-inflammatory interstitial space resolve, will exert increasing control over signaling and metabolic rhythms[6,7].

The Anti-Organ Interstitial Space Backwash Manifested from Disease Mosaics within the Interstitial Space Becomes a Systemic Anti-inflammatory Immune Suppressant

When scarring or other anti-organ interstitial space disease processes control signaling and metabolic rhythms, they will encrypt an exocytic *backwash* through the capillary and downstream endothelium and into the systemic circulation that will tweak molecular configurations of circulating immune arsenal to where they no longer cater to anti-inflammatory interstitial space outcomes. The circulating immune arsenal conversion processes will enable the interstitial space anti-organ to exert better control over immune funneling cohorts that will be better suited for specific anti-organ duties. As this occurs, interstitial space capillary cell dance step derived anti-inflammatory processing interstitial space immune remnants becomes increasingly less effective towards resisting proinflammatory rhythms [5,6,7]. As backwashed proinflammatory signaling and metabolic rhythms into the interstitial space become de rigueur, they anti-inflammatory immune suppress as they simultaneously serve anti-organ functional interests (Figure 18, appendix). In the case of end organ interstitial space amyloid and fibrous scarring, mesenchymal, monocyte and lymphocyte cells will be signal weaponized in the processing of these outcomes.

These cascading interstitial space chronic inflammatory signaling rhythms will be associated with a metabolic prodrome of increasing insulin resistance, biased pH acidification and reduced oxygen tensions that in aggregate contributes to a backwash signaling momentum into the systemic circulation that postures proinflammatory adipokines, increased angiotensin II and abundant proinflammatory proteins with an increased portfolio of AGEs, small particle LDL cholesterol, triglycerides and non HDL cholesterols. All of this circulating proinflammatory momentum will favor an ongoing chronic inflammatory interstitial space bias of disease expressions. The momentum of these gathered chronic inflammatory rhythms becomes a powerful anti-inflammatory immunosuppressive that will transition multi end organ interstitial spaces until disease mosaics that will in some fashion involve scar production.

As interstitial space scar lattices mature, their architecture and the metabolic microenvironment they nurture will favor respiting cancer cells and assorted infectious agents [7]. The maturing of the amyloid/fibrous manifold becomes a *metabolic adjuvant* for a multilateral interstitial space disease initiative. Using its lattice as a protective shield, when coupled with its inert status and proclivity for oxygen deprivation, the microenvironment its enables will become low lying fruit for cells that readily utilize fermentation to produce energy while metabolically benefitting from the harsh realities of insulin resistance, acidic pH and aberrant osmolarity gradients. This type of interstitial space detail will almost always preclude a proinflammatory interstitial space bias that will signal convert mesenchymal and lymphocyte cells, platelets and clotting factors into chronic inflammatory contributors. In aggregate their rhythms make the evolving infrastructure of the scar lattice even more attractive to other disease consorts to birth expression. This anti-organ interstitial space mosaic will virilize intent as it reciprocates a diminished anti-inflammatory reserve from the capillary cell dance steps. This makes chronic inflammatory signal pirating of its diminished outer membrane complex more likely and self-fulfilling as anti-organ rhythms coalesce intentionality.

Chapter Thirteen

How Infectious Agents Tie into and Extend End Organ Interstitial Space Proinflammatory Signaling Rhythms

How Infectious Agents Become Anti-Organ Add-Ons

As persistent vascular inflammatory interstitial space free radicals eventually enable the processing of chronic inflammatory signaling rhythms, they simultaneously marginalize anti-inflammatory intent. This interstitial space "fork in the road" occurs when their pester and fester effect precludes capillary cell dance step rhythm counterbalance that will subsequently diminish its nitric oxide combustion cycle and the purpose fulfillment it processes. The capillary cell's inability to effectively refurbish its infrastructure makes it a functional pariah in processing anti-inflammatory multipurpose. As anti-inflammatory rhythms diminish purpose fulfillment, the interstitial space signaling void is taken up by chronic inflammatory rhythms that process milieus that conform immune arsenal, mesenchymal and pericytes towards their intent. In this setting vascular inflammatory interstitial space free radicals become a chronic inflammatory magnifier that will mature disease consorts which include the harboring of infectious agents (Figures 11-17, appendix)[5,6,7].

This conversion of the interstitial space to a free standing chronic inflammatory signaling and metabolic hub involves the transitioning of many moving parts that first and foremost s punctuated by the loss of the capillary cell's capacity to anti-inflammatory immune choreograph interstitial space outcomes. This deterioration pauses anti-inflammatory interstitial space multipurpose execution as funneled immune arsenal become increasingly prone to chronic inflammatory manipulation. This will inevitably facilitate the transitioning of the end organ's interstitial space into a chronic inflammatory signaling and metabolic reservoir that will become a magnet to disease expression.

The functional effect of these evolving chronic inflammatory interstitial space signaling and metabolic hyperbolas is to bias rhythms that will render infectious agent seeding more likely[7]. As the interstitial space chronic inflammatory conversion process evolves, signal converted immune remnants will stream cytokines, enzymes, free radicals, inflammatory proteins and electromagnetic wavelets that will bias the spillover of infectious agents into the interstitial space. As this occurs, signal converted mesenchymal, pericyte and white blood cells as well as immunoglobulins, platelets, clotting factors and complement will process a microenvironment conducive to infectious agent birthing. In this chronic inflammatory collaborative, infectious agents will find the interstitial space increasingly attractive to their physical, metabolic and functional requirements.

The maturing of chronic inflammatory anti-organ outcomes that include the expression of the various infectious agents into the interstitial space will require:

✓ a decreasing capacity for the capillary cell's dance step rhythm to provide sufficient anti-inflammatory immune trajectories into the interstitial space to timely remove inflammatory breach

✓ the diminishment of the capillary cell's mitochondrial nitric oxide combustion cycle with the subsequent loss of its capacity to replete its infrastructure

✓ the loss of the critically important infrastructure of its outer membrane complex making precise interstitial space anti-inflammatory immune funneling less intentional and purpose effective

✓ a progressive conversion of interstitial space immune arsenal towards proinflammatory purposes

✓ the expansion of intentional chronic inflammatory interstitial space intent that will favor the harboring of various infectious agents (Figures 16 and 17, appendix)[5,6,7]

As the capillary cell's anti-inflammatory dance steps become inept, its increasingly pseudocapillarized outer membrane complex will transition to incentivize chronic inflammatory interstitial space purposes that should include the harboring of infectious agents.

The Invasion of Interstitial Space Infectious Agents and How They Co Link with Preexisting Chronic Inflammatory Rhythms

As chronic inflammatory interstitial space rhythms mature, the signaling and metabolic transitioning they impose can predispose to the harboring of infectious agents. Viruses, bacteria or other infectious intruders will likely find the preexisting chronic inflammatory signaling and metabolic rhythms advantageous to their own intrinsic rhythms. Many will particularly find metabolic advantages within the chronic inflammatory interstitial space milieu as reduced oxygen tensions and increased insulin resistance synergize with their underlying metabolic biases associated with fermentation and preferences for sugar oxidation. In this manner, infectious agents could flourish in an interstitial space that feels hostile to the capillary and end organ cell[6,7]. The chronic inflammatory interstitial space interface will potentially enable a variety of different infectious agents to find functional comfort. They do so by utilizing their saprophytic properties as they borrow metabolic synergies from preexisting proinflammatory interstitial space rhythms[6,7,32]. When this occurs, the addition of infectious agents into the interstitial space becomes *additive and collaborative* to the prospects of other anti-organ outcomes.

Infectious agents are ubiquitous end organ interstitial space invaders as they come in a variety of shapes, sizes, solubilities and functional utilities linked to their saprophytic nature. Generally, the smaller and more lipid soluble varieties do their dirty work in stealth (such as prions or viruses) as they penetrate membranes and cellular infrastructure utilizing several different mechanics. Whether by inhalation or through being absorbed through the skin or mucous membranes, or from being intestinally processed through the microbiome, these smaller infectious agents can find their way into a variety of different cells and their vulnerable organelles. As they penetrate, they will coopt the cell's infrastructure mechanics to process their replicative cycles. In this manner, they will integrate their replicative rhythms with the cell's infrastructure to camouflage their intent. As they hack and functionally coalesce with the mechanics of nascent cellular infrastructure, they redirect the cell's purpose towards their own fulfillment. In the setting of chronic interstitial space inflammation, the attacking virus, prion or small particle will utilize the functional loss of a weakened nascent cell to rearrange infrastructure signaling and metabolic priorities to accommodate their own purpose fulfillment. In this manner, the virus will replicate as the nascent cell continues to become a victim of infrastructure decay which most likely be associated with unbalanced signaling and metabolic rhythms and loss of functional counterbalance. In the end organ cell, increases in the nitric oxide combustion cycle will bias signaling rhythms that conjure cellular replication of which the infectious agent will tag along with to nurture their own. The cross linkage of chronic interstitial space inflammatory rhythms with a persistent capillary cell dance step energy combustion cycle (and an associated end organ cell nitric oxide combustion bias) will enable the harbored infectious agent opportunity to signal harness into these rhythms to enhance their replicative machinery.

Other infectious agents such as bacteria, fungi, amoebas, parasites and worms can also propagate to expand their interstitial space reach as they too will find replicative advantages in the chronically inflamed interstitial space. In these cases, the larger and more immune exposed infectious agents will utilize other physical properties other than camouflage to posture resistance against immune surveillance. Some of these properties include their outer membrane support structures that will barrier against immune attacks or how they secrete various substances that inhibit immune surveillance against them. In these instances, resistance to immune degradation is based on their size, physical properties and predilection for specific types of end organ interstitial spaces. Their capacity to immune resist will be based on multiple factors that include size, solubility, the degree to which their outer membranes can barrier resist, and how their infrastructure and coalesce their replicative cycles with preexisting chronic inflammatory signaling and metabolic rhythms [6,7,32,33].

Regardless of which infectious agent finds refuge within a given interstitial space, the combination of their own proinflammatory signaling and metabolic rhythms coupled with those that are already chronic inflammatory will foster increasingly anti-inflammatory resistance towards their removal while at the same time rendering the interstitial space less end organ cell productive as the functional utility of the capillary cell's dance step rhythm continues to decay[6,7]. When infectious agent functional rhythms control interstitial space signaling and metabolic mechanics, it becomes a potential hotbed for other disease consorts such as scarring or oncogenesis which in aggregate keeps the interstitial space anti-inflammatory immune suppressed.

More on How Infectious Agents Utilize Preexisting Chronic Inflammatory Rhythms to Coopt Their Own Replicative Purpose

Infectious agents are consummate interstitial space *saprophytic adapters* to proinflammatory microenvironments meaning they can utilize preexisting proinflammatory signaling and metabolic towards mastering their own purpose fulfillment. As these interstitial space rhythms remaster, they will process a chronic inflammatory intransigent signaling and metabolic momentum that will favor the replicative recycling of infectious agent expression. Interstitial space metabolic rhythms that incentivize this bias include pH acidification, oxygen deprivation and increasing insulin resistance that frequently couple with hypoosmotic pressure gradients[7]. The evolution of these chronic inflammatory interstitial space metabolic rhythms will give the infrastructure of many infectious seeds a sizeable advantage compared to nearby end organ cells whose functional algorithms fare much better with counterbalanced interstitial space pH, optimal oxygen delivery and ideal metabolically responsive glucose/fatty acid ratios. In these chronic inflammatory interstitial space settings, many infectious agents will parlay these underlying conditions with their own signaling and metabolic nomenclature to foster increasing anti-inflammatory resistance and replication[6,7].

The chronic inflammatory-infectious agent functional consolidation is further virilized by the coupling of their interstitial space rhythms with other disease venues. This will typically increase additional anti-inflammatory immune suppression that will preclude increasing rates of infectious agent mitosis and possible metastatic spread to other end organ interstitial space. The virulence of these chronic inflammatory interstitial space reverberations will enable the increased funneling through the disabled capillary cell outer membrane complex of purpose neutral and easily signal turned immune arsenal that can be easily reprogramed by preexisting proinflammatory rhythms to cater to the replicative expression of invading infectious cohorts. With interstitial space maturity, the harbored infectious agent will not only replicate but will cause other infectious agents or disease venues to find the interstitial space chronic inflammatory rhythms to their liking. Visiting viruses and prions become increasingly more intracellular capable in their replicative cycles while bacteria, fungi, protozoans and amoebas can also take advantage of the chronic inflammatory interstitial space microenvironment to bolster their claim towards replication. The processing of these infectious agent interstitial space bouquets will serve to harden their collective resolve to remain anti-inflammatory resistant.

While bacteria and viruses are considered to be the most common saprophytic interstitial space stewards, other infectious agents given the in the right end organ and chronic inflammatory signaling and metabolic context can be just as dangerous. Using a variety of different signaling, metabolic, functional and physical attributes, these infectious agent collectives will utilize many of the same chronic inflammatory interstitial space metabolic and signaling rhythms that bacteria and viruses utilize to consolidate their interstitial space positions as they fuse and collaborate with preexisting chronic inflammatory rhythms[6,7]. As with their viral and bacterial brethren, their interstitial space reverberations will bully the metabolic and signaling atmosphere as they increasingly coopt interstitial space purpose away from nurturing end organ cell functional utility.

How Infectious Agents Marginalize Interstitial Spaces

A key to an infectious agent's capacity to propagate within an interstitial space is its capacity to marginalize anti-inflammatory signaling and metabolic rhythms as their own rhythms simultaneously fuse and collaborate with preexisting chronic inflammatory rhythms. [5,6,7]. As chronic inflammatory rhythms coopt interstitial space purpose, infectious agents will exploit them for their own replication.

In summary, the expression of interstitial space infectious seeding is accomplished by:

- the increasing displays of virilized chronic inflammatory interstitial space signaling and metabolic rhythms that are buoyed by vascular inflammatory free radical impingements and signal turned immune arsenal
- the capacity of the infectious agent to utilize these rhythms to propagate and possibly *camouflage* intent
- the capacity of the infectious seed to utilize metabolic rhythms that are hostile to nearby end organ cells
- the capacity of the infectious agent to utilize signaling and metabolic rhythms form other disease consorts towards their own replicative benefit
- by utilizing their unique saprophytic properties 'to take what it needs' from nascent cellular membranes or organelles [6,7,,22,31,32,33].

In these biased chronic inflammatory interstitial space settings, infectious agents will find significant signaling, metabolic and functional advantages over nearby nascent cells as they can readily adapt and thrive within these proinflammatory rhythms whereas end organ cells can't [6,7]. As they propagate, infectious agents will produce intentional signaling rhythms that further pirate immune funneling content into the interstitial space that will fortify their own intent benefit as they simultaneously marginalize the capillary cell dance steps, rhythms and anti-inflammatory multipurpose. As they multiply and consolidate signaling and metabolic rhythms within the interstitial space, the infectious agent (s) will signal initialize rhythms that will make the space vulnerable to other disease consorts that will in turn integrate within the context of the infectious agent's signaling and metabolic hierarchy. The reverberation or these coalescing rhythms will consolidate chronic inflammatory virulence as they propagate their own brand of interstitial space ricochet and circulatory backwash (Figures 13 and 17, appendix).

How Infectious Agents Coopt Preexisting Chronic Inflammatory Interstitial Space Rhythms

With the addition proinflammatory interstitial space signaling and metabolic threads that emanate from propagating infectious agents, chronic inflammatory intent becomes both intentional and virilized [7]. As interstitial space funneled and signal turned white blood cells, platelets, clotting factors and immunoglobulins collect, their signaling threads degrade a declining anti-inflammatory purpose fulfillment as they convert the interstitial space into a chronic inflammatory haven. This interstitial space deterioration coincides with a declining capillary cell dance step rhythm and purpose coopted outer membrane complex as the purpose of the interstitial space changes hands from the anti-inflammatory rhythms of the pulsed capillary cell dance steps to those of the chronic inflammatory matrix and anti-organ.

The process of converting interstitial space funneled immune arsenal towards chronic inflammatory intent becomes much easier when their purpose identity has been rendered neutral form being molecularly tweaked from chronic inflammatory backwashed cytokines prior to their interstitial space arrival. As the capillary cell's functional anti-inflammatory rhythms degrade, it loses its capacity to sanitize the interstitial space, service end organ cell functional needs or provide the necessary signaling rhythms for infrastructure refurbishment. The continuum of interstitial space anti-inflammatory degradation and proinflammatory consolidation will cause ae and exchange of interstitial space purpose that will incentivize infectious seeding.

Once these new found interstitial space rhythms find tractions, their reverberations will lobby the increasingly disabled capillary cell's outer membrane complex to funnel immune remnants into the interstitial space that will prop up the replicative directives of the seeded infectious agent. This immune interstitial space transitioning towards becoming purpose responsive to a proinflammatory context becomes increasingly advantageous to the infectious agent(s) capacity to multiply. With anti-organ interstitial space signaling and metabolic consolidation, the disabled capillary cell's outer membrane complex becomes it's funneling agent as the anti-organ ricochets and backwashes to and from the capillary cell rhythms that foster the infectious agent's propagation on the one hand and a systemic anti-inflammatory immune suppression on the other. In these persistent chronic inflammatory salvos, the capillary cell's outer membrane complex, mitochondria and nuclear chromatin have all become more or less subservient to anti-organ purposes that will include infectious agent propagation.

Once interstitial space infectious agents harness control of preexisting chronic inflammatory rhythms, they will utilize their unique physical and functional attributes and saprophytic underpinnings to interpose their collective will on the interstitial space and nascent epi and endothelial cell membranes, organelles and infrastructure. They will enable them to find replicative opportunities in conditions whereby the end organ cell has withdrawn its functional priorities[6,7]. This allows them to integrate within microenvironments that are typically anti-inflammatory immune suppressive. In this manner infectious agents will find interstitial space proinflammatory microenvironments to their replicative advantage as the end organ cell's functional utility withers in the same context.

As infectious agent signaling and metabolic rhythms fuse with those of preexisting chronic interstitial space inflammation, they will process their own replication while simultaneously threading rhythms that degrade anti-inflammatory immune resolve [7]. In this manner the *transitioning* of the interstitial space towards the consolidation of chronic inflammatory signaled and metabolic rhythms will include all allied mesenchymal and pericyte cells thereby making the habitat more anti-organ intentional. When this occurs, chronic inflammatory will virilize intent, increasingly marginalize the anti-inflammatory intentions of the capillary and downstream endothelial cell network, and predispose the interstitial space to a mosaic of disease outcomes.

How an Infectious Agent Accelerates Outer Membrane Complex Pseudocapillarization

As the propagation of an infectious agent transitions seismic signaling and metabolic shifts within the interstitial space, funneled immune arsenal increasingly identify with and respond to preexisting proinflammatory rhythms. This in turn will help process anti-organ sustainability which will enable further interstitial space transitioning towards a diversification of disease consortiums [5,6,7]. The increasing precision of chronic inflammatory interstitial space signaling and metabolic rhythms towards becoming anti-organ compliant will involve many different moving parts that include the serial diminution of the anti-inflammatory capillary cell's dance steps and the corresponding decay of mesenchymal and end organ cell function that are both codependent of dance step outcomes. Once anti-organ signaling and metabolic rhythms go full throttle, the functional fate of these allied cells either declines or gets converted to a proinflammatory purpose. The outcome is to enable the evolution of a chronic inflammatory interstitial space *lattice* that nurtures chronic inflammatory outcomes that includes the seeding of infectious agents.

The speed of this anti-organ transitioning will be predicated on how consuming these chronic inflammatory rhythms are towards the degradation of anti-inflammatory resolve. As the dance step rhythm deteriorates, so does its capacity to hybrid a sufficient anti-inflammatory resolve within the interstitial space. To the degree that it can't is to the degree that chronic inflammatory rhythms will consolidate intent. The rate of interstitial space transitioning will be proportional to:

- the degree to which the capillary and downstream endothelial cells have degraded their infrastructure as their dance steps have become increasingly unbalanced and anti-inflammatory non-compliant
- the rate of functional decline within the capillary cell's organelle lattice, with specific reference to its outer membrane complex, but also to its mitochondrial reserve and ROS cross linked nuclear chromatin

- **the increasing functional dysrhythmia of capillary cell's dance step anti-inflammatory-pace, stem ricochet and backwash effects** [6,7].

When the capacity of the capillary cell's dance step anti-inflammatory rhythm degenerates, its purpose clarity within the interstitial space does so as well as chronic inflammatory rhythms consolidate and virilize intent. With this level of interstitial space transitioning, the signaling and metabolic door opens for the expression of infectious processes [7]. In this context, the functionally weakened and purpose pirated capillary cell outer membrane complex becomes the anti-organ processing membrane.

The Infectious Agent's Physical and Chemical Properties Enables its Fusion to Chronic Inflammatory Expression

With the loss of the capillary cell dance step rhythm and the sustained momentum of chronic inflammatory interstitial space expression, infectious agents will find the signaling and metabolic rhythms within the interstitial space conducive to their propagation [6,7]. In these desirable interstitial space settings, infectious arrays will seed and propagate based on how anti-inflammatory vulnerable the interstitial space has transitioned it's signaling rhythms. This would mean that interstitial space microenvironments become increasingly more inviting to specific infectious agents as the space transitions its signaling and metabolic rhythms away from the capillary cell dance steps and towards a proinflammatory countenance. It is within this interstitial space context that infectious seeds can tie into proinflammatory rhythms before they can be identified by the weakened anti-inflammatory surveillance as a foreign entity. Their replicative expression is fortified by antecedent chronic inflammatory interstitial space metabolic rhythms that center on acid-base imbalances, reduced oxygen tensions and increased insulin resistance. Within these metabolic settings, the infectious agent will find opportunities to replicate by:

- ❖ **processing their replicative cycles with preexisting chronic inflammatory signaling and metabolic rhythms**
- ❖ **to utilize these chronic inflammatory interstitial space rhythms to camouflage their intent**
- ❖ **by finding inherent nascent cell physical or chemical barriers within or without the cell that hide and protect the infectious agent's infrastructure against anti-inflammatory surveillance**
- ❖ **to become increasingly saprophytic to the nascent cell's rhythms in order to integrate and then manipulate the cell to its functional (replicative) purpose.**
- ❖ **to utilize all manner of passive or active transport mechanics to integrate with the nascent cell's functional rhythms**
- ❖ **once linked into in a nascent cell's signaling, metabolic and functional rhythms, the infectious agent will directly or indirectly utilize nascent cell organelles to express their intent**
- ❖ **the harbored infectious agent will find replicative resolve by fusing its purpose to the functional rhythms of nascent cell mitochondria, nuclear chromosomal DNA/RNA and its outer membranes**
- ❖ **these processes will directly involve harbored virus or prions but could also kindle replicative cycles of other infectious agents such as bacteria, amoeba, fungi or parasites** [6,7,32,33]

In the setting of chronic inflammation, smaller and more soluble infectious agents will use their physical properties to directly penetrate the nascent cell's outer membranes to enter their cytoplasm and interact with organelles. When they do, they will attempt to manipulate the cell's infrastructure and organelle apparatus to process their replicative cycles with the organelle's signaling rhythms and purpose identity. The capacity for an infectious agent to functionally integrate with and even control a portion of the nascent cell's infrastructure will become dependent upon:

> - the volume the infectious agent interstitial space inoculum
> - the capacity of the infectious agent to utilize preexisting chronic inflammatory rhythms to fuse and align its purpose fulfillment
> - the degree to which anti-inflammatory rhythm decay has been transitioned towards a chronic inflammatory interstitial space makeover
> - the degree to which infectious agent can utilize these rhythms to camouflage intent away from waning anti-inflammatory surveillance
> - the degree to which the infectious agent can posture anti-inflammatory resistance even when they have become immune identified [6,7]

Bacteria are examples of how an infectious agent has been able to defensively posture its physical and molecular underpinnings within the interstitial space in order to prevent with an immune discovery or its degradation if discovered. Besides evolving layers of protective outer membrane gear consisting of both infrastructure and secretion of various mucopolysaccharides, bacteria have also evolved a highly effective chromatin accessory known as a nuclear plasmid. These code adaptable appendages allow bacteria to produce proteins that counter and protect them from potentially hostile cytokines, enzymes, antibiotics, leukocytes or macrophages making them increasingly resistant to most immune counteroffensives. In addition, through the production of camouflaging secretagogues or by hiding within scar tissue or other types of chronic inflammatory processes, bacteria become a cause and effect of cascading anti-inflammatory interstitial space disarray that in turn will weaken the immune system, dampen the capillary cell dance step rhythm and significantly limit effective anti-inflammatory immune surveillance.

When bacteria can evoke a facile anaerobic metabolism to produce energy via fermentation, as when interstitial space oxygen tensions have been compromised, their capacity to thrive as other anti-inflammatory cells fail gives them a leg up towards prospering in proinflammatory interstitial space environments. When this is coupled with abundant interstitial space sugars to augment the fermentation process through glycolysis, bacteria will have made the occupied space a safe and dependable haven for their propagation. In this scenario, what oxygen is afforded the bacteria, will be shuttled into their mitochondrial nitric oxide combustion mechanics whereby the induction of growth factor assisted replication will occur in relentless fashion. It is within this end organ interstitial space context that infectious agents in general and bacteria specifically will do more than just survive[6,7,31,32,33].

How Infectious Agents Disrupt the Capillary Cell Outer Membrane Complex

By coopting purpose intentionality within the context of preexisting chronic inflammatory interstitial space rhythms, infectious agent(s) will stream signaling impulses to and from the capillary cell's outer membrane complex that will damage the capillary cell's anti-inflammatory rhythms as they exert increasing control over a mosaic of chronic inflammatory interstitial space outcomes. As damage hinge interstitial space signaling and metabolic rhythms that foster chronic inflammatory intent, anti-inflammatory degradation is occurring at multiple levels fueled primarily by decaying capillary cell dance steps, persistent vascular inflammatory free radical impingements, and assorted arrays of signal converted interstitial space immune arsenal. This progressive weakening of the anti-inflammatory interstitial space response to prevailing chronic interstitial space rhythms that are signal conferred by infectious agents, will virilize proinflammatory resolve as the anti-organ processes purpose-intentional immune remnants into the interstitial space that will aid and abet disease consorts that include infectious agent propagation[6,7].

The processing of chronic inflammatory interstitial space signaled and metabolic maneuvers will escalate disease venues as it simultaneously shuts down anti-inflammatory chain reactions that would oppose it[5,6,7,29]. As the capillary cell's functional senescence increases, the maturation of chronic inflammatory interstitial space rhythms will enable infectious agents to seed, find respite and begin propagation. As they exert more control over chronic inflammatory rhythms, the interstitial space becomes a birthplace for other types of disease consorts. When all of this chronic inflammatory interstitial space momentum has materialized, the capillary and downstream outer membrane complex has atrophied. The thinned glycocalyx has become an adhesive shell of what it once was, the continuous outer membrane has lost pores, adhesion receptors, transport processes and voltage potential and the abluminal basement membrane has typically thickened from chronic inflammatory residuals making it less responsive to both the end organ cell and assorted immune derivatives. The outer membrane complex *pseudocapillarization effect* plays into the anti-organ's signaling and metabolic hand as it creates an interstitial space biosphere that becomes ideal for the spreading of infectious agents [6,7]. As the anti-organ pulses chronic inflammatory interstitial space signaling and metabolic venues that foster infectious agent spread, it simultaneously backwashes cytokine and free radical rhythms into the central circulation that suppresses blood plasma immune constituents thereby rendering them useless towards an anti-inflammatory interstitial space purpose.

The Infectious Agent's End Game: Immune Suppression, Sepsis and End Organ Capitulation

As chronic inflammatory signaling and metabolic expression continue unabated, end organ interstitial space infectious agent replicative cycles are enabled. When the interstitial space becomes overwhelmed with infectious agents, they functionally compromised capillary and endothelial cell outer membrane complex will backwash the infectious agent into the central circulation thereby producing a systemic compromise as immune derivatives are released to cause fever, hypotension, increased insulin resistance and reduced oxygen delivery to multiple end organs. With this level of systemic acute and chronic inflammatory collapse, anti-inflammatory rhythms have become so chaotic and dysrhythmic that they can offer insufficient resistance to the burgeoning proinflammatory chain reactions of sepsis. Without rigorous interventions, this type of infectious outcome will yield multi end organ failure and death.

Part of the proinflammatory collapse is not just the systemic infusion of circulating infectious agents and chain reactions they elicit but also the chronic inflammatory immune suppression that had previously occurred from a compromised capillary cell dance step rhythm and the chronic inflammatory backwash that had occurred that rendered circulating immune remnants less anti-inflammatory capable. In this sense chronic interstitial space inflammation set up the end organ's interstitial space and blood plasma to fail if positioned with infectious agent overgrowth and systemic spreading. The failure of the capillary and endothelial cell dance step rhythm to procure a sufficient anti-inflammatory resistance to anti-organ posturing becomes the mechanic that enables infectious agents to potentially collapse multiple end organs. These chronic inflammatory antics will afford various disease consorts generally and infectious agents specifically sufficient interstitial space signaling and metabolic capability to empower explosive replication cycles that will outcome a septic conglomerate. In this end game, the highly saprophytic effective yet commensally end organ dependent infectious agent can ultimately become too successful as it produces signaling and metabolic chain reactions that collapse its end organ commensal partner. As it does the infectious agent would appear to marginalize its own survival as it likely succumbs to the effects of other infectious agents and their degradative "dust to dust" processes.

Chapter Fourteen

Hyper Coagulopathies and Thrombosis: How the Chronically Inflamed Endothelial Cell Interstitial Space *"Double Whammy"* Induces End Organ Hypoxia and Ischemia

The Harvesting of Chronic Inflammatory Interstitial Space *Signaling and Metabolic Threads* that Invoke Hyper Coagulopathies

The chronic inflammatory end organ interstitial space signaling and metabolic chain reactions that are fueled by vascular inflammatory free radical impingements and cytokines from purpose converted white blood cells, platelets and mesenchymal cells, become pivotal adjuncts towards the elicitation of abnormal clotting and thrombotic outcomes. These oft auto perpetuated chronic inflammatory rhythms are processed from the metabolic undercurrents of upstream underperforming oxygen delivery and increased insulin resistance to become the signaled underpinnings of chronic inflammatory willfulness[5,6,7]. As downstream endothelium and upstream capillary cell outer membranes pseudocapillarize from the effects of chronic interstitial space inflammation, the reduced anti-inflammatory nomenclature they convey will only further incentivize additional chronic inflammatory interstitial space rhythms. In what becomes a repetitive recycling of cause and effect, the anti-organ will signal convert platelets, complement and clotting factors towards harmful coagulopathies and thrombosis that threaten the functional viability of all involved end organ cells but particularly the very oxygen sensitive upstream varieties.

In this context of chronic inflammatory chain reactions, the anti-inflammatory interstitial space signaled and metabolic collective will weaken and is commensurate to the declines in the capillary and its downstream endothelial cell's loss of dance step rhythm, two step counterbalance and multipurposed anti-inflammatory fulfillment. As anti-inflammatory rhythms denature, the evolving and increasingly virilized chronic inflammatory interstitial space prodrome will chain react signaling and metabolic rhythms that will bias the activation of platelets and clotting factors into malignant thrombotic events that will damage end organ cells. Because these thrombotic outcomes can involve any endothelial cell's luminal or abluminal surface, the chronic inflammatory potential increases for a *double whammy effect* that will be felt particularly hard within the upstream capillary cell's interstitial space. It is within this context that downstream luminal thrombosis and subsequent upstream oxygen cutoff will not only predispose to additional capillary interstitial space platelet activation and clotting irregularities, but the loss of upstream oxygen delivery will cause the oxygen dependent end organ cell to seize up on its functional prerogatives. As endothelial cell interstitial spaces become monopolized by chronic inflammatory rhythms that employ hypercoagulable properties, the process is synergized by concomitant reductions in upstream oxygen delivery and increased insulin resistance. Both of these chronic inflammatory metabolic overtures will process an interstitial space microenvironment that will not only cater to platelet activation and a potential clotting megalopolis but will also set the stage for other disease consorts to find interstitial space traction. In this manner, infectious agents, scar tissue and cancer cells will utilize the same chronic inflammatory metabolic rhythms for their own propagation. It becomes possible for several disease venues to coexist within a single interstitial space that has become conducive for all of them to propagate in some fashion. When this chronic inflammatory prodrome occurs, the upstream capillary cell's outer membrane complex uncouples from its nearby end organ cell's outer membrane to instead form persistent signaling threads with previously signal converted mesenchymal and other immune cells that are now conveying a chronic inflammatory expression.

With less capacity for downstream endothelia to regulate and deliver upstream blood flow and oxygen, the upstream capillary cell becomes increasingly incapable of responding to the mitochondrial combustion needs of its oxygen dependent end organ cell partner. With less upstream to downstream functional collaboration of upstream blood flows, anti-inflammatory signaling and metabolic rhythms throughout the arterial tree dissipate with particular reference to the interstitial space effects on the upstream capillary cell. In these settings, chronic interstitial space inflammation will mature as proinflammatory signaling and metabolic rhythms favor the activation of clotting factors, complement and platelets towards unwanted transluminal thrombosis and sudden blood flow and oxygen cutoff.

In the case of downstream arterial vessel endothelium, the loss of dance step interstitial space anti-inflammatory interconnectedness and functional intimacy with its smooth muscle cell partner, will nifestake its on its basement membrane as free radical impingements such as small particle LDL cholesterol, attach, pester and fester a chronic inflammatory immune response that thickens its walls and prevents the facile exchange of information between it and its mesenchymal and end organ cell outer membranes. As basement membrane thickening escalates to plaque formation in larger and bifurcating arterial lumens upstream oxygen delivery becomes shoddy and less end organ cell predicable. What is more, the upstream capillary cell does not have any infrastructure tricks to manufacture more oxygen delivery to satisfy its end organ cell's functional demands. With less oxygen delivery and no reliable means of getting more, and with the capillary cell having to battle the same chronic inflammatory interstitial space rhythms as its downstream endothelial cell partners, its becomes clear that the upstream capillary cell becomes functionally trapped in a double whammy stranglehold. With less oxygen delivery and with the potential for increasing insulin resistance, the capillary cell's interstitial space becomes a chronic inflammatory processor that will earmark outcomes that include the activation of platelets, clotting factors and complement. This combination not only triggers coagulopathies but will also bias proinflammatory chain reactions that favor autoimmune mishaps as deranged complement activation will trigger aberrant immunoglobulin attachments. Much of this upstream chronic inflammatory decree will become dependent upon how asphyxiated the upstream interstitial space has become which in turn becomes a reflection of how much downstream luminal blood flow constriction has occurred.

The upstream to downstream chronic inflammatory double whammy effect will chain react a host of chronic inflammatory (anti-organ) interstitial space rhythms that will not only predispose to coagulopathies and end organ cell hypoxia and ischemia, but also to the expression of infections, oncogenesis, autoimmune complexes and amyloid/fibrous scar tissue [4,5,7,25,26,34]. These rhythms not only block anti-inflammatory interstitial space resolve up and down the arterial tree, but the proinflammatory signaling and metabolic makeover the create will process chain reactions that predispose to a host of luminal and abluminal disease outcomes as the ricochet and backwash through the capillary cell favors their propriety[5,7,26,30]. This transitioning of the interstitial space towards chronic inflammatory outcomes will occur as the capillary cell's anti-inflammatory dance step rhythm fades and becomes no longer capable of regulating interstitial space hygiene, processing transcellular restitution or acknowledging the functional needs of its end organ cell partner.

The "*Double Whammy Effect*" Becomes a Downstream Endothelial Cell Betrayal to Upstream Distress Signals

This signaling and metabolic anti-inflammatory interstitial space void that occurs throughout the arterial tree from the pervasiveness of chronic inflammatory rhythms will negate upstream capillary cells from controlling the functional utility of its interstitial space. The inability of downstream endothelium to signal and functionally respond to upstream capillary cell distress signals calling for more oxygen assistance becomes a root cause to upstream anti-inflammatory interstitial space failure. This will make all upstream anti-inflammatory interstitial space endeavors less purpose fulfilled while simultaneously creating a signaling and metabolic void that precludes additional chronic inflammatory behaviors[4,5,7]. The bias towards platelet aggregation and potential occlusive thrombosis becomes a fundamental mechanic of chronic inflammatory disease outcomes up and down the arterial tree.

The chronic inflammatory issues that hallmark the failure of upstream oxygen delivery and the double whammy effect will place the upstream end organ cell in functional jeopardy and will not only predispose to atrophy and loss of functional reserve but also to the possibility of death. With its functional utility declining, the interstitial space will venue the spread of disease consorts that are signaled to inherit the landscape that has become void of oxygen but ripe with sugar reserves.

It goes without saying that the capillary cell has long since lost its dance step reserve making anti-inflammatory interstitial space countenance far less likely. The capillary cell will flail in desperation as it attempts to increase upstream oxygen delivery via growth factor assisted angiogenesis. Unfortunately, due to endothelial cell basement membrane thickening or obstructive plaque, the flow of upstream blood has been reduced and upstream attempts to mobilize additional delivery becoming refractory as downstream arterial vessels become akin to rigid and increasingly narrowed pipes. Without a downstream reversal of basement membrane thickening of obstructive plaque, no amount of upstream capillary cell angiogenesis will amplify oxygen delivery, let alone counterbalance multipurpose of its dance step rhythm. As upstream oxygen deprivation increases, not only do chain reactions facilitate increased clotting and thrombosis, but the increasing insulin resistance that frequently accompanies it will facilitate other disease consorts to find functional propriety in these proinflammatory vulnerable interstitial spaces.

The loss of reliable shifts of upstream oxygen delivery based on demand will become part of a chronic inflammatory big picture that denatures anti-inflammatory interstitial space intent as its rhythms promote chronic inflammatory outcomes up and down the arterial tree.[5,6,7] In the setting of chronic upstream oxygen deprivation, interstitial space funneled *platelets, monocytes, lymphocytes, complement, clotting factors* and *inflammatory proteins* become chronic inflammatory pawns as they signal convert to increase clotting risks up and down the arterial tree. In this scenario, chronic inflammatory converted cells will elicit cytokines, enzymes, free radicals and electromagnetic wavelets that produce ricochet targets within the interstitial space that will identify with matrix and anti-organ outcomes. As these rhythms process disease outcomes, they will accentuate a backwashed anti-inflammatory immune suppression that will accelerate the transcellular aging of all end organs.

Large Arterial Vessel Thrombosis is Facilitated by the Weight, Mass and Chronic Inflammatory Momentum of Basement Membrane Obstructive Plaque

The intertwining of chronic inflammatory interstitial space signaling and metabolic processes up and down the arterial tree that negatively impact the anti-inflammatory performance of downfield endothelium and upstream capillary cells will bias their corresponding end organ cells towards adverse aging dynamics that include atrophy and apoptosis[5,7]. Transition noteworthy is how futile upstream capillary cells have become in how they have evolved coping strategies to restricted blood flows and oxygen delivery. Given sufficient downstream endothelial cell dysfunction, upstream capillary cells have no viable answers to discrepant end organ cell functional oxygen demands due to persistent reductions in upstream blood flows. The blood flow transgression becomes upstream end organ cell oxygen asphyxiating as the loss of downstream luminal flexibility precludes oxygen appropriate upstream delivery. As the tourniquet like effect tightens downstream, it will eventually slow the flow of blood through the constricted narrowing to where upstream oxygen supplies are unable to compensate for end organ cell functional disparities while making the downstream narrowed lumen a trap for clotting, thrombosis and occlusion.

Before downstream luminal occlusion occurs, the signaling framework will have been laid within the narrowed luminal space as well as within interstitial spaces where hypoxia is occurring for the activation of platelets and clotting factors that will bias variable levels of microvascular thrombosis. The momentum of these rhythms will contribute to further upstream oxygen deprivation and subsequent end organ cell atrophy and apoptosis with the rate of asphyxiation allowing for the potential of other disease venues (infections, cancer cells) to take advantage of increasing anaerobic and insulin resistant conditions within affected interstitial spaces[5,6,7]. The progression of upstream oxygen deprivation becomes self-fulfilling as downstream obstructive plaque matures it's abluminal mass and size to impinge luminal blood flows from its increasing weight. The increasing mass effect will slow luminal flows to a trickle prompting proinflammatory clotting chain reactions that places the constricted lumen at risk for an occlusive thrombosis as upstream end organ hypoxia-ischemic risks escalate. Making matters worse, the upstream chronic inflammatory interstitial space backwash into the systemic circulation will amplify proinflammatory cytokines that will tweak circulating immune arsenal to become surrogates to additional anti-organ interstitial space outcomes that will include pro clotting rhythms.

The chronic inflammatory outcomes from large arterial vessel endothelial cell basement membrane obstructive plaque can take on many different occlusive forms and outcomes. These include the luminal trickle effect that leads to an intraluminal hyper coagulable state and subsequent thrombosis or there can be other types of abluminal complications from the growing obstructive plaque. These include plaque *ulceration or basement membrane dissection* which increases risk for catastrophic aneurysmal membrane rupture or proclivity for the showering of multiple upstream occlusive micro emboli[5,7]. Regardless of what outcome occurs, the upstream end organ cell damage will be significant and could place the entire end organ at serious functional risk for decline or death.

The Direct Causal Relationship of the *Double Whammy Effect* to Proinflammatory Lifestyles

The chronic inflammatory double whammy effect to upstream capillary cell dysfunction will find its vascular inflammatory free radical foundation in most cases, not from inherent genetic proclivities, but rather from repetitive proinflammatory lifestyle choices [4,5,6,7,21,24,30]. Repetitive lifestyle missteps involving the ingestion of sugar, salt and food processing, or from other addictive lifestyle choices involving alcohol, drugs or tobacco will birth and auto perpetuate chronic inflammatory signaling and metabolic perturbations throughout the arterial tree that will process the double whammy upstream capillary cell effect. The proinflammatory lifestyle mechanic involves a steady and repetitive infusion of vascular inflammatory free radicals into end organ interstitial spaces which disrupt endothelial and capillary cell anti-inflammatory dance step counterbalance thereby making its rhythm multipurpose untenable. By allowing these free radicals to persist within interstitial spaces, the loss of dance step purpose execution will chain react declines in its outer membrane complex to process anti-inflammatory purpose precise immune contingents into the interstitial space. As its outer membrane complex does not dance step refresh its infrastructure, it will enable the processing of immune funneling errors into the interstitial space which not only become less capable of removing inflammatory breach but also more inclined to purpose convert to become chronic inflammatory surrogates. Most of these lifestyle choices begat each other's proclivity to process their continued indulgence meaning sugar and salt will prosper if coupled with alcohol and tobacco which in turn will increase pain or anxiety and process the need for opioids or anxiolytics as end organ interstitial spaces accelerate a chronic inflammatory expression. When these behaviors couple, depression and stress increase, sleep is impaired, metabolic syndrome increases and interest in exercise, vegetable based eating or other anti-inflammatory rhythms wane. As risky proinflammatory behaviors escalate vascular inflammatory free radical interstitial space impingements increases within all end organs to virilize the upstream capillary cell double whammy effect and subsequent multiple chronic inflammatory outcomes.

The common thread to the capillary cell double whammy effect is the persistence of vascular inflammatory free radical interstitial space impingements, the pan disruption of capillary cell dance step efficacy and the purpose betrayal of funneled interstitial space immune contingents. Since this proinflammatory interstitial space processing is pan endothelial cell, all end organs will exhibit some level of functional decline (aging) based on how chronic inflammatory rhythms process the transitioning to disease consorts with upstream end organ oxygen deprivation foreshadowing the development of other disease consorts that include infections, cancer or scarring that take advantage of reduced interstitial space oxygen reserve and increased insulin resistance. The free radical recycling that occurs from addictions becomes a perfect chronic inflammatory interlude that enables interstitial space transitioning. As addictions auto manipulate cognitive, motor and sensory the brain and peripheral nerves processing, they build up a chronic inflammatory resistance towards anti-inflammatory penetration that will involve multiple end organs with the brain and peripheral nerves serving as powerful addiction surrogates as they process the physical and psychological aspects of pleasure, pain and withdrawal cycles. The persistent neurochemical imbalances that are derived throughout the brain, spinal cord and peripheral nerves will enable the cause and effect of various types of neuro degeneration that will also include bipolar depression, dementia, psychosis and schizophrenia. The recycling of proinflammatory effects from these addictive behaviors will revamp multi end organ interstitial space priorities as they potentially express disease pleiotropy that will initially prioritize end organ cell hypoxia/ischemia, small/large vessel vascular thrombotic occlusions and the capillary cell double whammy effect.

The Direct Relationship of Progressive Downstream Basement Membrane Thickening and Obstructive Plaque Development to Upstream Suboptimal Oxygen Delivery and End Organ Disease Consortiums

The downstream to upstream endothelial to capillary cell compromise of optimal oxygen delivery becomes the foundation of the *double whammy effect* to upstream capillary cell dysfunction, the loss of dance step functional counterbalance, efficacy and anti-inflammatory multipurpose. The downstream endothelial cell incidentals to the upstream capillary cell double whammy effect include:

- A pan endothelial cell block of their outer membrane complex and mitochondrial combustion pivot and swing dance step rhythm that will subsequently nullify anti-inflammatory multipurpose fulfillment up and down the arterial tree based on persistent vascular inflammatory free radical impingements and a funneled and progressively misaligned interstitial space immune arsenal.
- the progressive loss of capillary cell anti-inflammatory signaling and functional interface within their interstitial space domain to include their allied mesenchymal and end organ cellular partners.
- The collapse of the capillary and downstream endothelial cell counterbalanced anti-inflammatory signaling, metabolic and functional rhythms that are purveyed into the interstitial space and backwashed into the blood plasma.
- the eventual conveyance of end organ interstitial space expression of anti-organ disease consortiums initially manifested as oxygen deficits and end organ hypoxia/ischemia but with progression to include scarring, infections, oncogenesis and autoimmune complexes. Interstitial space oxygen deprivation and progressive capillary cell dance step dysfunction will escalate all major types of chronic inflammatory anti-organ disease consorts with any given end organ's interstitial space potentially occupying several disease entities at the same time [5,6,7].

As downstream arterial vessel endothelial cell basement membranes thicken, stiffen and form varying levels of plaque to become a functional blood flow albatross, the persistently muted oxygen delivery they harbor upstream will keep chronic inflammatory interstitial space rhythms in play as they deteriorate capillary cell dance steps, anti-inflammatory multipurpose and end organ cell function. In this setting, the capillary cell chronic inflammatory double whammy effect will unleash a variety of upstream signaling and metabolic rhythms that enable anti-organ interstitial space outcomes based on oxygen deprivation and its first cousin-insulin resistance.

A Summary of the Double Whammy Upstream End Organ Interstitial Space Signaling and Metabolic Makeover

The double whammy effect to upstream capillary cells and their muted capacity to emit dance step anti-inflammatory multipurposed rhythms becomes an ideal signaling and metabolic backdrop to upstream chronic inflammatory interstitial space functional organization[5,6,7]. By producing consistent waves of ineffectual upstream oxygen delivery to support end organ cell functional utility, interstitial space rhythms are set into motion that convert the interstitial space into a functional proinflammatory machine. The persistent inability to deliver upstream oxygen places the capillary cell's dance step rhythm on its keester and makes the interstitial space a chronic inflammatory signaling and metabolic haven as it decapitates end organ cell functional capacity. When progressive capillary cell dance step withering, their corresponding interstitial spaces and non-refurbished infrastructure become signaling fodder for chronic inflammatory manipulation. With anti-organ interstitial space maturation, large and small vessel coagulopathies, thrombosis and upstream oxygen cutoff will occur as platelets and clotting factors become more reactive in oxygen deprived luminal and abluminal spaces. It is in these conditions that other disease consorts will find attractive for propagation.

Specifically, the upstream capillary cell double whammy effect and its inability to solve oxygen deprivation towards the functional utility of its end organ cellular partner will empower the maturing of chronic inflammatory interstitial space functional outcomes that will potentially involve multiple different displays of disease consorts. This will universally manifest as:

> The loss of functional crosstalk between downstream endothelium and upstream capillary cells which in turn will isolate the functional prerogatives of the upstream end organ cell as oxygen delivery stays persistently muted and the interstitial space chronically inflamed.

> An interstitial space signaling and metabolic "hypoxic milieu" that will intensify oxygen deprivation, insulin resistance, dyslipidemias and the subsequent activation of procoagulant cascades that bias hyper-coagulopathies.

> An increase in upstream chronic inflammatory interstitial space anti-organ outcomes that favor mismatched anti-inflammatory immune cells, anaerobic fermentation, and the proliferation of simple sugars and metabolic free radicals.

> A pan endothelial cell interstitial space effect that auto-perpetuates the upstream capillary cell double whammy effect to virilize chronic inflammatory outcomes throughout the arterial tree.

> To cause an auto perpetuated chronic inflammatory interstitial space ricochet and backwash effect that will exacerbate a systemic *immune suppression* that will further potentiate chronic inflammatory outcomes [4,5,6,7].

As chronic inflammatory interstitial space signaling and metabolic rhythms consolidate as a residual from the upstream capillary cell double whammy effect, the capillary cell's dance steps degenerate as do their anti-inflammatory rhythms and functional outcomes. The metabolic residuals of chronic interstitial space oxygen deprivation will further hasten interstitial space compromise which becomes the signaling and metabolic backdrop to disease consorts.

The Mechanics of the Double Whammy Effect on End Organ Interstitial Space Chronic Inflammatory Virilization

As upstream end organ interstitial space chronic inflammatory signaling streams and metabolic rhythms gain momentum as a result of persistent ineffectual upstream oxygen delivery, their expressions will eventually mosaic a compilation of anti-organ disease consorts predicated on persistent oxygen deprivation[6,7,32,34]. As these rhythms mature within interstitial spaces, they consolidate virilization of intent meaning they become more purpose intentional and refractory to waning anti-inflammatory immune resistance. In the setting of the upstream capillary cell double whammy effect, as reduced upstream blood flows and oxygen delivery reproduce end organ cell hypoxia, atrophy and death, the chronic inflammatory signaling and metabolic momentum they generate will predispose to additional disease cohorts.

In these reverberating chronic inflammatory interstitial space rhythms, disease seeds will find these rhythms conducive to their propagation as they utilize oxygen deprivation, insulins resistance and vascular inflammatory free radical dyslipidemias to their own advantage. Examples of how disease consorts process proinflammatory interstitial space metabolics include:

- The capacity to easily adapt to anaerobically-ferment glucose rich interstitial space microenvironments via glycolysis to produce energy which becomes a natural fit for certain bacteria, other infectious agents and cancer cells which then use what oxygen is available to mitochondrial combust nitric oxide to boost their replicative cycles.

- The capacity of infectious agents, such as bacteria, fungi or amoebas to release endotoxins or secretagogues that both increase and subjugate acute inflammatory responses towards their purposes as they emit confusing signals that increase anti-inflammatory resistance towards their elimination while simultaneously decoying their replicative intent.

- These anti-organ disease mosaics will often further accentuate interstitial space oxygen deficits, insulin resistance, pH imbalances and adverse osmolar states which in turn facilitate replicative purpose fulfillment of cancer cells or assorted infectious agents. The replicative recycling can occur against the interstitial space backdrop of abnormal platelet aggregation and activation of clotting factors that predispose to luminal and abluminal coagulopathies.

- The increased production of amyloid and fibrous scar tissue by signal and functionally converted mesenchymal, monocyte and white blood cells.

- The likelihood that interstitial space disease mosaics will fuse and consolidate their signaling and metabolic rhythms and purpose fulfillment with each other as they virilize intent through their collective operational pyramids[7].

As the upstream capillary cell double whammy effect begats increasing chronic inflammatory interstitial space disease consolidation, the collective rhythms they emit will blend with their purpose fulfillments. With the capillary cell locked out of its anti-inflammatory dance step rhythm and with no hope for downstream endothelia to come to their collective rescue, the persistent upstream oxygen deficits will pace chain reacting rhythms that overwhelm the fading anti-inflammatory counter resistance[7]. The increasing functional senescence of the downstream endothelial and upstream capillary, mesenchymal and end organ cellular axis becomes the interstitial space signaling and metabolic pariah towards the compilation of disease mosaics.

The Persistent Reduction of Upstream Interstitial Space "Oxygen Tensions" Becomes the Anti-Organ's "Mother Lode" of Disease Fulfillment

When chronically reduced multi-end organ interstitial space oxygen tension occurs it will signal and metabolically bias an adjoining chronic inflammatory momentum that will stem a variety of disease cohorts that feast on the signaling and metabolic outcomes of interstitial space chronic hypoxia [5,6,7,8,9,10]. As dance step driven anti-inflammatory interstitial space resistance declines, hypoxic driven increases in insulin resistance, dyslipidemias, advanced glycation end products, acidic pH and assorted hypo osmolar states will couple with anti-inflammatory purpose disillusioned immune arsenal and mesenchymal cells to posture increasing resistance against anti-inflammatory immune mechanics as they simultaneously fortify anti-organ purpose fulfillment. The upstream double whammy drag on ineffectual oxygen delivery becomes an auto perpetuated stimulus against anti-inflammatory interstitial space rhythms as it amplifies chronic inflammatory metabolic mechanics and intent to become the growth engine of duplicitous disease mosaics. This results in a transitioned interstitial space that becomes anti-inflammatory refractory as ignored infectious agents and cancer cells couple with chronic inflammatory signal converted mesenchymal and lymphocyte cells to reset their signaling, metabolic and functional priorities.

In all end organs, but particularly in very *oxygen sensitive* ones such as the brain, heart, retina and spinal cord, the upstream capillary cell's double whammy effect, that has no viable long-term answer to upstream oxygen deficits. In that sense the functionally beleaguered cell becomes a surrogate to the chronic inflammatory anti-organ signaling and metabolic rhythms that *"mother lode"* the birth and propagation to a variety of disease expressions that are facilitated by the chain reactions created from reduced interstitial space oxygen tensions [4,5,6,7]. As upstream oxygen deficits apply increasing pressure on the end organ cell's functional viability, the disabled capillary cell's dance steps become enablers to proinflammatory chain reactions that facilitate interstitial space insulin resistance, dyslipidemias, acid base anomalies and hypo osmolar states. When these interstitial space chronic inflammatory metabolic amalgams merge with other midlife proinflammatory prodromes, the obligatory increases in hypertension, obesity, adult diabetes, the metabolic syndrome, obstructive sleep apnea, and anxiety/depression will in aggregate will, not only contribute to end organ hypoxic-ischemic events, but also to the development of end organ cancers, scarring, autoimmune complexes and various infectious invasions. The evolving multi end organ interstitial space chronic inflammatory anti-organ outcomes that can arise from persistent upstream oxygen deprivation will posture a metabolic interstitial space transitioning that will mediate proinflammatory outcomes that gives the anti-organ "executive privileges" towards interstitial space content.

Chapter Fifteen

The Lethal Integration of Cancer Cells into Chronic Inflammatory Signaling Streams and Metabolic Rhythms

Introducing the Chronic Inflammatory Signaling and Metabolic Enhancements that Occur from Anti-inflammatory Ignored Interstitial Space Cancer Cells

When capillary and downstream endothelial cells are performing in a counterbalanced and anti-inflammatory synchronized *dance step cadence* their interstitial space domains will be incidentally protected from the chronic dispersals of proinflammatory rhythms. The signaled, metabolic and functional counterbalance of the upstream capillary cell dance step rhythm, not only signal paces the downstream endothelial cell dance steps to coordinate anti-inflammatory multi, but the cadence and purposed execution of each dance step quality assures the anti-inflammatory purposed execution of the next dance step and so on (Figure 9, appendix) [6,7]. The counterbalanced functional rhythm of consecutive dance steps creates a pulsing of signaled and metabolic *circadian shifts* within the capillary and downstream infrastructure that extends to include the signaling rhythms of the interstitial space and allied cells that reside in their domain as they integrate their purposes within the confines of the capillary cell's anti-inflammatory dance step purpose fulfillment. The purposed execution within the dance step cadence includes the timely removal of vascular inflammatory free radical impingements, the optimization of interstitial space hygiene, the refurbishment of its infrastructure and the scaling of sufficient oxygen and nutrient loads to the interstitial space to satisfy the functional demands of the nearby end organ cell.

The *execution* of the dance step rhythm will pace, stem, ricochet and backwash many interlocking intracellular, interstitial space and blood plasma chain reactions and cellular contingents that find function anti-inflammatory patronage from the outer membrane complex permeability pivot and mitochondrial combustion swing of the capillary cells reverberating dance step rhythm. The back-and forth dance step process will salvo anti-inflammatory chain reactions that couple multipurpose execution within its interstitial space domain to its outer membrane complex permeability adjustments and subsequent swinging of mitochondrial combustion from energy to nitric oxide. When this rhythm is counterbalanced and multipurpose executed, the anti-inflammatory rhythms virilize expression which keeps the interstitial space hygienic, the end organ cell functionally optimal, and all allied cells within the capillary cell's domain infrastructure rejuvenated.

Central to successful dance step purpose execution is how it regulates immune choreography into the interstitial space to timely remove various types of inflammatory breach. In this manner the capillary cells outer membrane complex becomes the equivalent of a hired immune funneling agent as they spigot specific immune elements into the interstitial space that transact the elimination of various types of vascular inflammatory free radical interstitial space impingements. As the capillary cell's outer membrane complex permeability gradient fluxes to liberalize the mobilization of immune constituents into the interstitial space, it releases powerful signaling confluences to nearby mitochondria to increase energy combustion and begin the processing of the dance step execution of inflammatory breach removal. As energy is released to support the active transport of specific immune contingents that support B cell driven responses, nitric oxide combustion is subverted and all of its functional rhythms associated with it become quiescent. When this outer membrane complex permeability pivot and mitochondrial combustion swing dance step is executed and functionally counterbalanced with the next dance step, the capillary cell's dance step rhythm becomes a powerful anti-inflammatory multitasker as its dance steps a pace, stem, ricochet and backwash of anti-inflammatory rhythms into and out of the interstitial space and blood plasma[5,6,7].

This recurring stature of the multipurposed dance step rhythm will include within its cadence the restitution of its infrastructure (as well as that of its allied partnered cells) which enables future durability to its anti-inflammatory performance. The timely dance step anti-inflammatory processing will backwash immune boosting cytokines into the systemic circulation that will tweak circulating immune arsenal molecular configurations in such a manner as to make them better anti-inflammatory performers when called upon to be capillary cell funneled into an end organ's interstitial space.

Included within the context of the capillary cell's dance step rhythm removal of inflammatory breach would be the timely "processing" and molecular constituent recycling of interstitial space cancer cells[7]. The removal process will utilize immune funneled agents in a similar rhythm as removing vascular inflammatory free radical impingements as cancer cells are systematically immune identified opsonized and reduced to basic molecular contingents (carbon dioxide, water, nitrogen, amino acids and other trace minerals) with the ladder used as metabolic signaling fodder towards the initiation of the next dance step. In this manner, the anti-inflammatory dance step removal of cancer cells becomes circadian similar to the removal of other types of interstitial space inflammatory breach including vascular inflammatory free radical impingements.

The anti-inflammatory mechanics of cancer cell opsonization and molecular recycling when completely reduced to elemental units may require extra steps due the complexity of their metabolic breakdown that include phagocytosis from macrophages. Nevertheless, the processing of their removal can contextually fit within the dance step infrastructure and time frame of vascular inflammatory free radical interstitial space removal. Within the venue of the various types of interstitial space inflammatory breach removals, many different cell types and anti-inflammatory chain reactions will be required within the choreography of funneled immune contingents to handle the various displays and volumes of inflammatory contingents. In addition, continuous signaling input to the capillary cell's outer membrane complex is required from nearby interstitial space mesenchymal cells as they provide intelligence about the type and volume of inflammatory breach which helps the capillary cell adjust the rate and volume of specific immune funneling agents. It is this the volume and specificity of the mesenchymal cell "all hands-on deck" signal that stretches the confines of detailed immune funneling efforts into the interstitial space that includes polymorphonuclear white blood cells, both helper and killer lymphocytes, monocytes, immunoglobulins, complement, platelets and clotting factors. Their funneled integration into the interstitial space anti-inflammatory effort towards inflammatory breach removal will in turn process cytokines, free radicals, enzymes and electromagnetic wavelets that chain react the execution of the processing details. Included in this anti-inflammatory signaling amalgam are explicit messages to the capillary cell's basement membrane that in turn provides the necessary information to the continuous outer membrane and glycocalyx that will facilitate the sequential and detailed funneling of immune elements into the interstitial space. When the autologous cancer cell or other forms of inflammatory breach have been successfully degraded, the mesenchymal cell's cytokine inhibitory "all clear" signal will stream back to the capillary cell's basement membrane, which will cause a fundamental shift in its outer membrane complex permeability gradients away from further interstitial space immune funneling. When this occurs, the capillary cell's anti-inflammatory dance step rhythm will signal the next pivot and swing dance step that will fulfill a completely different anti-inflammatory purpose identity [5,6,7].

Just like the removal of other vascular inflammatory free radical interstitial space impingements, the removal of cancer cells from the interstitial space microenvironment will involve anti-inflammatory rhythms generated form the capillary cell dance steps with the additional caveat requiring a bit more immune sequencing to accomplish a satisfactory outcome. This built-in dance step derived anti-inflammatory interstitial space signaling and metabolic process to timely remove and reduce cancer cells fits within the context of optimal endothelial and capillary cell interstitial space *stewardship* in the management of its sanitation[7].

The Interstitial Space Microenvironment that Enables Cancer Cell Expression and Propagation

In contrast to optimally functioning end organ cells, cancer cells will find functional interstitial space utility in metabolic conditions where there will likely be less oxygen reserve and more insulin resistance. It turns out that when cancer cells utilize anaerobic metabolism to produce energy for its basal energy requirement, it becomes a perfect signaling and metabolic deference that enables what oxygen is available to be used for its mitochondrial nitric oxide combustion and subsequent growth factor assisted replication reverberation. The capacity to use abundant sugars in fermentation for basal energy metabolism gives it a distinctive leg up compared to its nascent cell ancestors that utilize huge quantities of oxygen for the specified functional purposes. Since cancer cells for the most part could care less about participating in those functional rhythms, it can go about its business autonomously by processing oxygen into its nitric oxide combustion rhythms to emphasize replication and increased propagation of cancer cell mass. In the setting of chronic interstitial space inflammation, not only are cancer cells increasingly immune ignored, but the rhythms generated by the weakened capillary cell dance steps actually feedback loop to the cancer cell signals that nurture nitric oxide combustion and replication dynamics. In this manner and within cancer cell metabolism, pyruvate is postured within mitochondrial combustion of acetyl co A to facilitate nitric oxide combustion and ribosomal protein synthesis as cancer cell liposomes are stimulated to manufacture longer fatty acid chains for the enablement of lipogenesis, protein synthesis and subsequent cancer cell replication[7]. These metabolic chronic inflammatory tweaks, that are nurtured by chronic inflammatory interstitial space rhythms and a persistent capillary cell energy combustion cycle, produces within a cancer that has been retrofitted with infrastructure that nurtures oxygen deprivation and insulin resistance, a better chance of functional utility, replicative propagation and an increased expression of cancer cells into masses.

It is the chronic inflammatory interstitial space processing of interstitial space chain reactions that not only biases nascent end organ cells to become increasingly oncogenic and to be immune ignored, but also supplies the necessary signaling and metabolic detail to allow the aberrant cell to multiply with impunity. In this chronic inflammatory setting, not only do cancer cells become more likely to be interstitial space displayed, but the rhythms generated within the interstitial space produce a greater likelihood that they find their own functional utility as they simultaneously escape a weakened anti-inflammatory immune surveillance from a dysfunctional capillary cell dance step rhythm. As their replication is enhanced, the persistence of its nitric oxide combustion cycle will produce sufficient RNS exhaust to increase additional nuclear chromatin cross linkages and further functional independence from its nascent cell ancestors as its replicative cycling increases. As the interstitial space chronic inflammatory transitions reduced oxygen reserves and increased insulin resistance, it becomes a perfect storm for cancer cells to express increasing cell division and greater autonomy from its nascent cell ancestor.

In summary, the interstitial space processing of cancer cell/mass virilization occurs on the basis of several converging chronic inflammatory interstitial space signaling and metabolic rhythms that divest the space away from the capillary cell dance step rhythm. This transitioning includes:

- a diminished capillary cell dance step derived anti-inflammatory interstitial space cadence
- increased interstitial space insulin resistance and oxygen deprivation
- diminished displays of anti-inflammatory precision purposed immune contingents within the interstitial space that increasingly ignore cancer cell identification but by becoming signal turned contribute to their identity development and replicative expression
- the increasing reconciliation of chronic inflammatory interstitial space intentionality as signaling rhythms generated by purpose converted immune arsenal signal pirate funneled immune content into the interstitial space that actually increases the purpose identity of the growing cancer mass.
- doing so will also increase interstitial space risks for the seeding of infections, autoimmune complexes, coagulopathies, thrombosis and scarring as part of a chronic inflammatory interstitial space disease conglomerate

As cancer cells replicate and continue to signal divest the chronic inflammatory interstitial space microenvironment, they will cause and effect additional proinflammatory metabolic rhythms that become an integral part of their replicative expressions. As they metabolically process reduced interstitial space oxygen tensions and increased insulin resistance, they cause and effect a metabolic admixture that becomes ideal suited for their replicative expressions as well as metabolic fodder for other disease venues. With increasing interstitial space chronic inflammatory rhythm consolidation and intentionality, the growing cancer mass will incorporate more of a defensive posturing towards protecting its infrastructure against anti-inflammatory incursions. Individual cells within the cancer mass not only begin to differentiate purposes in order to support the growing mass lattice, but they will also align their combustion mechanics with chronic inflammatory interstitial space signaling and metabolic chain reactions that enhance a replicative expression.

In contrast to its nascent cell ancestor, the cancer cell/mass will *adapt* and benefit from chronic inflammatory interstitial space signaling and metabolic rhythms that in turn have become unfavorable to the functional utilities of their nascent cell ancestors. The cancer mass may also tie into the functional rhythms generated from other interstitial space disease venues or the hormonal influences that are produced from distant end organ cells, both of which could lend themselves to their replicative rhythms. Through this coupling of mutual self-interest, this emerging chronic inflammatory interstitial space signaling and metabolic foundation will cause the cancer mass to grow exponentially as its nearby end organ cell ancestor atrophies or even dies.

As the cancer mass increases in size and interstitial space signaling influence, it will manufacture extending devices such as microtubules and growth factors that will provide the mass with the necessary resources, such as sugars and oxygen, to process their replication skill sets[7]. As cells within the cancer mass acquire and specialize their functioning, their expressions will transition the interstitial space into what can be described as an *anti-organ industrial complex*. This transitioning will deaden the interstitial space to anti-inflammatory rhythms as they parlay cancer mass replication and the potential layering of other disease consorts.

The loss of the anti-inflammatory capillary cell dance step rhythm becomes a chronic inflammatory and cancer mass fertilizer. This transitioning is highlighted by:

- The increased chronic inflammatory interstitial space signaling and metabolic rhythms that reduce anti-inflammatory proclivity to recognize cancer cell budding or to respond to them once they are made aware of their presence.
- The metabolic transitioning of the interstitial space towards oxygen deprivation and abundant sugar supplies both of which support cancer cell replication.
- The interstitial space metabolic combination of reduced oxygen reserve and increased simple sugars will be processed in the cancer cell as glycolysis induced energy production and mitochondrial nitric oxide combustion processed replication.
- The excessive and non-oxidized RNS exhaust from nitric oxide combustion will contribute towards additional nuclear chromatin cross linkage which will increase cancer cell/mass autonomy from its nascent cell ancestors as well as its replicative virulence.
- With cancer mass cellular differentiation, nitric oxide combustion within these cells will produce growth factor assisted production of mass extenders such as with microtubule displayrs and the processing of tumor angiogenesis.
- The cancer mass will integrate signaling and metabolic rhythms from other disease consortiums to increase its replicative and nascent cell autonomous expressions[7].

Trans Nascent Cell Aging and Cancer

With persistent chronic interstitial space inflammation, the capillary and downstream endothelial cells lose dance step rhythm, signaling and metabolic counterbalance and functional anti-inflammatory quality assurance. As their outer membrane complexes pseudocapillarize and mitochondria lose volumes, mass and size, their corresponding nuclear chromosomal DNA become increasingly code and protein synthesis silenced from ROS cross-linkage. This process defines capillary cell senescence and becomes the recipe for senescence of its cellular interstitial space allies.

Aging of the capillary and downstream endothelial cells, as well as the allied cells within its interstitial space domain, can slow or speed up based on how the interstitial space transitions chronic interstitial space signaling and metabolic influences. These rhythms will push capillary and downstream endothelial cell infrastructure towards increasing signaling and metabolic imbalances which will extoll persistent increases in their mitochondrial energy combustion cycles that will be counterproductive to the purposes derived from the diminished nitric oxide combustion cycle. When this occurs, excessive capillary and downstream endothelial cellular outer membrane complex permeability biases that keep immune remnants funneled into the interstitial space will keep their mitochondrial combustion fixed in energy production so that larger immune molecules can buck various permeability gradients and be actively transported into the interstitial space for inflammatory breach mediation. With this persistent energy combustion to nitric oxide combustion mismatch, the overproduction of *reactive oxygen species* exhaust becomes toxic to the cell as they do not get sufficiently reduced from exhausted antioxidant. Their lingering within the cell makes membrane and DNA surfaces vulnerable to their attachment. When ROS excessively attaches to nuclear chromatin, it silences its capacity to code for operational sustenance rendering the cell vulnerable to functional cracks and aging dynamics. The rate of ROS to nuclear chromatin cross linkage will determine the pace of cellular aging regardless of where or which cell is involved. The aging of all human cells therefore is *rate limited* by the degree to which capillary and downstream endothelial cell's nuclear chromatin has become code silenced from ROS cross linkage which is a reflection of how counterbalanced and functionally quality assured the capillary cell's dance step rhythm has been maintained. In the end organ cell, the problem with increasing senescence will more than likely involve code silencing from excessive *RNS* mitochondrial exhaust and DNA cross linkage [5,6,7].

When senescence occurs to the capillary-downstream endothelial cell axis, the endothelial system cannot execute optimal anti-inflammatory effects into and out of the interstitial space and blood plasma. This will ensure less than optimal interstitial space hygiene, the likely persistence of the vascular inflammatory free radical interstitial space pace pester and fester effect, the inability of the endothelial cell system to stage any meaningful infrastructure refurbishment, the increased predilection for immune funneling errors into the interstitial space, and the likely degradation of end organ cell functional utility. The degree and rate of endothelial cell system senescence becomes an independent risk factor towards the increasing virulence and intentionality of chronic inflammatory interstitial space signaling and metabolic expressions that by their nature will limit the anti-inflammatory capacity to survey and remove all types of inflammatory breach that would also include cancer cells. The senescent capillary-downstream endothelial cell axis becomes its own risk factor for the interstitial space fulfillment of oncogenesis.

In summary, increasing interstitial space cancer cell expression is enabled from the increased rate of functional senescence from the capillary and downstream endothelial cell as a manifestation of:

- **Loss of a system wide capillary endothelial cell dance step rhythm, signaling and metabolic counterbalance and functional quality assurance which makes the funneled immune operatives less likely to identify or remove cancer cells due to increased immune funneling miscues**
- **The inability of the capillary cell to oversight optimal interstitial space sanitation mechanics as its anti-inflammatory pace, stem ricochet and backwash effects have been irreparably compromised by invasive chronic inflammatory rhythms.**
- **The reduced capacity of the capillary-endothelial cell system to functionally address end organ cell oxygen, nutrient or other metabolic (pH, osmolality gradients) interstitial space requirements.**
- **The persistent inability of the capillary cell dance step rhythm to eliminate chronic inflammatory interstitial space signaling and metabolic dynamics rhythms which become increasingly anti-inflammatory purposed outliers.**
- **The increased likelihood that both end organ and mesenchymal cells become part of the chronic inflammatory tour de force as the capillary-downstream endothelia cell system become functional surrogates to the signaling displays of anti-organ rhythms that include the expression of cancer cell replication and mass expansion[7].**

The Cancer Cell *Masquerade Effect*

To avoid detection as it begins to functionally integrate its signaling and metabolic rhythms within an interstitial space, the cancer cell will utilize camouflage techniques as it processes its operational mechanics in stealth [6,7]. This camouflage process allows the cancer to masquerade its identity and purpose from interstitial space anti-inflammatory immune mechanics allowing the cell/mass to utilize preexisting chronic inflammatory rhythms to amplify its replication cycles. The capacity for cancer cells to find functional utility in these interstitial space circumstances gives them a competitive advantage over their nascent cell ancestors as they adapt and incorporate preexisting chronic inflammatory rhythms into their infrastructure and replicative purpose.

The cancer cell/mass can further outsource the masquerade effect to avoid anti-inflammatory degradation by integrating their signaling and metabolic rhythms with other disease venues such as when finding refuge within scar tissue crevices or integrating within the functional rhythms of infectious agents that are also harbored within the interstitial space. In this manner cancer cell/mass expression becomes a pleiotropic continuum of signaling adjustments based on prevailing proinflammatory interstitial space rhythms as well as ongoing adjustments towards anti-inflammatory interstitial space incursions that seek of identify and eliminate the cancer cell. In these situations, scar tissue, infectious agents or even autoimmune complexes or other types of cancer cells may enhance the cancer cell/mass by enabling the masquerade effect while at the same time continuing to compromise anti-inflammatory immune resistance from a declining dance step rhythm [6,7]. In summary, the cancer cell/mass *masquerade effect* will increase its interstitial space virilization via:

> Enabling the integration of the mass signaling expressions with interstitial space chronic inflammatory signaling and metabolic cues as it takes advantage of a depleted anti-inflammatory capillary cell dance step rhythm.
> Will boost its purposed intentionality and how its masquerades its expression via incorporating into other disease venues.
> Will enable the evolving cancer mass the opportunity to exploit chronic inflammatory interstitial space metabolic rhythms towards its r functional benefit that would include persistently reduced oxygen tensions and increased insulin resistance.
> Signal align with other preexisting chronic inflammatory interstitial space rhythms to extort additional proinflammatory immune funneling content into the interstitial space that would enable replicative resilience [6,7].

The Mechanics of a Chronic Inflammatory Interstitial Space Signaling and Metabolic Milieu that Favors Oncogenic Expansion

As chronic inflammatory rhythms transition a virilized interstitial space intent, the reduction of anti-inflammatory resistance will further incentivize additional proinflammatory signaling and metabolic rhythms which in turn ignite unmitigated nascent end organ cell oncogenesis[6,7]. This continuous processing of interstitial space cancer cells will become part of the chronic inflammatory signaling resistance that auto perpetuates the block of the capillary cell's dance step rhythm as the proinflammatory signaling crescendos continue to *recruit and convert* funneled interstitial space immune arsenal into chronic inflammatory purposes. The loss of the capillary cell's dance step rhythm becomes the gain of increasing chronic inflammatory interstitial space expressions whose sway will favor the expression of nascent cell oncogenesis. The process of oncogenic expansion virilizes as chronic inflammatory interstitial space rhythms begin to intentionally signal pirate the capillary cell's outer membrane complex to enable a virilized and specific chronic inflammatory signaling expression (Figures 16 and 17, appendix).

As chronic inflammatory interstitial space signaling and metabolic rhythms mature to increase purpose virulence, their expressions will signal loop and functionally integrate with those of the antecedent cancer mass. Their intentional expressions will virilize chronic inflammatory immune funneling rhythms from the central circulation that will conform to the growth needs of the replicative cancer cell/mass[7]. As the cancer cell mass evolves microtubules projections and angiogenesis to improve oxygen and nutrient delivery, these operatives will also foster the further conversion of immune contingents being funneled into the interstitial space to signal convert and facilitate the further processing of cancer mass replicative expression. When immune arsenal signal convert, their released cytokines, enzymes, free radicals and electromagnetic wavelets will not only conform to the growth and defense of the growing cancer mass but will also enable other disease venue expression as anti-inflammatory interstitial space prerogatives fade.

The building of the cancer mass into a virile signaling and metabolic interstitial space consensus of replicative purpose execution will create an anti-organ juggernaut that becomes capable of exerting its functional will on all interstitial space membrane surfaces to extort what it requires from the blood plasma through the disabled capillary cell's outer membrane complex. In this manner, the rhythms it generates within the interstitial space microenvironment will virilize cancer mass replication as it transitions other disease consort expressions.

How Cancer Cells, and Subsequent Mass Development Envelop the Transcendental Interstitial Space Signaling and Metabolic Milieu to become its *"Favored Son"*

The continuously adaptive metabolic and signaling lattice that composes the infrastructure of the growing cancer mass will bias interstitial space rhythms that make it increasingly anti-inflammatory resistant towards its degradation[7]. Because of the capacity of the cancer mass to adapt to, participate in and benefit from chronic inflammatory microenvironments its metabolic propensity will be to thrive in oxygen challenged interstitial space situations that will also preclude increased sugar reserves. Its growing capacity to utilize these metabolic mechanics to their advantage as these same metabolic venues remain hostile to their nearby nascent cell relatives as they make the interstitial space environment increasingly more conducive towards the replicative expression of the cancer mass.

As chronic inflammatory metabolic and signaling rhythms organize the cancer mass replicative processes are enhanced as reduced oxygen concentrations, acidic pH, increasing insulin resistance and hypo osmolar states intensify. It is within these interstitial space microenvironments, that are increasingly hostile to the functional rhythms of the end organ cell, where cancer cells and other disease consorts can escort their propagation. Central to this metabolic propitiation is how cancer cells (unlike their native ancestor cells) utilize fermentation to produce energy for their basal requirements. Doing so, places a high demand on sugar as a fermentation resource thereby making insulin resistance an important antecedent towards fermentation utilization. When enabled to produce energy in this fashion, the cancer mass can divert what oxygen it does consume to its mitochondria in the production of nitric oxide which will enhance growth factor induced replication. When this occurs, increased RNS exhaust will betray and cross link with its nuclear chromosomal DNA to increase further functional disparities between the cells within the cancer mass and the feedback loops they will be responsive to and the nearby nascent cells from which they were derived. In this context, the utilization of the metabolically desperate interstitial space microenvironment by the cancer cell/mass towards its robust replicative fulfillment makes these cells the *favorite son* of the interstitial space. As the cancer mass becomes increasingly more signal and metabolically independent form their nascent cell ancestors it will extol their own brand of functional pressure on the interstitial space microenvironment that will require the disabled capillary cell's outer membrane complex to funnel form the blood plasma immune contingents that will signal convert and cater to their functional demands[5,6,7].

In the early stages of cancer mass transitioning, their progenitor cells will have become refractory to the signaling feedback loops within the interstitial space that the nearby nascent cell ancestors utilize for their functional output. When they do so, they become interstitial space *independent contractors* as they deploy their own sets of signaling indicators that execute a much different purpose (replication) compared to the functional rhythms of their ancestor relatives. This signaling divergence makes cancer cells and mass refractory to the feedback loops and other interstitial space accessories that their what their nascent cell ancestors will utilize to optimize their functional output. As the cancer mass continues to disable its DNA from RNS cross linkage this divergence becomes even more desperate as the cancer mass becomes more rogue and resistant to anti-inflammatory degradation. The evolving cancer mass not only becomes increasingly more functionally autonomous but its metabolically deranged infrastructure finds replicative utility within the context of increased interstitial space oxygen deprivation and insulin resistance.

As the cancer mass causes and effects interstitial space signal and metabolic transitioning, the rhythms its generates will increasingly compromise the beleaguered capillary cell dance step rhythm to where it has severely marginalized both its functional counterbalance and anti-inflammatory multipurposed quality assurance. The loss of dance step anti-inflammatory resolve, makes the interstitial space signaling and metabolic rhythms favorable towards cancer mass replicative cycles as nitric oxide combustion within the cells of the cancer mass is signal biased. This signaling bias not only enhances cancer mass expression but will also incentivize nearby nascent end organ cells to offshoot more cancer cells that will likely be able to escape anti-inflammatory immune surveillance due to the decay of interstitial space functional resolve[6,7]. When this proinflammatory perfect interstitial space storm materializes, the moribund capillary cell dance steps will enable signaling and metabolic rhythms to prosper the intensified growth of cancer mass replicative expressions[5,6,7].

As the cancer mass strengthens its signaling and metabolic hierarchy, its emitted rhythms become user friendly towards other disease expressions [5,6,7,25]. The evolution of these other venues will further magnify the virulence and intentionality of chronic inflammatory interstitial space rhythms that will reduce corresponding anti-inflammatory resolve. These increasing interstitial space functional imbalances will further constrain what might be left of the capillary cell's dance steps and its corresponding anti-inflammatory rhythms. As the cancer mass virilizes intent and transitions the interstitial space signaling and metabolic prerogatives, the rhythms it generates will posture both replication and protection of its assets[7]. In this manner, the signaled expressions of the cancer mass become a chronic inflammatory interstitial space predator and aggressive anti-organ *agent* that will transition the functional mechanics of the interstitial space into a virilized anti-organ amalgam.

One major goal of a maturing cancer mass is that its replicative expressions become refractory to *anti-inflammatory degradation*[7]. As the cancer mass remasters the interstitial space signaling and metabolic hierarchy, it will foster increasing control of immune operatives as it pirates their purpose towards its own fulfillment. As it does this, it keeps the capillary cell dance step disabled as it prevents it from resuscitating any anti-inflammatory interstitial space vibrato. This will keep the interstitial space locked into signaling and metabolic rhythms that virilize both cancer mass and chronic inflammatory purpose fulfillment.

The Signal and Metabolic *Predator Effect* of the Growing Cancer Mass and the Manipulation of Synchronized Chronic Inflammatory Interstitial Space Rhythms

As the end organ's interstitial space cancer mass replicates and virilizes its expression, it captures an increasing control of interstitial space signaling and metabolic bandwidth. This enables its transmitted signals to become aggressive *predators of* chronic inflammatory purpose fulfillment that will *synchronize its effects* within the evolving collateral rhythms of anti-organ dispersals. The fusion of these anti-organ signaling projections will serve to virilize cancer mass purpose fulfillment as it collateralizes the necessary signaling and metabolic overtures within the interstitial space to harvest other disease venues. This chronic inflammatory synchronizing effect will convert funneled and signal vulnerable immune remnants towards the chronic inflammatory interstitial space precipice that will become instrumental in shaping the direction of interstitial space rhythms that support cancer mass expression[7].

In this scenario, the increasingly virilized and purpose intentional chronic inflammatory signaling and metabolic rhythms will transition the interstitial space to become more proinflammatory responsive and cancer mass inductive[7]. Its corresponding rhythm displays will extort and consort a chronic inflammatory consensus to express the potential for multiple disease consorts to cohabitate and express a multi leveled purpose fulfillment. When this occurs, cancer expression will enable infectious agents and scar formation to occur within the interstitial space and visa-versa.

The signaling mechanics behind the consolidation of cancer mass expression will be to amalgam preexisting chronic inflammatory signaling and metabolic threads towards its replicative expression. The transitioning interstitial space process will include the alignment of the disabled capillary cell outer membrane complex as it becomes the go between of what the cancer mass requires form the blood or lymph plasma [6,7,25].

The Cancer Mass will Likely Overutilize Interstitial Space Signaling and Metabolic Resources that will Ultimately Contribute to the Death of the End Organ and its Own Subsequent Demise

A rapidly growing and purpose consolidating cancer mass will become so purpose virilized that it will overutilize the prevailing interstitial space natural resources to where it not only suffocates future growth prospects but also fosters the demise of the end organ cell constituency[6,7]. When this occurs, its autonomous and replicative momentum will become extinguished as it overruns interstitial space oxygen and nutrient reserves. When this occurs, the mass may have to contract, hibernate its replicative expression or backwash malignant cells into the central circulation to potentially seed in other locations. Which direction the cancer mass will take is predicated on the interstitial space microenvironment and ill often involve combinations of all three responses as the mass simultaneously weighs in on the prospects of tapping into additional oxygen or sugar reserves. It will also become dependent on how much resistance can be mustered from anti-inflammatory immune resuscitation which is codependent on how much resolve the capillary cell has in retooling its dance step rhythm given the right signaling and metabolic propensities within the interstitial space. Much of this reversal will become dependent on how vascular inflammatory free radical impingements have been interstitial space tamed.

For the cancer mass to succeed and further express replicative expansion, it will require sufficient volumes of delivered oxygen, sugars and a persistent display of vascular inflammatory free radical interstitial space impingements that will keep the disabled capillary cell network purpose distracted and dance step paralyzed. The proclivity and preponderance of these chronic inflammatory overtures, will not only run contrary to the overmatched and less capable anti-inflammatory immune alternatives, but their signaling momentum will convert purpose neutral immune cells towards their functional prerogatives[7]. When this occurs, chronic inflammatory interstitial space rhythms will virilize their own intentionality that will include the expression of cancer mass expansion.

A consequence of the expansive power and signaling control of the cancer mass will be how its rhythms induce the expression of other disease venues which mutually fulfill each other's purpose fulfillment [6,7]. Thus interstitial space bacteria, virus, scar tissue or even pro clotting biases will co link with chronic inflammatory rhythms to support further cancer mass expression and visa-versa.

How Fasting, Exercise and Reducing Insulin Resistance become Anti-Inflammatory Weapons that can Stall Out Cancer Mass Growth by Facilitating Capillary Cell Dance Steps and by also Reducing Interstitial Space Pyruvate Concentrations

When strategizing an anti-inflammatory response towards blocking cancer cell replication, given the dire anti-inflammatory interstitial space circumstances and decayed capillary cell dance step rhythm, aggressive external attempts to restore anti-inflammatory impetus could have merit is stalling out further cancer cell/mass expression. In this scenario, *fasting, regular exercise, and reducing insulin resistance* should in aggregate contribute to reducing interstitial space pyruvate concentrations. This should cause an incredibly potent effect on antagonizing cancer cell replication through the following mechanics:

- To feedback loop the cancer mass restriction of glycolysis to ferment energy thereby requiring the cells within the cancer mass to utilize oxygen to combust energy thereby overriding its nitric oxide combustion and replicative bias. This same strategy holds true in the case of limiting bacterial replication.
- As cancer mass mitochondria utilize fatty acids and beta oxidation for energy combustion, there will be less of them available for liposomes to process lipogenesis for cancer cell replication.
- The push for cancer mass cells to make their mitochondria produce energy will cause the signaling rhythms within these cells to have a more counterbalanced ROS/RNS exhaust thereby making them more likely to be antioxidant reduced and less likely to linger within the cell and cross link nuclear chroman thereby making the cancer cell less likely to become purpose anaplastic and more likely to maintain some features that resonate with their nascent cell ancestors.

If this lifestyle intervention plays out, it becomes clear that when combined with other external medicinal intervention, will produce a direct hit on deferring cancer cell/mass growth as cancer cells within the mass must scramble to adjust to prevailing interstitial space metabolic concerns that run contrary to their replicative bias. The manipulation of interstitial space pyruvate would suggest that its reduction could stall out cancer cell/mass replication which could be operationally supported by simple lifestyle interventions that are coupled with basic medicinal support.

Robert L Buckingham, MD, FACP

The Evolution of the Chronic Inflammatory *Anti-Organ* "Team"

To achieve recurring cellular replication, cells within the cancer mass will acquire and express a signaling and metabolic sway within the interstitial space that will repress anti-inflammatory resistance. The chronic inflammatory signaling and metabolic forces within the interstitial space will rely on the combination of abundant vascular inflammatory free radicals, the processing of signal turned immune arsenal and mesenchymal cells, and an increasingly dysfunctional capillary cell dance step rhythm to extort the necessary rhythms that process cancer cell/mass replication[7]. For the cancer mass to achieve this replicative pinnacle the interstitial space will have aligned with:

- Metabolic reflections that couple increasing insulin resistance and reduced oxygen tensions to a persistent chronic inflammatory signaling bias that will involve signal converted immune and mesenchymal cells.
- The persistent inability of capillary cells to any anti-inflammatory dance step traction as its infrastructure fails to keep up with refreshing its outer membrane complex or mitochondrial volumes and mass.
- The increasing interstitial space chronic inflammatory virilization of purpose that will rely on anti-organ signal pirating of immune content form the blood and lymph plasma.
- A persistent chronic inflammatory interstitial space backwash that incentivizes a systemic anti-inflammatory immune suppression through the cytokine induced molecular manipulation of circulating immune arsenal.
- The convergence of these rhythms within the interstitial space to virilize anti-organ intent (Figures 17 and 18, appendix) [7]

In the context of expansile chronic interstitial space inflammation, it becomes increasingly unlikely that the disabled capillary cell will find sufficient resolve to reconstitute its fully functional dance step rhythm. The unwinding of intransigent chronic inflammatory interstitial space signaling and metabolic rhythms, that are coupled to other disease venues that include the expressions of cancer mass growth metrics, will be exceedingly difficult for anti-inflammatory rhythms to counteract. Even with a sustained reduction in vascular inflammatory free radical interstitial space impingements, for the capillary cell to find sufficient dance step resolve to reconstitute its anti-inflammatory multipurpose would require the cell' nuclear chromatin to code for and enable protein synthesis to refurbish much of its outer membrane complex and mitochondrial functional reserve. Both of these organelle resuscitations must occur to counter the chronic inflammatory signaling and metabolic offensive that has been generated by the aggressive signaling streams from an oxygen/nutrient hungry cancer mass or other disease venues. In these cases, cancer mass signaling expression has developed some semblance of control over interstitial space signaling and metabolic rhythms that will preclude or at least antagonize the return of anti-inflammatory dance step rhythms. In these setting, external "allopathic" manipulation of the cancer mass reserve will likely have to occur in the form of stem cell rejuvenation, chemotherapy, radiation or surgery[7].

When the ladder is employed, some manner of cancer mass debulking will occur which should nullify some of its overwhelming signaling and metabolic interstitial space influences, that when coupled with the return of the capillary cell dance step rhythm, should provide sufficient interstitial space signaling momentum for the return of anti-inflammatory homeostasis. In this setting, this will mean that the cancer mass will have been either eliminated or shrunk to where it has become signal isolated and unable to manipulate or control interstitial space signaling and metabolic rhythms. As the capillary cell dance steps find traction and their anti-inflammatory rhythms reenergize the interstitial space, they will disrupt the logistics of chronic inflammatory rhythms that will include the isolated cancer mass as funneled immune and mesenchymal cells rekindle their anti-inflammatory purposes and reconnect to the capillary cell dance steps. The dance step reharmonization will displace cancer cell/mass fermentation-mitochondrial combustion rhythms that will in turn block the un recoiled utilization of nitric oxide combustion to disperse replication cycles[6,7] (Figure 19, appendix).

The anti-inflammatory interstitial space hinge that will trigger cancer mass regression will likely occur from a combination of a resuscitated capillary cell dance step rhythm and external allopathic interventions that debulk the control of cancer mass interstitial space control of signaling and metabolic rhythms. The interstitial space will signal transform to convey the anti-inflammatory pace, stem, ricochet and backwash interests of the resuscitated capillary cell dancer steps[7]. As the capillary cell dance step rhythm recovers its anti-inflammatory multipurpose, the pulsed interstitial space rhythms it conveys will resist, neutralize and disassemble the signaling and metabolic rhythms of the anti-organ and its dispersed disease consorts including those of the cancer mass.

The Transcellular Aging Effect and Oncogenic Predisposition

As human cells age, their nuclear chromatin becomes increasingly code silenced from accumulated free radical translocation on its DNA. This in turn restricts the capacity for ribosomes and rough endoplasmic reticulum to synthesis a full complement of refurbishment proteins that would otherwise resuscitate the cell's infrastructure to enable it to perform a full capacity. In the capillary cell, this manifest loss of silenced DNA coding, will limit its capacity to multipurpose fulfill its anti-inflammatory dance step rhythms. The speed of capillary and downstream endothelial cell nuclear decay becomes codependent on the *veracity* of chronic interstitial space signaling and metabolic rhythms and the disease outcomes they enable. This is turn will hinge on the flow of vascular inflammatory free radical interstitial space impingements and the subsequent increasing incompetence of immune arsenal that have been funneled into the interstitial space to neutralize them[5,6,7]. The capillary cell's nuclear chromatin cross linkages will code silence to where the lack of protein replacement in various organelles will chain react a host of broken anti-inflammatory rhythms that will include a less reliable processing of funneled immune choreography into the interstitial space from an adhesion receptor and pore compromised outer membrane complex and diminished mitochondrial reserve. As capillary cell infrastructure becomes increasingly less dance step rhythm purpose capable, the interstitial space and end organ cell become vulnerable to increasing chronic inflammatory intentionality, signaling manipulation and disease consort cohabitation which includes end organ cell oncogenesis. As the capillary cell loses precision to accomplish dance step multipurpose, its interstitial space domain becomes a signaling and metabolic watershed for cancer cell expression.

The aging and subsequent code silencing of capillary cell nuclear chromatin makes the cell increasingly interstitial space vulnerable to chronic inflammatory signaling and metabolic penetration. This means that as the capillary and downstream endothelial cell becomes senescent, it will require *fewer* vascular inflammatory free radical interstitial space impingements to disrupt the functional integrity of the interstitial space. As the capillary cell's infrastructure deteriorates, its outer membrane complex and mitochondria become increasingly less capable of delivering anti-inflammatory multipurpose execution as all things transcapillary become increasingly more error prone. This will make even small numbers of vascular inflammatory free radical interstitial space impingements at risk for enabling a chronic inflammatory immune response directed at them from capillary cell outer membrane complex miscalculation of required anti-inflammatory immune dispersals. As the outer membrane complex loses capacity to anti-inflammatory immune choreograph, immune funneling errors will increase and will likely signal convert once in the interstitial space to a chronic inflammatory purpose.

This will include the ignoring of cancer cell identification and elimination and perhaps even contributing to their replicative expressions. As the dance step rhythm falters and transcellular anti-inflammatory multipurpose declines, the interstitial space signaling and metabolic format transitions to become a chronic inflammatory predator towards disease consorts.

The DNA transcellular aging effect makes the capillary and downstream endothelial cell dance step expression less anti-inflammatory multipurpose capable thereby opening the signaling and metabolic interstitial space door to chronic inflammatory rhythms intentionality and the unmitigated expression of cancer cell/mass propagation[7]. The lack of capacity for the capillary and downstream endothelial cell to refurbish infrastructure makes it more likely that their dance step rhythm becomes less reliable which makes their interstitial space domains vulnerable to a virilized chronic inflammatory signaling and metabolic proforma that will inevitably include oncogenic expression.

Chapter Sixteen

How Immunoglobulins Lose their Anti-Inflammatory Edge to Become Interstitial Space Signal Maligned

An Introduction to the Proinflammatory Signal Turning of Immunoglobulins Towards the Facilitation of Chronic Inflammatory Interstitial Space Rhythms

The foundation for the maturing of chronic inflammatory end organ interstitial space signaling and metabolic rhythms into disease consorts has many different interconnected feedback loops and chain reactions. Ultimately, these rhythms can lose anti-inflammatory dance step derived functional counterbalance making these chain reactions vulnerable to chronic inflammatory transitioning and the subsequent pacing of disease venues[5,6,7,8,9]. This transitioning process will include the cytokine directed *molecular reconfiguration* of circulating immunoglobulins, that when funneled into the interstitial space, will facilitate lack immunoglobulin misreads and erroneous attachments to nascent cell membranes and infrastructure rather than to the membrane surfaces of foreign invaders or vascular inflammatory free radicals. This loss of capillary cell dance step rhythm will enable the active transport of purpose improvised immunoglobulins into the interstitial space where they can be signal manipulated by preexisting chronic inflammatory signaling rhythms to process erroneous nascent cell membrane and organelle attachments. The subsequent inflammatory mediators they attract towards their erroneous attachment will cascade further chronic inflammatory interstitial space disarray with their attachment creating a "B cell antigen-antibody memory" that will facilitate the same attachment mistake with subsequent immunoglobulin forays into the interstitial space.

The loss of the capillary cell pivot and swing rhythm and the subsequent disarray of anti-inflammatory counterbalance will feature the transitioning of proinflammatory reconfigurations of funneled immune remnants into the interstitial space that cater to chronic inflammatory rhythms that will also include immunoglobulins. In this interstitial space discourse, increasing chronic inflammatory functional dysrhythmias will transform the interstitial space purpose to manifest disease consorts that include autoimmune immunoglobulin misreads[6,7].

As funneled interstitial space immune remnants signal convert to extol chronic inflammatory signaling and metabolic virtues, their rhythms will cause and effect anti-organ virilization and intentionality which is executed via signal pirating the capillary cell's outer membrane complex to bias immune funneling towards their purpose fulfillment. This will include the help of both B and T cell lymphocyte lines which in the former involves the funneling of molecularly reconfigured and chronic inflammatory prone IgG and/or IgM immunoglobulins. Once transported into the interstitial space, these immunoglobulins will be signal manipulated to target nascent cell membrane and organelle attachments as part of a chronic inflammatory interstitial space expression that will likely include other disease consorts. The attachment misreads might just as well be considered the equivalent of a proinflammatory cluster bomb, as the newly formed nascent cell "antigen-antibody complex" attracts complement, cytokines and other opsonizing agents that will process the reduction of the complex. The opsonizing process becomes chronic inflammatory as the B cell plasma cell line that produced the immunoglobulin will stem the memory of the same attachment thereby creating a repetitive attachment mistake over time. These attachments can be to outer membrane surfaces or to nascent cell infrastructure that include its organelles, mitochondria and nuclear chromatin.

These autoimmune attachments not only compromise the membrane function they attach to, but will chain react additional nascent cell functional mistakes that are linked to the disrupted membrane. The chronic inflammatory signaling and metabolic wedge that ensues within the nascent cell becomes one of several anti-organ foundational pieces that will further entrap the capillary cell's dance step rhythm and anti-inflammatory prerogatives.

Within the evolving chronic inflammatory interstitial space signaling and metabolic nomenclature, rogue immunoglobulin-nascent cell membrane attachments become part of anti-organ interstitial space scaling of other disease consorts. The autoimmune complex reverberation will make the interstitial space a signaling and metabolic enabler for other disease mosaics as chronic inflammatory chain reaction will fortify:

> Declines in capillary cell anti-inflammatory dance step reserve.
> The further consolidation of chronic inflammatory interstitial space signaling and metabolic rhythms.
> Promote the additional pirating of specific chronic inflammatory immune content into the interstitial space.
> Will help facilitate the scaling up of other interstitial space disease venues [7].

The Mechanics of Immunoglobulin Misalignment

Exactly how and when circulating IgG or IgM (and perhaps IgE) immunoglobulins become signal misaligned could involve several different steps and locations beginning with HOW STEM CELLS process their molecular memory. The immunoglobulin misalignment can extend into the systemic circulation whereby proinflammatory adipokines and other cytokines molecularly reconfigure the circulating immunoglobulin to conform to proinflammatory signaling biases. Once these "tweaked" immunoglobulins are actively transported into the interstitial space as part of a comprehensive B cell intervention, they can be further modified or redirected by proinflammatory streams of cytokines, enzymes or electromagnetic wavelets towards a nascent cell attachment. In any of these chronic inflammatory scenarios interstitial space funneled immunoglobulins could be swayed into alignment mistakes thereby making them easy prey towards the facilitation of chronic inflammatory chain reactions. Regardless of where, when or how the immunoglobulin goes rogue, the aggregate of these chronic inflammatory effects on the immunoglobulin will virilize a proinflammatory attachment as these immunoglobulins go rogue and disavow anti-inflammatory functionality[6,7]. The immunoglobulin chronic inflammatory "transitioning" is completed when proinflammatory interstitial space signaling streams *guide* the immunoglobulin towards its attachment mistake. The immunoglobulin interstitial space "turning process" has been enabled by the increasingly dysfunctional capillary cell outer membrane complex which has become an enabler of funneling misaligned immunoglobulins into the interstitial space.

When immunoglobulins have been suitably proinflammatory reconfigured, whether in the bone marrow, blood plasma or interstitial space, they become vulnerable to being *signal manipulated* by preexisting chronic inflammatory interstitial space signaling streams[7]. In these scenarios, preexisting chronic inflammatory signaling rhythms will make the rogue immunoglobulin transition into an anti-organ tour de force.

How Can Anti-Inflammatory Immunoglobulins Maintain Purpose Precision

In contrast to the chronic inflammatory interstitial space signaling ruminations and the rogue immunoglobulins they enable, when the capillary cell's outer membrane complex and mitochondria are pivot and swinging in full dance step throttle, the elicited anti-inflammatory rhythms they exude will keep circulating and funneled anti-inflammatory immunoglobulin purpose precise. Their anti-inflammatory reach will even include keeping the bone marrow stem and plasma cells from manufacturing immunoglobulins that would be prone to misaligned attachments. Their backwashed anti-inflammatory cytokine and enzyme rhtyhms would extend to circulating adipokines that would keep these blue chip B cell facilitators in line with anti-inflammatory purposes within interstitial spaces as they stay focused on attaching to foreign proteins and harmful vascular inflammatory free radicals [5,6,7]. The functionally counterbalanced capillary cell's dance step rhythm becomes akin to an anti-inflammatory immunoglobulin interstitial space salve that produces many crosschecking signaling rhythms and streams that facilitate the appropriate immunoglobulin attachment. Their timely attachment against a foreign interstitial space protein will ensure proper opsonization in what becomes a dance step derived signaling and metabolic crescendo and decrescendo that enables the nearby mesenchymal cell to render the cytokine inhibitory "all clear" signal that shifts the capillary cell to the next dance step. The signaling rhythms will carry the capillary cell's outer membrane complex and mitochondria into a different dance step and structure multipurpose that will be facilitated by a decrease in the outer membrane complex permeability gradient and the accentuation of nitric oxide combustion.

The weakest link within the dance step anti-inflammatory context is how the capillary cell can timely manage the sequential immune funneling steps of the antigen-antibody opsonization process. If this process cannot be timely managed within the context of the dance step rhythm, the purpose fulfillment could eventually become prone to chronic inflammatory manipulation as the counterbalanced dance step rhythm begins to fail. When this occurs, the dance step rhythm will lose anti-inflammatory purpose clarity. This will diminish and delay dance step anti-inflammatory outcomes that include the capillary and downstream endothelial cell's capacity to pulse precision choreographed immunoglobulin movement into the interstitial space.

This chronic inflammatory interstitial space indicator will deescalate the capillary cell's nitric oxide combustion cycle thereby restricting the cell's capacity to rejuvenate its infrastructure making the cells capacity to execute a comprehensive multipurposed dance step rhythm going forward, less effective. In this scenario, anti-inflammatory immune funneling into the interstitial space will become precision and purpose compromised including the actively transported IgG and IgM immunoglobulins.

The loss of capillary cell mitochondrial nitric oxide rejuvenation makes it less likely that anti-inflammatory purposed immunoglobulins are actively transported into the interstitial space making them less amenable towards free radical opsonization and more likely to resonate a nascent cell attachment. The loss of the capillary cell's nitric oxide induced infrastructure refresh, that when coupled with proinflammatory prone circulating immunoglobulins, will become a double whammy benefit to interstitial space anti-organ concerns as autoimmune complexes will serve to magnify the chronic inflammatory interstitial space window. None of this interstitial space functional compromise will occur if the capillary cell's dance step rhythm remains counterbalanced and anti-inflammatory quality assured. Within this dance step context, actively transported anti-inflammatory purpose specific immunoglobulins will enter the interstitial space and be directed by anti-inflammatory cytokine streams to a purpose specific foreign protein attachment that will be timely opsonized and degraded to its elemental forms so as to facilitate the accurate timing and precision of the next dance step.

The Functional Ramifications of the Different Immunoglobulin *Families*

Within a given end organ's interstitial space, the manifestations of vascular inflammatory free radical breach will require different computations of funneled or actively transported immune arsenal that will include circulating immunoglobulins [5,6,7]. The *IgG, IgM* and *IgE* immunoglobulin families will be actively transported into interstitial spaces for different inflammatory breach reasons but will always be funneled from the blood plasma for their sequential removal. These immunoglobulin families are produced from *plasma cells* within the bone marrow or lymph tissue. After production they are released into the blood plasma where their preconceived immune purpose makes them a foundational towards specific end organ interstitial space inflammatory breach removal that is also known as a *B lymphocyte cell humoral* immune response. Their journey into an end organ's interstitial space may begin with an adhesive attachment to the capillary cell's luminal glycocalyx. The glycocalyx adherence stages the immunoglobulin to find integration within a continuous outer membrane transport process such as *vesicle* or *transcellular transport channel* whereby they will be actively transported to the interstitial space against various concentration or pressure gradients for their preconceived purpose fulfillment.

Under ideal dance step conditions and upon entering the interstitial space, the immunoglobulin will be assimilated into the anti-inflammatory signaling hierarchy as these activated cytokines, enzymes and free radicals will interact with the immunoglobulin to both reconfigure its outer membrane architecture and facilitate guidance of the immunoglobulin towards its foreign protein attachment target. Once attached the antigen-antibody configuration will become *opsonized vulnerable* from a series of signaling and metabolic chain reactions that will activate and assist the propagation of complement molecules towards the attachment while also sending out signals that facilitate monocytes and macrophage maneuvering towards the antigen-antibody entity. Together these immune components will work *sequentially* but also within a timely circadian threshold to process the denigration of the antigen-antibody-complex to an *elemental form* whereby these constituents become signaling fodder to nearby mesenchymal cells for the potent release of *inhibitory cytokines* that facilitate the purpose clarifying "all clear" signal and subsequent adjustment in capillary cell dance step pivot and swing nomenclature. The immunoglobulin antigen-antibody attachment could be the result of a variety of different types of foreign protein exposures from classic displays of vascular inflammatory interstitial space free radicals to other forms of a matured inflammatory breach that involve infectious agents, allergens or cancer cells.

The effective removal of an interstitial space foreign protein from an immunoglobulin attachment will be facilitated by several factors that facilitate a virilized anti-Inflammatory purpose fulfillment. This will include the purpose responsiveness of all of its opsonization partners with the detail of the response requiring the precision clarity from its plasma cell production within the bone marrow as well as its anti-inflammatory molecular tweaking once it enters the central circulation. This anti-inflammatory processing will involve various circulating anti-inflammatory cytokines, enzymes and free radicals that have been generated from the capillary cells dance step backwash. When this tweaking occurs, it provides further specificity and preparation of the immunoglobulin towards its capillary cell's outer membrane complex target. This means that the immunoglobulins capacity to anti-inflammatory purpose fulfill within an interstitial space requires several preparatory steps that can be disrupted by dispersed chronic inflammatory cytokine, enzyme or free radical mediators that can compete with their anti-inflammatory antagonists. The precise immunoglobulin purpose fulfillment within an interstitial space becomes dependent on the precision of all the *ancillary pieces* that are involved in the immunoglobulin preparatory work before, and after it reaches its interstitial space destination.

Within the context of a chronic inflammatory capillary cell dance step rhythm fallout, it will become likely that one or more of the sequential anti-inflammatory B-cell mediated step involving immunoglobulin proficiency towards a foreign protein target will become compromised making the eventual dissolution of the protein less effective and more likely to be delayed, contribute to a chronic inflammatory response, or worse yet, attach to the wrong protein altogether. As capillary cell dance steps fail in multi end organs, it becomes more likely that their backwash is chronic inflammatory tainted and the subsequent anti-inflammatory systemic immunosuppression it causes will yield circulating immunoglobulins that have been molecularly tweaked to become ineffectual executioners of anti-inflammatory interstitial space purpose fulfillment[6,7].

The increasing propensity for a systemic chronic inflammatory multi end organ interstitial space signal and metabolic rhythm, not only renders circulating immunoglobulin less anti-inflammatory attachment responsive, but will also compromises the capacity all the other anti-inflammatory pieces that are involved into the opsonization and foreign protein reduction process. This would include the anti-inflammatory responsiveness of complement, monocytes and macrophages that would also be engaged int the foreign protein reduction processes[5,6,7]. A summary of the misguided mechanics of interstitial space immunoglobulin attachment misfires that would occur under a chronic inflammatory signaling and metabolic auspice include:

- A sustained and suboptimal anti-inflammatory signaling manifesto that twill involve both the interstitial apace and central circulation. The ramifications include all the associated anti-inflammatory constituents that are connected to the antigen-antibody complex degradation as they have become purpose compromised from chronic inflammatory signaled manipulation.
- The aggregate of this ancillary anti-inflammatory immune ineptitude will further reduce the purpose clarity of the already molecularly compromised and anti-inflammatory disabled circulating immunoglobulin.
- Once capillary cell attached, their active transport into the interstitial space by chronic inflammatory compromised vesicles and transport channels becomes uneven and haphazard creating interstitial space delays while creating opportunities within the transport process for the immunoglobulin to become less attachment capable.
- Once within the interstitial space, the chronic inflammatory signaling confluence will distract the immunoglobulin from its preferred target to delay its attachment or cause a complete misfire in where it does finally attach.
- Once the immunoglobulin has erroneously attached to a nascent cell protein and has consummated the opsonization response, immune memory has been created meaning that bone marrow plasma cells will be called upon to produce the same type of chronic inflammatory tweaked immunoglobulin thereby enabling future attachment mistakes.
- These mistakes become aligned with and cadenced to chronic inflammatory *metabolic rhythms* that include interstitial space acidosis, insulin resistance, reduced oxygen tensions, and disparate osmotic and other pressure gradients.
- The chronic inflammatory immunoglobulin attachment rhythms will be further facilitated by the signal conversion of other interstitial space immune combatants including lymphocytes,

monocytes, macrophages and mesenchymal cells. The anti-inflammatory loss of these immune facilitators will further sway signaling and metabolic momentum towards chronic inflammatory outcomes [6,7].

The Pros and Cons of Immunoglobulin "Memory" Depends on what Signaling and Metabolic Rhythms are In-Charge of the Interstitial space

The persistence of chronic interstitial space inflammation will eventually cause the capillary cell's dance step rhythm to fail which will incentivize the funneling of ineffectual anti-inflammatory immune arsenal into the interstitial space that will include the uneven active transport of IgG, IgM and IgE immunoglobulins [6,7]. When these repurposed immunoglobulins "antigen-antibody" attach, the chronic inflammatory response the will likely be associated with will not only make opsonization less complete but will cause additional attachment miscues involving other nascent cell proteins. As the autoimmune nascent cell decapitation process continues, the involved cell becomes prone to malfunction, senescence and even oncogenesis. As these rhythms mature, chronic interstitial space inflammation becomes more intentional to virilize and nurture multi anti-organ disease mosaics which become proportional to end organ cell functional declines. Ironically, as other disease consorts become interstitial space involved, their presence may springboard additional autoimmune immunoglobulin dispersals to either increase virilization or be signal redirected towards the permutations of other disease purposes.

The recurring misaligned immunoglobulin attachments to a nascent cell outer membrane or organelle proteins will invoke a sufficient immune memory within bone marrow plasma and stem cells that if not mitigated will eventually cannibalize the involved end organ nascent cell operations while potentiating other anti-organ interstitial space operatives [7]. This means that anti-inflammatory immunoglobulin attachment failures will incentivize further end organ interstitial space disease vulnerabilities that would make the induction and propagation of viruses, bacteria and cancer cells more likely as well as contributing to signaling and metabolic rhythms that enable interstitial space scarring or hypercoagulability states. In these virilizing chronic inflammatory interstitial space venues, one disease consort such as erroneous immunoglobulin attachments will support the propagation of other consorts thereby making potential autoimmune mishaps more likely to facilitate the framing of other disease mosaics.

Once immunoglobulin attachment mistakes become part of the chronic inflammatory signaling and metabolic inventory, not only are other disease consorts more likely to become interstitial space vested, but anti-inflammatory resuscitation of the interstitial space becomes far reaching [6,7]. A robust anti-inflammatory interstitial space resurgence will require that the capillary cell dance step rhythm will reconfigure enough capacity to full throttle it's multipurposed rhythm meaning that its nuclear chromosomal DNA has not ROS denatured to where it can't code for a maximal level of protein replacement. In addition, a successful anti-inflammatory interstitial space reversal will also require across-the board reductions in vascular inflammatory free radical access to the interstitial space which in turn will help baby step the return of a counterbalanced capillary and downstream endothelial cell dance step rhythm. This resuscitation will unlock the cell's nitric oxide combustion cycle thereby allowing for the refurbishment of its infrastructure. The unlocking of the capillary cell's counterbalanced dance steps could provide a sufficient resuscitation of its anti-inflammatory rhythms whereby its interstitial space domain will have the return of a pace, stem ricochet and backwashed rhythms that successfully mitigate chronic inflammatory influences that would include the subversion of future autoimmune prerogatives.

The return of a systemic multi end organ interstitial space anti-inflammatory algorithm, will not only derail chronic inflammatory rhythms and potential immunoglobulin attachment mistakes, but its reverberating backwash into the blood plasma will further anti-inflammatory immune enhance its circulating immune partners as backwashed anti-inflammatory cytokines, enzymes and free radicals chain react within the blood plasma a host of immune cell and immunoglobulin molecularly reconfigurations that will contribute to a systemic anti-inflammatory enanthema,[24,30].

The Vastly Different Mosaics of Interstitial Space Immunoglobulin Mediation: From Anti-inflammatory Purpose Fulfillment to Anaphylactic "Cytokine Storms" to Chronic Inflammatory "Allergic" Reactions

Whereas IgG, IgM and IgE immunoglobulin families are produced by plasma cells mostly within a bone marrow milieu, other immunoglobulins (IgD, IgA) appear ubiquitously within certain end organ interstitial spaces[6]. Immunoglobulin IgE, while produced by plasma cells within the bone marrow, will respond to a different set of transmitted signaling cues from end organ interstitial spaces compared to their IgG and IgM circulating cousins. In this manner, IgE becomes part of an end organ "allergic response" to a foreign protein. When interstitial space summoned, activated IgE can chain react a broad spectrum of acute and chronic inflammatory responses that can range from become life threatening (anaphylactic) to a more chronic and clinically debilitating variety that could involve a drippy-congested nose, headaches, itchy eyes, asthmatic cough or varying levels of abdominal pain and bloating.

The chronic inflammatory byproducts of IgE mediation will typically manifest as mucous secretions from oropharyngeal or nasal mucous membranes or as varying levels of constricted smooth muscle in lung airways and occur from various types of inhaled foreign "allergic proteins". While allergic responses can typically appear as annoying, they can occasionally be life threatening as activated IgE may trigger a host of vasoactive and other inflammatory enhanced mediators that induce end organ edema and systemic hypotension. In these settings, IgE will interact to cascade the activation of other *immune cell expanders* such as mast cells, basophils and eosinophils that in aggregate could release copious amounts of histamines, bradykinins and other potent vasoactive molecules that will substantially increase the acute inflammatory interstitial space response. The different magnitudes of these released vasoactive responses will chain react the intensity of the acute inflammatory response which can become overly exaggerated beyond the removal of the inhaled or ingested "allergic) foreign protein. When the response becomes excessive, it can trigger immune cascades that will form "a cytokine storm" that will trigger an "anaphylactic immune response" to the foreign protein within the end organ that can be life threatening as circulatory collapse typically will follow.

Similar to IgG and IgM immune responses, IgE mediated allergic responses can be *immune remembered* meaning that repeated exposures to the offending protein will induce a similar potentially life-threatening clinical effect. In the setting of end organ chronic interstitial space inflammation, the funneling precision of anti-inflammatory IgE into the interstitial space may be reduced which means that the IgE may be activated or utilized for inappropriate purposes as they become signal manipulated to be less anti-inflammatory effective and more chronic inflammatory supportive. This will make the subsequent removal of the interstitial space "allergic" foreign proteins less likely with the IgE generated inflammatory response anti-inflammatory distracted, suboptimal and chronic inflammatory subversive. When combined with a suboptimal capillary cell dance step rhythm, the inopportune mobilization of signal manipulated IgE into the interstitial space will likely trigger inflammatory responses that work against dwindling anti-inflammatory rhythms. It is in these situations that chronic "allergic" interstitial space manifestations occur that will increase secretions, itching, rashes and diarrhea while nurturing the emergence of other disease consorts.

The Chronic Inflammatory Effects of Interstitial Space Immunoglobulin IgA Deficiency States

Immunoglobulin IgA does not appear to circulate but rather is produced and subsequently imbedded within the interstitial spaces of the respiratory and intestinal tracts [5,6]. Its anti-inflammatory function within these premises remains poorly characterized, however its presence will adjunctively support B cell related immunity in the removal of inhaled or ingested toxins, proteins or particulates. In this opsonization context, IgA becomes an anti-inflammatory cog that will facilitate the necessary chain reactions for the successful removal of a foreign molecule while limiting additional interstitial space immune fanfare. In this endeavor its presence increases the efficacy of foreign protein opsonization which enables the involved end organ cells interstitial space to remain circadian rhythm attached to the capillary cell's counterbalanced dance step rhythm and multipurposed anti-inflammatory alignment.

When IgA is interstitial space deficient, be it *inherited, acquired, overutilized or underproduced*, it will become part of an anti-inflammatory *signaling void* that will reduce the capillary cell's efficiency towards the timely elimination of specific types of foreign protein exposures[7]. The IgA deficiency will foster cascades of anti-inflammatory signaling voids that make foreign protein opsonization efficacy less reliable. By *delaying* the elimination time of foreign protein removal, the risk increases for the subversive signaling rhythms of chronic interstitial space inflammation. As this interstitial space reverberates, the capillary cell's dance step rhythm becomes subjugated[7]. If this is left unabated, chronic inflammatory interstitial space signaling rhythms will pick up momentum that will eventually lead to their disease fulfillment. Thus, a deficient IgA will nurture chronic inflammatory interstitial space allergic responses that will lead to anti-inflammatory denaturing and an increased risk for other chronic inflammatory outcomes that include hyper coagulopathies, infections, cancers, scarring and autoimmune complexes.

Similar to the origins of other chronic inflammatory interstitial space rhythms, a persistently depleted IgA interstitial space immunoglobulin will bias a persistent increase in certain interstitial space foreign proteins that will not be effectively opsonized. This will delay and eventually destabilize the capillary cell's dance step rhythm to where the processing of funneled immune remnants into the interstitial space will cater to anti-organ disease mosaics. The IgA failure will eventually trigger and become participatory to enough chronic inflammatory interstitial space signaling and metabolic momentum to where it will transition diverse arrays of disease consorts.

Immunoglobulins, Plasma Cells and B Cell Immunity

All immunoglobulin families play important and integrative anti-inflammatory roles when it comes to the management of end organ interstitial space hygiene and the maintenance of the precision choreographed capillary cell dance step rhythm [5,6,7]. In the case of the immunoglobulin subsets, their capacity to timely execute an anti-inflammatory antigen-antibody complex that supports a B cell mediated opsonization of the foreign protein becomes anti-inflammatory integrative to interstitial space hygiene and the recapitulation of the capillary and downstream endothelial cell's dance step rhythm. The actively transported anti-inflammatory interstitial space immunoglobulin funneled IgG, IgM or IgE towards its intended foreign protein target will process a timely "circadian" rhythm degradation that will trigger the nearby mesenchymal cells cytokine inhibitory "all clear signal" that will pivot and swing the next capillary cell dance step. In this manner, circulating immunoglobulins become critical B cell mediated partners to anti-inflammatory interstitial space circadian rhythms that remove certain types of foreign proteins that keep the counterbalanced capillary cell dance step rhythm intact.

On the other hand, when interstitial space immunoglobulin forays do not correctly attach to a specified foreign protein inflammatory breach, but instead are purpose distracted or utilized for other purposes, chronic inflammatory interstitial space rhythms will escalate as the counterbalanced capillary cell dance step rhythm diminishes.[6,7]. When this occurs, interstitial space funneled immunoglobulins becomes increasingly purpose rogue with their nascent cellular attachments becoming part of an emerging chronic inflammatory interstitial space catharsis that will foster dark outcomes.

How Proinflammatory *Metabolic* Rhythms Bias Interstitial Space Immunoglobulin Attachment Mistakes

The cascading momentum of chronic inflammatory interstitial space signaling and metabolic chain reactions will scale the rate and degree to which interstitial space immunoglobulin attachments become error prone. This in turn will become interdependent on the escalation of capillary cell dance step dysrhythmias[5,6,7]. The propagation of misaligned immunoglobulin attachments will coincide with the increasing functional virulence of chronic inflammatory interstitial space rhythms that will include metabolic displays that coincide with reduced oxygen tensions and increased insulin resistance as well as acid-base anomalies and various desperate pressure gradients. As the interstitial space shifts towards a proinflammatory metabolic collective, it will bias immunoglobulin *molecular reconfigurations* that make them *chronic inflammatory inductive* thereby favoring nascent cellular attachments. These chronic inflammatory interstitial space metabolic escorts enhance signaling rhythms that will place additional attachment pressure on proinflammatory reconfigured immunoglobulins to make poor attachment decisions [5,6,7].

With end organ chronic inflammatory interstitial space reorganization, and the multi-end organ immunosuppressive backwash that it produces, the functional integrity of bone marrow plasma cell operatives become increasingly compromised,[7]. Bone marrow B cell progenitor cells become ensnarled with chronic inflammatory signal and metabolic streaming which will increase their DNA translocation and disrupt their capacity to produce a configurationally precise anti-inflammatory IgG, IgM or IgE immunoglobulin. When these anti-inflammatory ineffectual immunoglobulins enter the circulation, they will become configurational vulnerable to further chronic inflammatory molecular manipulation from circulating adipokines or other chronic inflammatory contributors. When they do get dispersed into interstitial spaces via capillary cell active transport their already compromised molecular configuration will come under further proinflammatory scrutiny by signaling streams that bias their repurposed navigation towards a nascent cellular membrane and organelle attachments.

Robert L Buckingham, MD, FACP

The Proposed Mechanics of How Interstitial Space Immunoglobulins become Lethal Chronic Inflammatory Weapons

Once a signal turned and molecularly reconfigured interstitial space transported immunoglobulin attaches to a nascent cell protein to form an *autoimmune complex,* it will collateralize additional chronic inflammatory chain reactions that increase additional proinflammatory momentum as they disrupt the functional integrity of the attached nascent cell membrane or infrastructure organelle. The proinflammatory processes that lead up to this attachment misalignment include how the immunoglobulin was "processed" before the attachment miscue. This would include how they were bone marrow configured, their molecular interactions within the central circulation with "proinflammatory" adipokines or other proinflammatory mediators, how they were chosen to be actively transported into the interstitial space by a purpose ineffectual capillary cell outer membrane complex, and finally how they become entangled with chronic inflammatory mediators and signaling streams once entered into the interstitial space. Any or all of these chronic inflammatory mechanics could cause and effect immunoglobulin attachment failures.

Once aberrantly attached to a nascent cell membrane or organelle, the autoimmune complex will chain react signaling displays consisting of activated cytokines, complement, enzymes and free radicals as well as cellular constituents like T killer/helper lymphocytes, macrophages and mesenchymal cells that will contribute to the opsonization and reduction of the autoimmune complex[6,7]. This B cell "humoral process" will in turn sequence reactive acute inflammatory mediators such as *IL-interleukin 1,6*, growth factors (*TNF* (tumor necrosis factor and *VEGF* (vascular endothelial growth factor) among others in the opsonization collective. All of these acute phase reactants to the antigen-antibody complex can be *either* anti or pro/chronic inflammatory based on the type of chain reactions they are responding to and the prevailing signaling and metabolic rhythms that are being conveyed within the interstitial space[6].

When these signaling crescendos are proinflammatory applied, the antigen-antibody attachment will more likely be an autoimmune complex, with the attachment causing loss of membrane or organelle functional aptitude. The opsonization "process" becomes immunoglobulin engrained thereby causing its future facilitation to the attached membrane protein to be auto perpetuated. Immunoglobulin memory, which can key a successful and recurring anti-inflammatory immunoglobulin purpose against a foreign protein within end organ interstitial spaces, can also be used by chronic inflammatory interstitial space rhythms to exact an autoimmune toll on nascent cell membranes and organelles.

In the ladder situation, the recycling of darker interstitial space immunoglobulins and their associated proinflammatory chain reactions becomes a virilized disease consort that will further escalate chronic inflammatory rhythms to enable additional disease venues. The Immunoglobulin attachment misfires can involve *any* nascent cell including endothelial, epithelial, immune or mesenchymal cell outer membrane or infrastructure proteins [6,7]. The virulence of these attachments will correlate with the controlling hierarchy of chronic inflammatory interstitial space signaling and metabolic rhythms.

Chapter Seventeen

The DNA Pothole

How Chronic Interstitial Space Inflammation Silences the Coding Processes of Capillary Cell Nuclear Chromatin

A primary flexion point for chronic inflammatory end organ interstitial space signaling and metabolic rhythms is to create an interstitial space identity while simultaneously limiting the capillary cell's capacity to implement an anti-inflammatory dance step rhythm. If successful the anti-organ will springboard control of the interstitial space to propagate disease consortiums[4,5,6,7,8,9]. As chronic inflammatory rhythms master interstitial space signaling and metabolic control, they will at the same time blunt anti-inflammatory algorithms and their end organ cell beneficial circadian outcomes. The loss of a pulsed interstitial space anti-inflammatory functional homeostasis will force changes to the functional integrity within the capillary cell and its dance step rhythm which gets signal transmitted to adversely affect the interstitial space and allied cells within its domain. This will inevitably deescalate the capillary cell's dance step rhythm and its anti-inflammatory signaling or metabolic rhythms and multipurposed outcomes as the interstitial space cedes rhythm control to chronic interstitial space inflammation.

The diminishment of capillary cell dance steps and their anti-inflammatory multipurpose will be replaced by proinflammatory signaling and metabolic rhythms that purport malignant purposes and anti-organ outcomes[7]. This interstitial space transitioning process will enable the anti-organ to express intent by signal pirating the disabled capillary cell outer membrane complex in order to escalate a disease consort mosaic[7]. The key to this interstitial space transformation is daggered by the loss of the capillary cell's dance step functional counterbalance and the diminution of its nitric oxide combustion cycle which is transformative to the cell's refurbishment and its sustainability of anti-inflammatory performance. Included in this recurring reconstitution is the restitution of its protective DNA telomere cap (via activated telomerase) which keeps free radicals from crosslinking DNA. Capillary cell dance step functional counterbalance also limits the distribution of ROS and RNS mitochondrial combustion exhaust products thereby limiting their potential effacement towards DNA cross linkage. The combination of these two key protective pieces that protect nuclear chromatin functional integrity enable the capillary cell's dance step rhythm to achieve operational sustainability as maximal numbers of proteins are coded for in order to sustain infrastructure restitution and subsequent functional potability.

The Capillary Cell's Code Silenced DNA: The Foundational Piece that Consolidates Anti-Inflammatory Interstitial Space Functional Desynchrony

As capillary and downstream endothelial cell DNA becomes increasingly code silenced, there will be an increasing ricochet and backwash signaling and metabolic anti-inflammatory *desynchrony* that will enable immune suppression and the subsequent auto perpetuation of chronic inflammatory interstitial space rhythms[5,6,7,23]. As this transitioning escalate, proinflammatory signaling and metabolic chain reactions will process chronic inflammatory intentionality while at the same time making the disabled capillary cell their interstitial space purposed gatekeeper. With an increasingly disingenuous mitochondrial nitric oxide combustion output, the capillary cell loses capacity to infrastructure replete which will include its processing of telomere lengthening. As its nuclear telomeres shorten, they expose its nuclear chromatin to increasing ROS cross linkages. With less codable DNA and less inclination for protein synthesis infrastructure refurbishment, the capillary and downstream endothelial cell loses its anti-inflammatory dance step resolve as its disabled lattice becomes a resource for chronic interstitial space inflammatory repurposing[6,7]. The escalation of these interstitial space rhythms will full court press the capillary cell and its disabled dance steps into a chronic inflammatory forbearance that will auto perpetuate proinflammatory immune funneling salvos that express chronic inflammatory directives.

The maturing of chronic inflammatory interstitial space signaling and metabolic rhythms will continue to bias the denaturing of capillary cell nuclear chromatin via the following mechanics:

> - The persistent diminution of nitric oxide combustion cycle, the loss of infrastructure refurbishment potability.
> - The increased predilection of ROS combustion exhaust to become antioxidant resistant and nuclear chromatin cross linkage virulent.
> - The loss of dance step counterbalance coupled with excessive mitochondrial energy combustion not only translates into more ROS exhaust but also increases in mitochondrial fission and autophagy and less fusion and replication.
> - The biased loss of nuclear telomere length thereby increasing nuclear chromatin exposures to ROS cross linkages.
> - The loss of capillary and downstream endothelial cell functional infrastructure will increase/ accelerate their functional senescence to become an anti-inflammatory outlier and a proinflammatory conduit[6,7].

The Chronic Inflammatory-Anti-Organ Interstitial Space Equation: Persistent Free Radical Impingements Plus Anti-Inflammatory Purpose Neutralized Inflammatory Mediators Equals Increased Capillary Cell Dance Step Desynchrony that will Bias Chronic Inflammatory Outcomes as the Capillary Cell Ages from its Nuclear Chromatin Becoming Code Silenced

As capillary cell mitochondria are signal and metabolically cornered to produce energy in support of the active transport of immune arsenal into the interstitial space that supports a chronic inflammatory rendering, the self-proclaimed anti-organ heir to the interstitial space will keep the capillary cell's anti-inflammatory functional prerogatives off balance through numerous proinflammatory signaling algorithms that in addition code silence its DNA and prevent the cell from refurbishing its infrastructure.

The combination of unmitigated mitochondrial ROS production that is also accompanied by its miscued attachment to nuclear chromatin renders the capillary cell's nuclear chromosomal DNA coding rhythms to be insolvent and increasingly time limited. When this restitution double whammy occurs over time, the capillary cell loses functional competency of its infrastructure that includes the functional breadth of its outer membrane complex and the combustion latitudes of its mitochondria. The nature of these functional defaults is to render the capillary cell increasingly incapable of distributing a competent anti-inflammatory interstitial space immune alternative to the prevailing chronic inflammatory signaling and metabolic nomenclature. This pervasive proinflammatory momentum will bias the interstitial space towards rhythms that de facto disease mosaics.

A Functionally Counterbalanced Capillary Cell Dance Step Rhythm Enables Anti-Inflammatory Multipurposed Interstitial Space Fulfillment

Within the context of a multipurposed fulfilled and functionally counterbalanced capillary cell anti-inflammatory dance step rhythm, pulsed concentrations of ROS and RNS combustion exhaust are released. In this scenario, they have a limited functional prerogative as each will membrane attach, elicit a membrane response that is anti-inflammatory additive to the dance step prerogative, and then is antioxidant degraded *before* it attaches to or crosslinks with nuclear chromatin or other membrane surfaces. The timeliness of these membrane attachments and their subsequent molecular degradation keeps both ROS and RNS within the context of their anti-inflammatory purpose while also preventing them from aberrant attachments.

With appropriate dance step ROS/RNS recycling, the integrity of each step's purpose fulfillment will be enhanced as both combustion end products become part of the overall anti-inflammatory rhythm and subsequent purpose execution of the dance step. This implies that even the level of mitochondrial combustion exhaust is rhythm coupled into the dance step equation of anti-inflammatory purpose fulfillment. In this context, both ROS and RNS become invaluable *free radical tags* that enhance each dance step's purpose execution. As they are produced, membrane attach and antioxidant degraded, they will magnify a timely anti-inflammatory expression before they are antioxidant relieved of their attachment duties. In this scenario, their *rhythm* becomes an integral part to the anti-inflammatory collective that is additive to the dance step's rotating signaling and metabolic hierarchy and multipurposed fulfillment[7].

Within the Capillary and Downstream Endothelial Cell, Accelerated Nuclear Chromatin Cross Linkage Will Occur from the Residuals of Excess Mitochondrial Energy Combustion

To enable capillary cell dance step counterbalance and effectively functionally pulsed ROS and RNS combustion exhaust, the capillary and downstream endothelial cell must remain capable of maintaining its dance step fortitude which in turn will always include the timely removal of vascular inflammatory free radical interstitial space impingements. This requires that the cell keeps its infrastructure intact to the largest extent possible and will include its anti-inflammatory purpose critical outer membrane complex and mitochondria.

When the rhythm remains in sync, its anti-inflammatory multipurpose fulfills while maintaining optimal functional counterbalance.

Most importantly, mitochondrial ROS combustion exhaust will not accumulate within the cell. In this manner, the capillary cell's dance steps, rhythm and functional outcomes become an interstitial space and allied cell *pacemaker* to counterbalanced anti-inflammatory chain reactions that execute a multipurposed alignment throughout its domain while extending this virtue as backwash to the blood plasma. This keeps cytokines (inhibitory and/or excitatory), free radicals (such as ROS/RNS among others), enzymes and electromagnetic wavelets in a functionally counterbalanced alignment with purpose fulfilled anti-inflammatory chain reactions. In this context, all organelles and their purposes within the capillary cell will fall in line with the execution of intentional anti-inflammatory fulfillment. As they do, the capillary cell's dance step rhythm remains counterbalanced, optimally *pulsed,* and functionally *quality assured.* In this setting, its chromatin DNA will be less likely crosslinked as its telomere caps remain long and DNA protective and mitochondrial free radical ROS/RNS exhaust timely antioxidant reduced.

In contrast, the consolidation of chronic inflammatory interstitial space signaling and metabolic rhythms will do the opposite to the capillary cell and its domain as they collude, fuse and virilize rhythms that derail the functional counterbalance of the capillary cell's dance steps. As capillary and downstream endothelial cell mitochondrial energy combustion surges, its ROS exhaust increases with its intracellular accumulation increasing aberrant membrane and nuclear chromatin cross linkages. The capillary cell's subsequent chronic inflammatory degradation will include:

- ✓ A metabolic intracellular, transcellular and interstitial space autocatalysis that occurs from the consolidation of an increasing chronic inflammatory metabolic diathesis consisting of a biased discourse of acidosis, insulin resistance, hypoxia, and membrane unfriendly osmolality gradients.
- ✓ The transitioning within the capillary cell of anti-inflammatory unfriendly and increasingly unbalanced fermentation mechanics (excessive gluconeogenesis), that will in turn chai react liposomal lipolysis (over lipogenesis), and the paradoxical mitochondrial utilization of fatty acid substrates over pyruvate for hub related acetyl co A production.
- ✓ The biased shuttling of mitochondrial acetyl CoA to the Krebs cycle (instead of ribosomes) as all manner of infrastructure protein synthesis is scuttled.
- ✓ The self-fulfilled auto perpetuation or these chronic inflammatory metabolic rhythms which in turn will chain react further free radical cannibalization of infrastructure membranes as well as mitochondrial and nuclear chromosomal DNA[6,7].

The Dance Step Fission and Fusion, Autophagy and Replication Cyclic Equation and How its Functional Counterbalance Protects the Capillary Cell's DNA (and Infrastructure) Lattice

Within the capillary and downstream endothelial cell, the pulsed and counterbalanced mitochondrial dance step production of energy and nitric oxide will include the ladder's activation of growth factors and other such inducements that favor infrastructure restoration and/or its replication. Within this dance step processing of mitochondrial (and intracellular) refurbishment there will be a counterbalanced *fission and fusion* mechanic that occurs that both culls and replenishes infrastructure components within the confines of the dance step rhythm. This recurring process of infrastructure restoration will include among others the its telomere absent clumps of mitochondrial matrix DNA. The counterbalanced fission and fusion reprocessing of its DNA makes it possible for it to sustain a maximal coding capacity for protein synthesis infrastructure repair over time as worn-out DNA fragments are fission culled and fused back into the DNA lattice in recurring cycles. If fission is excessive (as would occur from excessive mitochondrial energy combustion) or fusion too rambunctious (during a prolonged nitric oxide combustion cycle), the result would be a DNA coding lattice that becomes functionally deranged and inadequate for the restitution of the cell's infrastructure let alone its mitochondrial combustion apparatus[5,6,7]. When capillary cell infrastructure restitution is impaired that would include its own mitochondrial DNA, (typically from excessive energy combustion derived fission/autophagy) the DNA clumps within its matrix shrink to become increasingly code silenced with their denaturing from the combination of increased ROS cross linkage, excessive fission/autophagy and insufficient fusion/replication. The loss of capillary cell mitochondrial reserve will be one of several chronic inflammatory intracapillary cell chain reactions that compromises dance step anti-inflammatory multipurposed execution[5,6,7].

This capillary cell's restitution void becomes integrative to evolving chronic inflammatory interstitial space signaling and metabolic chain reactions as their increasing rhythms displays will outperform the diminishing anti-inflammatory reserves that have been registered by the increasingly disabled capillary cell dance steps. The loss of interstitial space anti-inflammatory signaling and metabolic counterbalance from the persistent displays of chronic inflammatory rhythms will cause the capillary cell's dance steps to lose functional anti-inflammatory cred as outer membrane complex loses pores, adhesion receptors and voltage gradient fortitude and nearby mitochondria shrink in size and volumes from combinations of fission, autophagy and underperforming matrix DNA.

The capacity for the capillary cell to *reverse or prevent* its functional senescence will become codependent on just how much functional capacity it can revitalize after its dance steps have been functionally reconstituted. This will involve may different interstitial space and intracapillary cellular moving parts that will be determined by the degree of anti-organ interstitial space consolidation, the degree to which this consolidation can be signal and metabolically outmaneuvered and how much non crosslinked nuclear chromatin reserve remains within the capillary cell's nucleus[7]. Assuming anti-organ interstitial space influences can be mitigated, to the extent that the capillary cell's nuclear chromosomal and refurbished mitochondrial DNA can code for a full complement of infrastructure replacement proteins in a reconstituted dance step rhythm will be to the extent that the capillary cell and its interstitial space domain can anti-inflammatory recover from the chronic inflammatory pestilence. In this scenario, it is implied that capillary cell mitochondrial DNA can fully recover its coding capacity via fusion and replication, the same cannot be said for its nuclear chromatin whose coding resuscitation will be limited by irreversible ROS cross linkage. This discrepancy of nuclear chromatin reversal becomes the Achilles heel towards a comprehensive capillary cell infrastructure refurbishment. This becomes one of the limiting factors that negates a comprehensive interstitial space reversal of chronic inflammatory outcomes[26].

The "Double Whammy Effect" from Trans-Endothelial Cell Accumulative Nuclear Chromatin Cross Linkage

When increasingly senescent upstream capillary cells come under persistent pressure from chronic interstitial space inflammatory rhythms (AKA, from the matrix and anti-organ), the capillary cell's dance step rhythm will lose capacity to anti-inflammatory maneuver the interstitial space with a corner piece to this marginalization being the loss of precision immune funneling choreography. As their nuclear chromatin comes under increased attack from ROS free radicals, there will be less of it code available for infrastructure refurbishment. When coupled with a diminished nitric oxide combustion cycle, and a prevailing signal no show from similarly senescent downstream endothelial cells, and the upstream interstitial space makings will process a chronic inflammatory makeover. This upstream to downstream and back again "double whammy effect" occurs because the interstitial spaces of all endothelium are being chronically inflamed from similar free radical impingements and associated signal turned immune cell compromises. In this scenario, there is a trans endothelial cell pseudocapillarization of their outer membrane complex, loss of mitochondrial reserve and increased nuclear chromatin ROS cross linkage based on the same chronic inflammatory functional mechanics within their respective interstitial spaces. These effects will transition endothelial cells up and down the arterial tree into a *collaborative functional senescence* which will provide signaling and metabolic fodder for the advancement of chronic inflammatory interstitial space initiatives[5,6,7].

The double whammy effect takes on increasing virulence when upstream capillary cells are denied functional responses from their downstream brethren as they clammer for more oxygen delivery for an increasingly desperate end organ cell's functional reserve. The lack of a sufficient downstream endothelial cell response will further propagate upstream chronic inflammatory interstitial space signaling and metabolic rhythms as the dying capillary cell flounders to reconcile the functional demands of their end organ cell oxygen deprive partners. This oxygen deprivation dilemma will create signaling and metabolic momentum that will affect the upstream capillary cell's capacity to combat increasing chronic inflammatory interstitial space resolve.

As downstream arterial endothelial cells increasingly underperform in their upstream oxygen delivery duties, their infrastructure as well as that of upstream capillary cells will transition senescence that will make them increasingly less capable of anti-inflammatory interstitial space deliverance or interactivity with the outer membranes of their end organ cell partner. In these chronic inflammatory interstitial space scenarios, the functionally deficient endothelial cell outer membranes have adopted an oval configuration making their basement membranes more responsive to the nearby but equally anti-inflammatory deficient mesenchymal cells. The functional divorce between the endothelial, capillary and end organ cell partners make downstream endothelium incapable of addressing upstream oxygen demands at several different levels as they not only are battling the residuals of chronic interstitial space inflammation but have also become increasingly incapable of engaging with the outer membranes of their smooth muscle "end organ" cell partner. This, along with increasing basement membrane dysfunction from vascular inflammatory free radical assault, makes their corresponding lumens refractory to diameter regulation that would adjust blood flow and upstream oxygen delivery. This "double whammy effect" places the upstream capillary cell in an untenable no win functional position as it has no tools in its tool box to win this battle as it helplessly watches its own functional reserve as well as that of its end organ cell partner dry up. The capillary cell can only watch its vitality diminish as its interstitial space domain and crippled allied cell partners surrender to prevailing chronic inflammatory interstitial space rhythms and functional intent.

Within both downstream endothelium and upstream capillary cell mitochondria, the chronic inflammatory double whammy effect reduces combustion reserve several different mechanics that involve fission and autophagy that reduced their size, volume and mass as ROS exhaust accumulates and increasingly crosslinks both nuclear and mitochondrial chromatin. The increasing virulence of proinflammatory rhythms within the capillary and downstream endothelial cell, coupled with the trans endothelial cell chronic inflammatory interstitial space consolidation, produces a windfall confluence of disease expression. These chronic inflammatory rhythms will fast track a trans endothelial cell functional degradation via:

- A diffuse outer membrane complex pseudocapillarization
- A sustained loss of mitochondrial combustion reserve
- A persistent increase of ROS attached nuclear and mitochondrial chromatin cross linkage
- A persistent chronic inflammatory interstitial space ricochet and systemic backwash effect that functionally isolates endothelial cell basement membranes from their end organ cell partner's outer membrane surfaces.
- The increasing fulfillment of chronic inflammatory interstitial space disease consortiums as their rhythms functionally auto perpetuate [5,6,7].

The Enablement of Interstitial Space Disease Consortiums: A Quid Pro Quo of Capillary Cell Code Silenced Nuclear Chromatin

As capillary cells slide into an accelerated functional senescence, and their nuclear chromosomal DNA becomes increasingly code silenced and functionally disabled, the cell's capacity to support anti-inflammatory interstitial space outcomes will disappear[6,7]. This transitioning will enable chronic inflammatory signaling cues and metabolic outcomes within the interstitial space to rhythm *fuse* to become increasingly purpose intentional. The evolution of the chronic inflammatory matrix will begin to process its own *purpose fulfillment* from these fused signaling streams and metabolic rhythms that will eventually pirate immune intent from and through the disabled capillary cell's outer membrane complex as funneled immune cells from blood and lymph plasma signal convert from these self-imposed chronic inflammatory streams to enhance their purpose virulence. Their dispersed chronic inflammatory interstitial space confluence will posture a focused intent based upon the following interstitial space features:

- The interstitial space outlay of assorted vascular inflammatory free radical impingements and the type of chronic inflammatory immune arsenal that has been interstitial space dispersed.
- The degree to which capillary cell dance step rhythm has become disabled.
- The level of which the capillary cell's outer membrane complex has been signal pirated.
- The pace of chronic inflammatory interstitial space rhythm consolidation (typically a reflection of the previous 3 bullets).
- The type or mosaic of disease venues that are interstitial space propagated.
- The degree to which the backwash effect has molecularly reconfigured and immune suppressed circulating immune arsenal.
- The inherent or acquired genetic makeup of the involved end organ cell(s) that will portend vulnerability towards specific interstitial space disease consorts [6,7].

In this chronic inflammatory interstitial space amalgam virilizes intent while simultaneously diminishing anti-inflammatory resistance, their rhythms and influence will procure the necessary interstitial space immune elements to process disease outcomes[7]. Further chronic inflammatory consolidation will occur from signal converted mesenchymal and pericyte cells.

A major development within this chronic inflammatory interstitial space transitioning will come from the loss of capillary cell dance step anti-inflammatory *compensatory mechanics* as its crippled infrastructure can no longer *adjust to* parabolic proinflammatory interstitial space signaling or metabolic initiatives. As capillary cell anti-inflammatory compensatory mechanics diminish, the interstitial space transitioning of chronic inflammatory purpose will escalate. When this occurs, the capillary cell's dance steps will have become so compromised and anti-inflammatory desperate that they can no longer process a chronic inflammatory mitigation. In these settings, maturing disease venues become chronic inflammatory mercenaries that will nurture and virilize each other's interstitial space propagation[7]. The principal feature of their increasing virulence will be how their rhythms decapitate the capillary cell's anti-inflammatory dance step rhythm. This is highlighted by the increasing ineptitude of the capillary cell's cross linked and code silenced nuclear chromatin as the cell surrenders its capacity to infrastructure self-repair. The lack of infrastructure restitution causes the capillary cell to become a "passive conduit" to chronic inflammatory interstitial space intent.

When the *Rate* of Capillary Cell Nuclear Chromosomal DNA Senescence Comes under Chronic Inflammatory Control

The aging of capillary cell DNA is dependent on its volume of aggregate ROS cross linkages which in turn is dependent on the interstitial space signaling pressure exerted from chronic inflammatory rhythms. Thus, the rate of capillary cell senescence will vary within each individual based on the anti-inflammatory care they can render to their end organ interstitial spaces. This becomes directly proportional to how vascular inflammatory free radical interstitial space displays can be mitigated.

As chronic inflammation within interstitial space accelerates intent, the capillary cell dance step rhythm denigrates. The increased capillary cell mitochondrial ROS exhaust concentration gradients will crosslink and accelerate the denigration of its nuclear chromatin which code silences its capacity to restore infrastructure. The rate of capillary cell aging and anti-inflammatory functional denigration will become dependent upon how much of their interstitial space domain has come under the signaling and metabolic control of anti-organ disease consorts[5,6,7]. The progression of nuclear chromosomal DNA code silencing will make the capillary cell subservient to these pervading interstitial space rhythms as they increasingly limit the cell's anti-inflammatory resolve to resist the chronic inflammatory pervasiveness. The rate of capillary cell DNA compromise becomes directly proportional to the degree to which its interstitial space has been persistently overrun with chronic inflammatory signal and metabolic transitioning.

When the capillary cell's dance step anti-inflammatory rhythms whither as its nuclear chromatin becomes increasingly code silenced, the cell loses all manner of anti-inflammatory rhythm dispersal that will preclude dance step inefficiencies that would have otherwise pulsed optimal interstitial space hygiene and end organ cell functional resolve. The loss of capillary cell anti-inflammatory functional reserve makes the interstitial space chronic inflammatory conducive with even smaller numbers of vascular inflammatory interstitial space free radical impingements producing potential disruptive effects to the circadian dance steps. As effectively funneled interstitial space immune support diminishes to remove the various forms of inflammatory breach, the rhythms within the space transition towards proinflammatory manipulation[7]. To summarize, the **rate** of capillary and downstream endothelial cell functional transitioning from an anti-inflammatory provocateur to a subservient chronic inflammatory enabler will become dependent upon:

> ➢ the persistence, type and volume of vascular inflammatory free radical interstitial space impingements with less of them being required as the capillary cell loses anti-inflammatory functional resolve
> ➢ the rate of functional decline to the capillary cell's infrastructure that defines dance step effectiveness which can be construed as outer membrane complex pseudocapillarization, reduced mitochondrial functional reserve and increased nuclear chromatin code silencing

> the level to which chronic inflammatory signaling cues are pirating functional intent form the blood plasma through the capillary cell's outer membrane complex
> the degree to which the interstitial space has become signal controlled from the naturing of disease propagation[6,7].

The rate of capillary and downstream endothelial cell nuclear chromatin code silencing will correlate with the degree to which the interstitial space has become controlled by disease hierarchies[6,7]. Capillary and downstream endothelial cell aging will translate into a reduced capillary cell dance step rhythm and multipurposed anti-inflammatory fulfillment and the increasing likelihood of a malignant chronic inflammatory interstitial space outcome(s).

What If?

Could a potentially reinvigorated capillary (or somatic cell be DNA stemmed or *transplanted* to harness a comprehensive nuclear chromatin repair in order to code restore the potential for a comprehensive anti-inflammatory dance step functional renaissance? One potential concept for capillary cell nuclear chromosomal DNA renewal may emulate the fission/ fusion autophagy/replication model of DNA restoration within mitochondria that is linked to the capillary cell's counterbalanced dance step rhythm. In this scenario, mitochondrial restoration including its DNA will use the signaling and metabolic rhythms of its dance and counterbalanced energy and nitric oxide combustion cycles to chain react fission/fusion, autophagy/replication rhythms that will include its DNA clumps to cull, replace and replicate its serviceable DNA thereby keeping it coding capacity fresh and comprehensively sustainable. In this model mitochondrial DNA will undergo fission and autophagy during energy combustion and fusion and replication within nitric oxide combustion cycle with the dance steps counterbalance keeping the culling and replacement mutually paired. Both are required to enable an auto perpetuated and code comprehensive mitochondrial DNA[6,7,29].

Could the capillary cell's nuclear chromatin use the dance step rhythm find a similar culling and restitution pattern of coding enhancements that is used by the more primitive mitochondrial DNA? In this *"what-if"* scenario, the fission/autophagy culling of ROS crosslinked nuclear chromatin could be followed with the fusion/ replication DNA enhancements that would occur during the nitric oxide combustion cycle. If this did occur, the capillary cell's nuclear chromosomal DNA's operational status would remain optimal over time as ROS cross linkages would be dance step removed by a recurring fission of the involved DNA strip during energy combustion which would then be replaced by fusion of a normal DNA strip during its nitric oxide combustion cycle. In this manner the cell would use its counterbalanced dance steps to signal for a repetitive nuclear chromatin repair that would enable the cell to stay youthful as it continues to yield a sharpened multipurposed anti-inflammatory dance step outcome. The recurrence of DNA culling, repair or replacement would make this dance step outcome a potent anti-aging-disease preventative. The anti-inflammatory ramifications would in turn be stemmed, paced, ricocheted and backwashed to its interstitial space domain, allied cells and systemic circulation to lengthen lifespans way beyond anything currently recognizable.

Chapter Eighteen

The Interstitial Space "Big STING"!

The Mechanics of Chronic End Organ Interstitial Space Inflammatory *"Sting Operations"* that *Extort* Interstitial Space Purpose Away from the End Organ Cell

The process of extorting an end organ's interstitial space purpose from an anti-to chronic inflammatory is most commonly insidious until the end game is reached where anti-inflammatory functional rhythms collapse from the weight and virilized outcomes of the chronic inflammatory anti-organ onslaught. The interstitial space "conversion process" is typically carried out in incremental signaling shifts whereby anti-inflammatory generated signaling displays gradually *wither* and are exchanged for chronic inflammatory rhythms processed from signal converted immune arsenal, mesenchymal cells and maturing disease consorts. As this conversion process intensifies, the chronic inflammatory matrix and then anti-organ consign signaling and metabolic rhythms to the interstitial space that virilize disease intentions. The exchange process will initially appear anti-inflammatory disruptive and a rhythm nuisance but over time becomes increasingly purpose focused and signal calibrated to the maturing of disease consorts. Early disruption of anti-inflammatory signaling rhythms will include the inability to timely remove vascular inflammatory free radical impingements from the interstitial space. These circadian delays will translate into decreasing capillary cell dance step rhythm efficiencies, loss of its nitric oxide combustion cycle and ineffectual retooling of the cell's infrastructure mechanics that only lead to further dance step irregularities. The persistent loss of functional dance step counterbalance will produce devastating infrastructure cracks within the capillary cell's signaling mechanics and feedback loop systems that nullify its capacity to execute dance step rhythm precise anti-inflammatory outcomes. As immune funneling mistakes increase into the interstitial space and signal convert to identify with a chronic inflammatory purpose, the capillary cell dance steps become increasingly anti-inflammatory maligned with its outer membrane complex, mitochondria and other organelle infrastructure becoming a pawn to chronic inflammatory processing.

As might be expected, with early marginalization of early anti-inflammatory interstitial space signaling rhythms, the capillary cell's dance steps will have a built-in capacity to compensate for these proinflammatory onslaughts without necessarily disrupting dance step functional utility. However, if these rhythms are allowed to auto-perpetuate, and with additional capillary cell infrastructure decline, the cell's capacity to "anti-inflammatory compensate" for these discrepant signals will fail, and chronic inflammatory interstitial space rhythms will gain stature as anti-inflammatory rhythms diminish. When this occurs, the capillary cell's increasingly pseudocapillarized outer membrane complex becomes signal vulnerable to chronic inflammatory interstitial space rhythms and subsequent functional pirating of intent from the blood plasma[7]. As the pirating process evolves, chronic inflammatory interstitial space rhythms become self-sustaining, functionally virilized and purpose intentional as they subvert less the responsive and purpose distracted anti-inflammatory immune cohorts.

As the capillary cell's outer membrane complex functionally withers, the interstitial space immune funneling mistakes it enables decimate anti-inflammatory outcomes, which in turn cause mesenchymal and end organ cells to fall in line with their purposed outcomes. The mesenchymal cell conversion will subvert most of their anti-inflammatory signaling displays and rhythms back to the capillary cell's basement membrane that would include the counterbalanced and purpose clarifying "all hands-on deck" and "all clear" signals, both of which are critical to the pulsing of the next capillary and downstream endothelial cell dance step. The interstitial space momentum of these signaling miscues not only make the capillary and allied cells chronic inflammatory signal manipulated, but radically change their purpose outcomes.

The lack of allied cell interstitial space signaling clarity or anti-inflammatory purpose identity, will further bias the disabled capillary cell's outer membrane complex to continue making immune funneling miscues that will cater to a chronic inflammatory purposed execution and an ongoing discrepant capillary cell dance step rhythm that overexaggerates energy combustion. The increasing misalignment of the interstitial space to a chronic inflammatory purposed outcome becomes an auto perpetuating signaling and metabolic rhythm that biases additional capillary cell "pseudocapillarization". Capitulation of the capillary cell's anti-inflammatory resolve will occur as its waning mitochondrial nitric oxide combustion cycle becomes unrecognizable. This will eventually reduce the capillary cell's anti-iflammatory dance step multipurpose to a functional shell.

The chronic inflammatory interstitial space transition will switch signaling and metabolic operatives away from the end organ cell's functional prerogatives to instead favor the signaling rhythms generated from disease venues [5,6,7]. As signal converted interstitial space immune arsenal increasingly volley proinflammatory signaling and metabolic rhythms, the functionally senescent capillary cell becomes their blood plasma conduit. In this context, the auto perpetuated chronic inflammatory reversal of interstitial space purpose will backwash through the senescent capillary and downstream endothelial cell a systemic anti-inflammatory immune suppression as expressed cytokines, enzymes and free radicals molecularly manipulate circulating immune remnants to conform to a proinflammatory purpose identity. When this occurs the newly reconfigured immune arsenal when interstitial space funneled will become signal converted hostages to the execution of chronic inflammatory intent. Their purposed outcomes will overshadow evolving and intransigent metabolic rhythms that will process less upstream oxygen delivery, more insulin resistance, increasing acid base discrepancies and non-pulsed osmolar discrepancies [5,6,7]. When this occurs, the interstitial space will manifest a veritable *who's who* of disease propagation that is hereto for characterized as the anti-organ's "***big sting***".

Capillary Cell Mitochondrial Energy Combustion and the How and Why it Caters to Outer Membrane Complex Permeability to Key the Pivot and Swing Dance Step

As the capillary cell's dance rhythm becomes increasingly nitic oxide combustion diminished, the *persistence* of its mitochondrial energy combustion and the corresponding functional rhythms it supports, becomes the *conscripted denigration* to the cell's infrastructure as it induces signaling and metabolic chain reactions that disrupt the cell's delicate signaling, metabolic and functional counterbalance. With increasing chronic inflammatory interstitial space exclamation points, the bloated capillary cell mitochondrial energy combustion cycle, will not only increase its infrastructure fission and autophagy, but will elicit signaling and metabolic rhythms that will metastasize dysfunction and loss of counterbalance within all other intracellular organelles that include the increasingly disabled outer membrane complex. The repetition of this loss of mitochondrial combustion counterbalance makes funneled interstitial space immune remnants signaling fodder for a chronic inflammatory habitat (Figure 3, appendix) [3,5,6,7,8,9,10,11].

The chronic inflammatory interstitial space processing of immune funneling content through the functionally disparaged capillary cell outer membrane complex will cascade a host of proinflammatory signaling and metabolic outcomes which in turn will auto perpetuate chronic inflammatory rhythms and disease consorts. The reduction in capillary cell dance step reserve will reenforce a proinflammatory interstitial space "tour de force" that provides a birthing bed for the "big sting" of auto perpetuated disease consorts into the interstitial space (Figures 16 and 17, appendix).

The Chronic Inflammatory Interstitial Space Signaling and Metabolic Synergies that Elicit the "Big Sting" are Contingent on Keeping the Capillary and Downstream Endothelial Cell's Mitochondria Stuck in Energy Combustion

As the capillary cell's mitochondrial energy combustion labors in a fixed production cycle, the consequences will yield a reverberation of persistently unbalanced rhythms throughout the capillary cell that will foment infrastructure decay while increasing resistance towards anti-inflammatory interstitial space outcomes [5,6,7]. The loss of capillary cell dance step signal, metabolic and functional counterbalance creates an anti-inflammatory quality assurance void to the dance step rhythm multipurpose that will gap increasingly ineffectual outcomes to the interstitial space and allied cells within its domain. This transitioning will eventually collapse the anti-inflammatory interstitial space with the signaling and metabolic mechanics becoming part of the "Big Sting" of interstitial space transitioning.

As dance step pivot and swing resistance increases and as the capillary cell loses its mitochondrial nitric oxide combustion cycle and subsequent infrastructure restitution, the cell will generate a host of unbalanced metabolic consequences that become a reflection of excessive mitochondrial energy combustion. These have been summarized previously and include the overutilization of fermented gluconeogenesis, a preponderance of fatty acid utilization to produce acetyl co A within mitochondria, the excessive processing of liposomal lipolysis and the forced utilization of acetyl co A in the mitochondrial Krebs cycle rather than for ribosomal protein synthesis. The persistent lack of dance step counterbalance will eventually deep six mitochondrial combustion reserve as its size, volume and mass within the capillary and downstream endothelial cell decreases from excessive fission and autophagy and not enough fusion and replication. None of this bodes well for the longer-term anti-inflammatory interstitial space initiatives that keep the space hygienic and the end organ cell functionally astute.

The diminished capillary cell mitochondrial nitric oxide combustion cycle and subsequent lack of transcellular restitution will also shrink the capacity of the cell's outer membrane complex to nuance anti-inflammatory multipurpose as its glycocalyx thins, basement membrane thickens and continuous outer membrane adhesion receptors, pores, transport vesicles and voltage gradients lose their pulsed capabilities [5,6,7]. When this occurs, the capillary cell's functionally desperate outer membrane complex will purpose recoil as it loses power to engage a meaningful anti-inflammatory interstitial space multipurpose fulfillment which in turn usurps the end organ cell's functional resolve. This interstitial space chronic inflammatory collective, in combination with newly emerging disease consorts, becomes the end organ's "big sting" prerogative[7]. As these rhythms auto perpetuate, vascular inflammatory free radical interstitial space impingements increasingly resist degradation, incoming immune arsenal are being pushed to chronic inflammatory signal convert and mesenchymal cells have become part of the chronic inflammatory "tour de force" as blood plasma circulating immune remnants have been molecularly reconfigured form the chronic inflammatory cytokine backwash to be repurposed to proinflammatory alignments.

The End-Game of an Interstitial Space Chronic Inflammatory Sting Operative: Introducing the *Anti-Organ* Functional Monopoly

The powerful counterbalanced anti-inflammatory fluxing of the capillary cell's dance step rhythm will trigger chain reverberating and pulsed reactions that facilitate interstitial space sanitation and revitalize allied cells while enhancing end organ cell functional viability [5,6,7]. In this manner the fulfillment of each dance step functionally protects the next step's purposed execution. These recurring dance step anti-inflammatory fulfillments enhance the functional integrity of the dance step through a sequential quality assurance of their outcomes as the timely execution of each dance step serves as its own control to its outcome while simultaneously laying out the signaling, metabolic and functional groundwork for the fulfillment of the next dance step. This keeps the dance step rhythm functionally counterbalanced as it paces, stems, ricochets and backwashes it's signaling, metabolic and functional rhythms to and from the interstitial space and blood plasma[5,6,7]. In this manner the capillary cell's dance step rhythm reanoints continuous flows of multipurposed anti-inflammatory chain reactions that connect the capillary cell's refurbished and functionally intact infrastructure with the functional rhythms of its interstitial space domain.

The fluxing capillary cell dance step process becomes the method of choice for how the cell maneuvers competent anti-inflammatory multipurpose over extended periods of time (Figures 4-6, appendix) [5,6,7,8,9]. These purpose fulfillments become inextricably linked to the capillary and downstream endothelial cells fluxing of its outer membrane permeability gradients and the swinging of its mitochondrial combustion which in turn triggers the reverberation of its pivot and swing functional outcomes that require each step to be rhythm counterbalanced with the previous. In this manner the sequential capillary cell dance steps facilitate the *recalibration* of a durable anti-inflammatory cellular, interstitial space and end organ cell functional hierarchy of both co and interdependency[7]. The beat-to beat outcomes to the dance step rhythm becomes the *anti-inflammatory language* that transmits transcellular legitimacy as well as their extended vitality while enabling a reliable interstitial space hygiene and transformative end organ cellular functional performance [5,6,7]. When the dance step rhythm is timely and operationally succinct, the executed anti-inflammatory rhythms it generates both counterbalance and quality assure a continuous dance step performance.

If or when the capillary cell dance step rhythm abates, it will be cause or affected by virilizing chronic inflammatory interstitial space signaling rhythms that will transition disease operatives that in turn will monopolize functional outcomes that "Big Sting" the interstitial space away from its original intent. When this occurs the virilized and intransigent anti-organ will diminish anti-inflammatory purpose weary capillary cells and their associated allied interstitial space partners with signaling and metabolic rhythms that push their anti-inflammatory counterparts to where they cannot resist. No matter what the capillary cell countering contingency plan is (attempts at more blood flow, oxygen delivery, immune cell dispersals etc.) the chronic inflammatory inertia will have mitigated it with its own set of signaling and metabolic contingencies that places the anti-inflammatory resistance on its heels to become even more purpose reactive. When this occurs, the "Big Sting" chronic inflammatory operative has organized to such a degree within the interstitial space that the signaling and metabolic monopolies that have incited result in a functional utility that hastens disease outcomes as it snuffs out what remains of end organ cell functional resolve. As the end organ cell atrophies or dies, the funneled white blood cells, immunoglobulins, platelets and clotting factors become signal converted chronic inflammatory surrogates that become participants in signaling rhythms that elicit chronic inflammatory outcomes. These outcomes will further weaponize the interstitial space landscape to "Big Sting" further control of its operatives.

The Anti-Organ "Big Sting" Operative will Outcome Disease Mosaics Based in Part on Inherent or Acquired End Organ Genetic and Functional Prerogatives

As chronic inflammatory interstitial space signaling and metabolic rhythms virilize intent, the capillary cell's capacity to dance step rhythm anti-inflammatory multipurpose will dissipate[7]. This will enable the anti-organ to capture a *purpose threshold* within the interstitial space that is uniquely suited to certain disease contexts. As chronic inflammatory interstitial space rhythms escalate, they will signal functional content to the disabled capillary cell's outer membrane complex that will purpose identify immune arsenal that will be suitable to these requests. When interstitial space funneled, they will signal to become ad hoc providers towards the expression of specific disease portals that would be unique to the functional and genetic algorithms of the end organ cell. Therefore, disease specificity within a given interstitial space is not just about how chronic inflammatory rhythms are randomly organized to express a functional purpose but it also involves how the end organ and its unique interstitial space domain will constitute a functional vulnerability to a specific *type* of disease entrée. This implies that different types of disease propagation will evolve in end organs not just based upon how the anti-organ organizes it's signaling and metabolic prerogatives but also on their functional and inherent or acquired genetic predispositions. Regardless of how these anti-organ prerogatives pan out, there will be a signaling and metabolic commonality within its functional fortress that will be common to all end organ interstitial spaces that will include:

> a persistent and intransigent portfolio of vascular inflammatory free radical impingements that will fuel the chronic inflammatory interstitial space dispersals

> a progressive interstitial space funneling of immune misfits that have become anti-inflammatory immune unresponsive but easily converted to anti-organ functional surrogates

> the increasing emergence of a purpose contrived anti-organ interstitial space *consciousness* that runs contrary to end organ cell functional prerogatives

> the compilated sets of interstitial space disease mosaics that are earmarked based on both anti-organ prerogatives and the functional and genetic vulnerability of the interstitial space and end organ involved [6,7].

As an example, the disease seeding within very oxygen vulnerable end organs and a tightly controlled interstitial space (such as the brain and its blood brain barrier), will often be connected to upstream oxygen deficits that will predispose to hypercoagulable, ischemic and thrombosis outcomes that are become part of the upstream capillary cell double whammy effect[5,6,7]. As the potential for upstream end organ cell hypoxia and ischemia plays out and as it loses functional reserve, the interstitial space will transition additional signaling and metabolic prerogatives that will incentivize additional disease consortiums within the end organ that will then cause and effect different types of neurodegeneration that will involve scarring, infections, cancers and autoimmune complexes. These mosaics will in part be determined by how the brain's infrastructure has become genetically prone towards their interstitial space involvement

In this manner, different end organs will posture different disease mosaics based on how the anti-organ perceives its unique signaling, metabolic and functional vulnerabilities. This will also become contingent on how the end organ has evolved a genetic predisposition to certain disease consorts as well as how inherently restrictive the capillary cell's basement membrane is to anti-organ prerogatives. When the capillary cell's basement membrane is inherently porous (liver, pancreas, intestines), the corresponding interstitial space becomes prone to a broader array of misfitted blood plasma immune contingents that will predispose to a wider spectrum of variable disease mosaics[6,7]. Regardless of which disease entity initiates the anti-organ procession, the signaling and metabolic rhythms they elicit will consolidate a chronic inflammatory interstitial space virilization that predisposes additional disease consorts.

The Mechanics as to How the Anti-Organ Consigns Interstitial Space Disease Hierarchies

The rate and hierarchal ascension of specific disease consorts within an end organ's interstitial space will become codependent on the degree to which the capillary cell's dance step rhythm has deteriorated, the decline of interstitial space anti-inflammatory resistance to the increasing chronic inflammatory consciousness, and how much anti-organ signal and metabolic control of the interstitial space has already occurred[6,7]. The aggregate of these factors in combination with the unique end organ vulnerability to a specific type of disease entrée will determine how the anti-organ will manipulate the interstitial space environment[6,7]. In the early stages of chronic interstitial space inflammation, the capillary cell dance step rhythm will be capable of compensating dance step intensity and duration to mitigate variable surges of proinflammatory free radical interstitial space inclusions and other signaling advances as it postures adjustments in the rate and intensity of immune funneling to fortify its anti-inflammatory defenses against increasing chronic inflammatory resistance. However, when persistent, chronic inflammatory interstitial space signaling, metabolic and functional salvos become intransigent, the resolve of the anti-organ can overcome the compensatory anti-inflammatory interstitial space rhythms to begin the breakdown process of the capillary and downstream endothelial cell dance steps.

Regardless of how and when disease seeds become interstitial space consigned, their propagation will become part of an autonomous yet self-fulfilling expression of intent that will process a de-escalation of anti-inflammatory signaling and metabolic resolve [5,6,7]. The rate and extent to which the end organ cell functionally declines becomes proportional to the interstitial space consolidation and signaling control of the anti-organ dispersed disease consorts. In these end organ cell hostile interstitial space settings, the disease venue will lay out the interstitial space anti-organ signaling and metabolic framework that will in turn "escort" the propagation of its fulfillment while also lending a signaling hand towards the propagation of a second or even a third disease consort within the same interstitial space. The ascension of these disease consorts is hereto fore called an anti-organ *disease hierarchy*. In the later stages of chronic interstitial space inflammation whereby the interstitial space signaling and metabolic rhythms have been anti-organ remastered, the processing of multiple disease entities will likely occur to collectively transition an *end game* to the end organ's life span. When this occurs, the end organ's functional decline will contribute to and rotates with an increasingly virile and multileveled anti-organ disease consortium that has completely remastered the purpose of the end organ's interstitial space (Figure 18, appendix).

With the decline to the increasingly senescent capillary cell's dance step rhythm, evolving interstitial space disease consorts will posture functional control over large swaths of interstitial space commerce which increasingly sanction the failing end organ cell's capacity to perform anything meaningful. Even with the solicitation of modern medical heroics, the inability of these interventions to find traction with functionally inept anti-inflammatory immune mechanics will make these endeavors against anti-organ auspices less than satisfactory. The ineffectiveness of allopathic treatments against the matured anti-organ, when coupled with the inability of these interventions to integrate their purpose with the defunct anti-inflammatory capillary cell dance step rhythm, makes anti-organ resistance against their effects more likely as its assembled disease consorts fuse signaling and metabolic prerogatives that will increasingly form resistance against these allopathic interventions.

The *Pace* of End Organ Cell Failure becomes Codependent on the *Rate of* Functional Anti-Organ Interstitial Space *Transitioning*

The progression of virilized anti-organ signaling and metabolic rhythms eventually become *predatory* towards the increasingly less capable anti-inflammatory immune signals thereby neutralizing their effectiveness[7]. The lost anti-inflammatory immune signaling and functional intentionality will coincide with the breakdown of the capillary cell's anti-inflammatory dance step derived pace, stem, ricochet and backwash rhythm as its protracted immune funneling efforts increasingly signal and functionally align with anti-organ prerogatives. In this manner, chronic inflammatory interstitial space rhythms gain unprecedented functional superiority to enable the transitioning of purpose control over broad swaths of interstitial space content. Chief among this conversion of interstitial space purpose is the gutting of the capillary cell anti-inflammatory functional utility as it manipulates rhythms that reduce the stature of its outer membrane complex, mitochondria and nuclear chromatin. The conversion process eventually enables the anti-organ to seize unlimited access to signaling and metabolic interstitial space pathways that will process disease fulfillment.

As proinflammatory interstitial space signaling, metabolic and functional rhythms consolidate intent, disease mosaics will become a natural offshoot with their purposed expressions pushing a chronic inflammatory interstitial space sprawl of anti-organ functional continuity that the disabled capillary cell and its allied cell axis has no answer for. This inability to anti-inflammatory resist the anti-organ becomes the "*big sting*" of the interstitial space (Figure 18, appendix).

Chapter Nineteen

The Dubious Conversion of End Organ Interstitial Spaces to Proinflammatory Signaling Streams and Metabolic Rhythms: A Fait Accompli?

The Sobering Realization that Aging and Trans-End Organ Cellular Decline Become Inevitable Intrusions from Anti-Organ Interstitial Space Outcomes

Anti-aging requires a sustained-functionally counterbalanced and quality assured capillary cell's dance step rhythm that is "circadian pulsed" to outcome a continuous flow of multipurposed anti-inflammatory fulfillment to and from the interstitial space and blood plasma[7]. In this context, most science-based observers would agree that cellular rhythms have a *life span* that will confer both a beginning and end of life with the rate of cellular denigration manifested by the increasing interference of chronic inflammatory signaling, metabolic and functional mediation both within the cell and outside of its outer membrane confluence. With regards to the aging of vascular endothelium, its collective vitality and functional longevity will be dependent on how long the integrity of its dance step rhythms can be maintained which in turn will forecast similar antiaging virtues to its interstitial space and allied cellular partners who utilize the dance step's pace and stem effects to their collective functional and restitution purposes. The enduring posterity of these transcellular relationships become codependent on the integrity of the capillary and downstream endothelial cell's counterbalanced dance step rhythm, the ongoing purposed fulfillment of its outer membrane complex permeability pivot and mitochondrial nitric oxide combustion swing, and how code compliant its nuclear chromatin remains to maximize protein synthesis for transcellular restitution. The recycling of transcellular rejuvenation, that becomes a manifestation of the capillary cell's pulsed dance step outcomes, becomes the primary determinant for capillary and allied cell health maintenance, functional longevity and disease prevention as each two-step of the dance step rhythm will process anti-inflammatory multipurpose. This keeps the capillary, downstream endothelial and all allied cells within their interstitial space domain purpose resilient and disease resistant.

A persistent multipurpose anti-inflammatory precise capillary cell dance step rhythm will by its two-step nature be signal, metabolic and functionally counterbalanced. This in turn quality assures sequential dance step functional outcomes. This pivot and swing two-step dance step process enables the recurring execution of a potentially *divergent yet purpose effective* set of corresponding anti-inflammatory rhythms that are precision crafted by the capillary cell's outer membrane complex to support the execution of optimal interstitial space hygiene. As interstitial space sanitation becomes dance step purpose fulfilled, it will signal escort the next pivot and swing dance step which processes a trans cellular functional revitalization as an increased uptick in upstream interstitial space oxygen delivery enables its end organ cell to optimally perform its function. This executed anti-inflammatory multipurposed dance step fulfillment will consign a pulsed and highly integrated set of signaling and metabolic rhythms that will elicit a multipurposed fulfillment that makes serial dance steps increasingly purpose enduring, anti-inflammatory resilient and multipurposed quality assured. In pragmatic terms this means that the dance step rhythm's multipurposed anti-inflammatory fulfillment includes a *restitution arm* that enables the dance step rhythm to remain functionally enduring as transcellular infrastructure gets reconstituted. When in dance step compliance, the entire endothelial arterial space and associated interstitial space collective should will remain anti-inflammatory functionally astute for greater than expected periods of time.

On the other hand, when trans arterial endothelial cell infrastructure does not get suitably refurbished, there will be a collective anti-inflammatory functional decline throughout the endothelial cell arterial tree. This will cause and effect a disingenuous and functionally unbalanced capillary and downstream endothelial cell dance step rhythm that will increasingly miscue interstitial space immune funneling that will result in ineffectual anti-inflammatory multipurposed outcomes. As vascular inflammatory free radical interstitial space free radicals pester and fester to expand chronic inflammatory influence and harken even more anti-inflammatory immune incompetent interstitial space funneling, the space will transition its purpose identity away from anti-inflammatory outcomes and towards the fulfillment of proinflammatory chain reactions. As this is occurring, the unbalanced dance step rhythm is not allowing for a genuine nitric oxide combustion cycle and trans endothelial cell restitution. Within the endothelial cell arterial complex, persistent delays in interstitial space inflammatory breach removal have pushed increases in mitochondrial energy combustion at the expense of a timely and dance step counterbalanced pivot and swing rhythm that would include a mitochondrial nitric oxide induced transcellular infrastructure restitution. The increasing inability of the endothelial cell system to process anti-inflammatory interstitial space rhythms allows for chronic inflammatory functional rhythms to gain increasing access to the signaling and metabolic hierarchy of the interstitial space. As anti-inflammatory losses mount, the capillary and downstream endothelial cells become anti-inflammatory purpose insolvent as their functional senescence will transfigure their identity to become an immune funneling surrogate to the increasingly intentional chronic inflammatory matrix and anti-organ [5,6,7,29].

The continued backdrop of lost dance step anti-inflammatory efficacy will correspond with the increasing intentionality of chronic inflammatory interstitial space rhythms as they form their own signaling and metabolic hierarchy to pace, ricochet and backwash to and through the capillary and downstream endothelial cell their own purpose. The result becomes a trans endothelial cell interstitial space domain that becomes anti-inflammatory defunct and proinflammatory enhanced, with the ladder processing increasing virulence and a mosaic of disease intentionality.

The Loss of Dance Step Rhythm's Circadian *Timeliness* of Purpose Execution Becomes the Interstitial Space's Signaling and Metabolic Window towards a Conscripted Chronic Inflammatory Expression

The driving force of a robust multipurposed anti-inflammatory capillary dance step fulfillment is its timely and recurring two-step execution that couples that performance with the existential refurbishment of its infrastructure. When in dance step compliance the capillary and downstream endothelial cell's outer membrane complex and mitochondria keep its interstitial space immune funneling effort purpose precise and outcome timely. When in rhythm the nearby mesenchymal cell(s) will pulse either a timely cytokine "all hands-on deck" or cytokine inhibitory "all clear" signal that becomes a powerful signaling beacon to the capillary cell's basement membrane to pivot and swing its dance step rhythm that will realign an adjustment to its anti-inflammatory purposes.

The recurring precise and timely endo and exocytic expressions through the endothelial cell, that mobilize anti-inflammatory multipurposed momentum shifts to and from the interstitial space and blood plasma, become the driving forces of dance step signaling, metabolic and functional counterbalance, quality assurance and outcome fulfillment. Within this context, consecutive dance step outcome fulfillment becomes the signaling and metabolic framework for the next dance step to process an equally successful but very different purposed execution. In this manner the anti-inflammatory "rhythm" that is conveyed becomes endearing as it *deters and prevents* chronic inflammatory interstitial space overtures [5,6,7]. As each dance step purpose fulfills, the signaling and metabolic reverberation of its outcomes will chain react an ongoing anti-inflammatory identity that will bias sequential dance step purpose fulfillment[5,6,7].

The dance step rhythm finds signaling continuity from the reverberated and pulsed fluxing of the capillary cell's continuous outer membrane's cAMP concentrations as it responds to the nearby mesenchymal cell "all hands-on deck" or "all clear" signals. This response will predicate the direction of the outer membrane complex permeability gradients and subsequent mitochondrial combustion swings. Its fluctuating levels will master switch a series of chain reactions within the capillary cell's outer membrane infrastructure that will enable up or down upticks to its permeability range which will determine the rate, intensity or lack thereof of funneled interstitial space immune arsenal. The two-step pivot and swing process will also either push or inhibit a cytokine backwash into the central circulation that further buffers and prepares circulating immune remnants to serve future anti-inflammatory interstitial space needs. The fluxing and counterbalanced outer membrane permeability Ying-yang process will invoke counter pulsed switch infrastructure chain reactions that facilitate either stimulatory or inhibitory immune permeability directives that in sum become a reflection of the real time permeability equation. This equation includes the adjustment of many outer membrane complex *permeability regulators* that involve continuous outer membrane voltage gradients, the exposures of luminal adhesion receptors, the activation of the gap junction orifice and channel immune funneling, and the endocytic luminal responsiveness of pores, vesicles and transcellular transport channels. In the opposite direction when immune funneling interstitial space recedes, it will process an exocytic backwash of anti-inflammatory immune enhanced cytokines into the central circulation that prepare circulating immune remnants for the next dance step interstitial space mobilization.

When immune funneling into the interstitial space is signaled to contract, capillary and downstream endothelial cell continuous outer membrane ATP and calcium ions will reaccumulate within the cytoplasm of the continuous outer membrane's interface. As they form concentration gradients, both will diffuse into the mitochondrial intermembrane space where they will process feedback loop signals with the inner membrane to activate matrix nitric oxide synthase and swing combustion to the nitric oxide cycle. These cyclical-signal and metabolically counterbalanced dance step driven chain reactions are driven by anti-inflammatory fulfillment and serve to quality assure future anti-inflammatory fulfillment to and from the interstitial space, capillary cell and blood plasma.

The pulsed volleys of precision purposed immune arsenal into the interstitial space will in most instances require energy surges to execute the funneling effort as their size, solubility and molecular perturbations must work against various concentration gradients. This becomes particularly relevant with the interstitial space funneling of B cell immunity as it will involve the penetration different types of immune cells, immunoglobulins, albumen, or other inflammatory proteins that are large, bulky and potentially resistant to osmolar or other gradients. In this context, *active transport mechanics* that will require surges of ATP and calcium ion support to the capillary cell's continuous outer membrane for the endocytic transport of these otherwise difficult to mobilize immune remnants becomes essential to process the removal of certain types of vascular inflammatory free radical impingements or other types of interstitial space inflammatory breach. The sudden and often dramatic continuous outer membrane ATP requirement for immune active transport will require the nearby capillary cell's mitochondria to combust the needed energy surges in order to carry out a successful dance step circadian purpose of certain types of inflammatory breach removal (Figures 3 and 4, appendix) [6,7]. When the dance steps are timely executed and then next step recalibrated, its counterbalanced rhythm keeps its vulnerable nitric oxide combustion cycle relevant [5,6,7]. This enables the capillary and mesenchymal cell's infrastructure to refresh and then perform the next step's execution with bravado.

Does Chronic Inflammatory Transcellular "Aging" Beg the Question of a *Fait Accompli?*

A primary consequence of sustained chronic interstitial space inflammation is the increasing functional senescence of the capillary and downstream endothelial cell network. As has been previously characterized, the capillary cell and its downstream endothelial cell brethren, lose dance step counterbalance that in turn suppresses their collective nitric oxide combustion cycles. As excessive energy combustion ROS accumulates within these cells their nuclear chromatin gets increasingly crosslinked and code silenced thereby interfering with the cell's capacity to refurbish thereby leading to transcellular functional senescence [5,6,7]. The irreversible loss of nuclear chromatin code capacity becomes the primary determinant of senescent endothelium.

The capillary and downstream endothelial cell's aging process becomes a virilizing life-extender to chronic interstitial space inflammation as it uses the loss of anti-inflammatory functional rhythms to process a collective interstitial space signaling and metabolic advantage. As this occurs, capillary cell aging will continue to escalate as the cell will accelerate its loss of anti-inflammatory functional reserve. The capillary cell's future dance step prospects become increasingly bleak as more of its functional apparatus becomes deleted, corrupted or irreversibly ineffective. This "transitioning" will enable the chronic inflammatory interstitial space amalgam to gain increasing intentionality to where its signaling and metabolic anachronisms will control vicious cycles of escalating proinflammatory rhythms.

When chronic inflammatory interstitial space rhythms escalate to control interstitial space outcomes to where there is marginal anti-inflammatory resistance, the capillary and downstream endothelial cell's functional attributes become chronic inflammatory facilitators (Figure 9, appendix)[7]. As the cell forfeits control of interstitial space landscape, not only do prevailing interstitial space signaling and metabolic rhythms cater to proinflammatory intent, but the exocytic backwash it manifests into the blood plasma will immune suppress to cause further chronic inflammatory interstitial space upheaval. Escalating chronic inflammatory rhythms on both luminal and abluminal sides of endothelium will foster overriding contingents of anti-organ prerogatives. As anti-inflammatory rhythms between the blood plasma, capillary cell and interstitial space hibernate, interstitial space disease venues escalate as the end organ cell loses functional viability. Short of a capillary cell chromosomal DNA *stem cell transplant* to rebuild capillary and endothelial cell infrastructure, the anti-inflammatory immune resistance against anti-organ prerogatives will be insufficient. Antiaging rhythms will deescalate within the interstitial spaces throughout the arterial tree as chronic inflammatory rhythms manifest a progressive existential dystopia of functional intent. In these interstitial space settings, the anti-organ outcomes become a lethal "a fait accompli".

The Capillary Cell's Loss of Dance Step Functional Utility Will Facilitate a Signaling Crosstalk of Interstitial Space Disease Consorts

With a reduced capacity to dance step and elicit purpose precise anti-inflammatory interstitial space rhythms and outcomes, the capillary and downstream endothelial cell's functional incompetence will bias pervasive arrays of chronic inflammatory interstitial space signaling rhythms that will trigger families of disease consorts to establish residence. his will not only bias reduced end organ cell functional utility, but will trigger the activation of growth factors within the cell from a pervasive nitric oxide combustion cycle that will bias unwanted replication cycles and RNS cross linkages. As end organ cells are nurtured to replicate with increasingly crosslinked nuclear chromatin, there will be heightened predilection for oncogenic interstitial space cell dispersal. As this occurs, the anti-inflammatory immune responsiveness to these dispersals is diminishing thereby allowing these cells to roam the interstitial space in search of favorable nooks and crannies to process amplification of their replicative and growth biases[6,7].

The persistence of capillary cell mitochondrial energy combustion and how it facilitates loss of dance step anti-inflammatory functional reserve, becomes an important chronic inflammatory *signaling and metabolic bridge* that will facilitate the necessary persistent signaling crescendos to the end organ cell and its dystopic offspring for the replicative development of oncogenic cell lines. The persistence of these rhythms, coupled with a diminished functionally insolvent anti-inflammatory immune contingent within the interstitial space, becomes an ideal microenvironment for cancer cells to find a replicative rhythm. As capillary cell dance step functional resolve diminishes, cancer cell propagation as well as that of other disease consorts such as infections, scar tissue or heightened levels of thrombosis, escalate. In aggregate they formulate the necessary signaling and metabolic tools to add credence towards the propagation of other disease consorts[6,7]. Hence, oncogenesis enhances infectious agent propagation and visa-versa, which turn could foster increased amyloid or fibrous scar tissue formation. All of the above will increase coagulation risks and posture autoimmune miscues. In this manner, the regardless of the inciting disease venue, the prevailing chronic inflammatory interstitial space rhythms will foster a heightened responsiveness to all forms of anti-organ mischievous (Figure 10, appendix).

The Persistently Unbalanced Capillary Cell Dance Step Rhythm will Accelerate its Own Senescence

The key to a robust capillary cell anti-inflammatory dance step rhythm is its functional counterbalance which processes anti-inflammatory multipurpose while mitigating proinflammatory signaling and metabolic innuendos within its interstitial space[6,7]. With dance step decay and an increasing anti-inflammatory to chronic inflammatory functional interstitial space gap, a proinflammatory signaling and metabolic crescendo will accentuate unmitigated vascular inflammatory free radical interstitial space impingements, immune funneling errors, end organ cell dysfunction and loss of transcellular restitution. Once more the preponderance of chronic inflammatory interstitial space rhythms will serve to begat itself as it magnifies an anti-organ signaling and metabolic predilection as it processes increased capillary and downstream endothelial cell dance step dysfunction.

The increasing capillary cell processing of chronic inflammatory interstitial space rhythms will make functional matters worse for its deteriorating outer membrane complex, mitochondrial reserve and increasingly crosslinked nuclear chromatin. The process self-fulfills increasing endothelial cell senescence as chronic inflammatory rhythms ratify their own functional purposes that become the antithesis to those derived from the capillary cell dance steps (Figures 14 and 15, appendix). With increasing capillary and downstream endothelial cell anti-inflammatory senescence, their interstitial spaces will transition functional derivatives that cater to disease consorts as mesenchymal, immune and end organ cells become transfixed into their functional rhtyhms.

The loss of capillary cell dance step rhythm becomes the functional equivalent of a blow torch to chronic inflammatory interstitial space prerogatives. Its persistence will only serve to magnify anti-organ interstitial space outcomes. The cell's increasing futility to provide anti-inflammatory resistance becomes self-fulfilling to the replicative cycles of infectious agents, cancer cells, scar tissue formation and misinformed immunoglobulins as well as the processing of interstitial space or transluminal hyper coagulable states [5,6,7].

Anti-Inflammatory Lifestyles can Make or Break Midlife Capillary Cell Anti-Inflammatory Dance Step Makeovers

The *rate* and *intensity* of capillary cell dance step decline becomes a direct reflection of how much loss of functional anti-inflammatory resolve has occurred within the cell's infrastructure[5,6,7,8,9]. Much of this capillary and downstream endothelial cell dance step "transitioning" is triggered by persistent midlife (ages 40-65) maladaptive lifestyles that have nurtured various addiction cycles. Their anti-inflammatory maladaptive and repetitive nature will produce enough vascular inflammatory free radical interstitial space impingements so as to exhaust dance step counterbalance, block its nitric oxide combustion and outsource increased immune funneling errors to in effect create a perfect interstitial pace venue for a chronic inflammatory signaling and metabolic pestilence. Addictions more or less assure a constant contingency of free radical interstitial space chronic inflammatory impingements that often couple with other malevolent addictions to render a recurrent recycling of even more aggressive free radical interstitial space assaults. This persistent multileveled free radical interstitial space firestorm becomes a virilized chronic inflammatory fuel as the recycling of interstitial space sugars, advanced glycation end products, trans and saturated animal fats, alcohol and its byproduct, drugs, tobacco products, and highly processed and refined foods become pallbearers to the declining capillary and downstream endothelia cell dance step rhythm [4,5,6,7,24]. To the extent that these free radicals comingle, malinger and persistently disrupt numerous nascent cell membranes and infrastructure is to the extent that the capillary cell and its interstitial space domain "transitions" into a chronic inflammatory apocalypse. This idealized interstitial space chronic inflammatory microclimate will speed up processes that transform signaling and metabolic rhythms into virilized disease outcomes. Addictive lifestyles and the disease consorts they enable are further framed by secondary interstitial space free radical rollovers that occur from inactivity, obesity, hypertension, adult diabetes, metabolic syndrome, stress, depression, and sleep disorders.

When lifestyle choices negate the addictive vascular inflammatory free radical interstitial space conveyor belt, anti-inflammatory dance step driven recycling of multipurpose will have a chance to be rhythm restored. The absolute and persistent reduction of highly reactive free radical interstitial space displays will enable the previously dysfunctional capillary cell to rekindle its dance step traction and begin processing anti-inflammatory resistance against prevailing chronic inflammatory interstitial space signaling salvos[5,6,7]. As the dance step rhythm restructures credibility, its rhythms will *synchronize* a functionally counterbalanced and quality assured multipurpose of outcomes that will incentivize reductions in chronic inflammatory intrusions. When this occurs, enhanced interstitial space hygiene and improved upstream oxygen flows I become additional anti-inflammatory deterrents towards improving end organ cell functional derivatives.

Will or Can Capillary and Endothelial Nuclear Chromosomal DNA *Self Repair* without a Stem Cell Intervention?

Could a genuine return of a pulsed signal, metabolic and functional anti-inflammatory interstitial space ecosystem from a revitalized capillary cell dance step rhythm include the capacity for capillary cell nuclear chromatin to self-repair? This type of DNA reconstitution appears to occur within mitochondria as their DNA clumps process repair via a recurring dance step derived fission/fusion, autophagy/replication operative that eliminates dead or crosslinked DNA and replaces it with fused viable types that can then be replicated to increase mass and volume within its matrix. That is, during mitochondrial energy combustion matrix DNA clumps appear to undergo a culling of its dead or code silenced DNA fragments via fission or autolysis only to have the DNA restored by fusion and replication during its nitric oxide combustion cycle. In a back-and forth rhythm that is best clarified with dance step mitochondrial combustion counterbalance. *BOTH* processes are required to keep the mitochondrial DNA coding capacity optimal to maximize the ribosomal processing of protein synthesis mitochondrial infrastructure repair and the maintenance of combustion efficacy.

In this dance step context, mitochondrial DNA volume and mass will expand and contract with each dance two step as its chromatin clumps are culled and then fused and replicated to restore its volume and coding capacity. If the mitochondrial DNA dance step DNA contraction and re expansion is purpose counterbalanced, it should theoretically maintain all of its functional viability over time. The process begs the question regarding a potential similar arrangement of ROS cross linked and code silenced capillary cell nuclear chromosomal DNA and weather it too could be functionally restored through the dance step rhythm.

The answer to this question is why not and then maybe. The problem with nuclear chromatin is that it is much more complex and signal interactive with a myriad of transcellular processes and organelles that coordinate dance step intent. This makes the processing of nuclear DNA resuscitation much more complex whereby the fission/fusion and autophagy and replication must play out within a dance step time constraint that would require a highly refined system that could systematically cull and fuse, remove and replicate DNA infrastructure on a much larger scale than the more primitive mitochondrial DNA clumps found in its matrix. On the other hand, if capillary cell nuclear chromatin could dance step self-repair itself it would have enormous long-term repercussions in terms of functional viability[5,6,7]. In this setting, the counterbalanced capillary cell dance step rhythm would facilitate the prevention of the longer-term coding consequences of ROS nuclear chromatin cross linkage. By incentivizing DNA self-repair, the sequential capillary cell dance step rhythm could keep its multipurposed execution fundamentally intact thereby preserving interstitial space hygiene and long-term end organ cell functional resolve while limiting signaling and metabolic rhythms that incentivize chronic inflammatory anti-organ outcomes.

The Murky and Often Unpredictable Process of Unwinding Chronic Inflammatory Interstitial Space Rhythms

The transitioning of an end organ's interstitial space from a chronic inflammatory signaling and metabolic haven to an anti-inflammatory functional powerhouse can be difficult due to intransigent chronic inflammatory roadblocks. For anti-inflammatory rhythms to regain an interstitial space continuity there must be a paradigm shift of sustained signaling momentum that can multilevel readjust of host of invasive chronic inflammatory functional mosaics. For this to occur, the capillary and downstream endothelial cell specifically and their interstitial space domains generally must revive operational anti-inflammatory rhythms that had been previously shut down by invasive chronic inflammatory encampments. The process of repositioning anti-inflammatory interstitial space rhythms that have been chronic inflammatory converted requires a reconstituted funneling of immune contingents into the interstitial space that are anti-inflammatory recalibrated. This will require a fundamental diminishment of infiltrated vascular inflammatory free radical interstitial space impingements that will give the arterial endothelial cell system a chance to revive its counterbalanced two step dance rhythm and begin processing a genuine nitric oxide combustion cycle and infrastructure rejuvenation. This will mean that emanated signaling and metabolic rhythms, that will include those derived from interstitial space immune and mesenchymal cells, will have the reinvigorated capability to process an anti-inflammatory resolve. The anti-inflammatory transitioning will require and the capillary and downstream endothelial cell to reposition its functional resolve to where it can redeploy a full complement of its dance step derived paced, stemmed, ricocheted and backwashed anti-inflammatory rhythms that allow little chance for chronic inflammatory processes to find interstitial space forbearance. In summary, for the interstitial space to transition a fundamental shift in purpose realignment it will require:

✓ A deep and sustained reduction in vascular inflammatory free radical interstitial space impingements.

✓ The unfettered capacity of the hibernating capillary cell to reestablish its dance step rhythm multipurpose given the aforementioned changes in interstitial space free radical dynamics.

✓ The return of capillary cell capacity to stem, pace, ricochet and backwash anti-inflammatory rhythms.

✓ The return to full capacity of the capillary cell's infrastructure to include its resuscitated outer membrane complex and mitochodnral reserve and the ability of the cell to respond dynamically to immune and mesenchymal cell anti-inflammatory immune signaling operatives (i.e., the "all-hands on deck" and "all clear" signals).

✓ The robust dance step responses to these interstitial space signals will clarify an intentional transitioning of repurpose that will process a virilized anti-inflammatory outcome that optimizes interstitial space hygiene while increasing end organ cell functional reserve [6,7].

The shifting of interstitial space signaling and metabolic rhythms back to an aligned anti-inflammatory purpose can amount to a *multi-level* tug of war between well-established chronic inflammatory disease consorts, their virilized signaled and metabolic threads, and the functional resolve of the resuscitated capillary cell's dance steps. The capacity of the capillary and downstream endothelial cell to redirect and position anti-inflammatory rhythms within the interstitial space will be based on the degree to which these cells can return to its counterbalanced dance step rhythm roots. It will be codependent on the how much signaling and metabolic control they can wrestle away from established anti-organ prerogatives. This becomes codependent on how much dance step recovery the capillary cell and its downstream brethren can muster and the degree to which the anti-organ's signaling rhythms can be penetrated to process an anti-inflammatory signaling transition[7]. Wrestling signaling and metabolic control away from a fully matured consortium of disease venues can be fundamentally difficult due to the degree of control they have interstitial space acquired.

Midlife often becomes the time period whereby the threshold of chronic inflammatory interstitial space resistance disallows its anti-inflammatory reconversion. This occurs due to the midlife accumulation of multiple chronic inflammatory vascular inflammatory free radical interstitial space risks that either cannot be suitably mitigated or there is insufficient resolve to aggressively process their reductions. These proinflammatory rhythms find virulence from the persistence of addictive behaviors that are typically chronic inflammatory enhanced with increased sleep deprivation, stress, inactivity, poor dietary habits and insulin resistance. These scenarios become a hotbed for a myriad of persistent vascular inflammatory free radical interstitial space impingements that become impossible for the disabled capillary cell and its downstream endothelial cell brethren to reestablish its dance step rhythms let alone its anti-inflammatory cred. The lack of effective chronic inflammatory mitigation becomes the midlife's nail in the coffin as disease consorts proliferate to yield dangerous, premature and often end organ lethal outcomes.

The Evolution of a Chronic Inflammatory Interstitial Space "Nebula" Propagates in Association with a Functionally Compromised Capillary Cell and Downstream Endothelial Cell System

When chronic inflammatory end organ interstitial space rhythms virilize intent, no matter the end organ involved, both their expression and expansion *require* the disabled capillary and downstream endothelial cells to become coparticipants in their endeavors. When this occurs, their signaling and metabolic salvos to the basement membranes of endothelia and capillary cells pirate intent from the blood plasma to the interstitial space that will be supportive to their functional endeavors. Incoming immune arsenal will have molecularly tweaked by proinflammatory backwash to become vulnerable to a chronic inflammatory signaled conversion that will be supportive to the anti-organ's disease expressions. When this occurs, the increasing interstitial space chronic inflammatory amalgam will precipitate declines to end organ cell functional reserve regardless of what end organ these rhythms are originating from[5,6,7]. As the end organ cell declines, the anti-organ functional reserve escalates as the chronic inflammatory interstitial space habituate becomes much more conducive to anti-organ prerogatives.

It is within these increasingly dark chronic inflammatory interstitial space end organ contexts that the expansion of disease consorts will live large and become increasingly resistant to many interventional forms of treatment against them. Best practice treatment mechanics will involve efforts that involve the resuscitation the of the capillary and downstream endothelial cell's dance step rhythm. Ideally, allopathic, homeopathic or naturopathic interventions will have a dual purpose as they directly weaken the disease consort while restoking the recovery mechanics of the capillary and downstream endothelial cell's pivot and swing dance steps. As treatment regime incentivize dual purpose, disease debulking will occur, vascular inflammatory free radical impingements are sharply diminished, immune funneling becomes increasingly more anti-inflammatory purposed and the revived capillary cell dance steps themselves will improvise an improving pace, stem, ricochet and backwash effect.

Unfortunately, with advancing age, an interstitial space proclivity for virilized anti-organ control, and a capillary cell that has diminished nuclear chromatin reversibility to maximally code for a full complement of infrastructure proteins, the capillary and downstream endothelial cell brethren may not be able to position a fully restored dance step rhythm, making disease consorts capable of lingering despite maximum external "allopathic" treatment interventions. For these reasons, in mid and late life when interstitial space is most anti-organ vulnerable, lifestyle management must be more aggressively anti-inflammatory *accommodative* to bias capillary cell dance step counterbalanced rhythms due to the reduced capacities of these rhythms to process a comprehensive anti-inflammatory resuscitation of the interstitial space. The anti-inflammatory lifestyle reset will cause both direct and indirect reductions in vascular inflammatory free radical interstitial space impingements thereby making their timely dance step removal more likely even when the capillary cell's dance steps are functionally compromised from the lack of a comprehensive infrastructure refurbishment.

Sometimes external treatment interventions will overshoot intended outcome against disease consorts to where they can actually do more harm than good. When this occurs, the capillary and downstream endothelial cell's dance steps are disincentivized to anti-inflammatory perform. This can occur from:

- ✓ The *harshness* of the external intervention(s) to where the treatment attacks the disease consort but also disables the signaling and metabolic rhythms of anti-inflammatory rhythms to a similar or greater degree. This will lessen the treatment effectiveness against the disease consort.
- ✓ The reduction in anti-inflammatory benefit could render the interstitial space susceptible to other disease consort propagation. As an example, overshooting treatment for an autoimmune disease could increase risk for interstitial space cancer or infectious propagation.
- ✓ The *repetitive recycling* of external treatment mosaics against a disease process can lessen the impact of inherent anti-inflammatory interstitial space rhythms against the disease entity thereby rendering increased resistance of the treatment paradigms from the disease entity. This is most commonly seen with some forms of chemotherapy or antibiotic treatments in the treatment of cancers or infections.
- ✓ For best treatment results, externally directed disease treatment interventions should also include the reduction of vascular inflammatory free radical interstitial space impingements whic would give the capillary and endothelial cell integrated signaling system the best chance of dance step recovery and inclusion with the external treatment towards the disease consort[7].

External Treatments that Integrate with the Repatriation of the Capillary Cell Dance Step Rhythm will Enhance Anti-Inflammatory Disease Treatment Outcomes

When planning external (allopathic, homeopathic, naturopathic) treatments to an expanding and openly signal expressive anti-organ disease process, urgent decisions are often required to prevent end organ failures. These interventions are often life-saving, but in themselves can be mistake prone and over time increase disease resistance when not coupled with attempts to restore the capillary and endothelial cell dance step rhythm. Disease treatments that are dance step inclusive will improve long term outcomes against the disease consort while also preventing other disease entities from becoming secondary interstitial space offenders. External treatments, when capillary and endothelial cell dance step integrative, become enhanced anti-inflammatory multipurposed forces that will support reductions in chronic inflammatory interstitial space rhythms while propping up the return of the counterbalanced capillary cell's dance steps[7].

The obvious universal treatment strategy in attacking the signaling and metabolic infrastructure of all disease consorts would be to include reductions in all vascular inflammatory free radical interstitial space impingements. Nurturing the return of the counterbalanced capillary cell dance step rhythm will augment external treatment effectiveness while decreasing the risk for interventional resistance form the underlying disease consort. With the coupling of disease treatment with the direct resuscitation of capillary and endothelial cell dance steps, the anticipated revival the upstream capillary cell's anti-inflammatory pace, stem, ricochet and backwash effects will occur to the extent that its nuclear chromatin will allow. This treatment paradigm will figure into an interstitial space "***root cause***" as the dance step resuscitated capillary and downstream endothelial cell will provide the necessary interstitial space signaling and metabolic details to transition rhythms away from anti-organ control.

It should be anticipated that the mechanics of external treatment interventions with capillary and downstream endothelial cell dance step integration becomes more complicated and with less desired benefit with advanced age or with complex interstitial space disease entrees. This makes external treatment successes in the elderly or in those with complex interstitial space disease mosaics more refractory to remission.

Anti-Inflammatory Lifestyle Transitioning is a Moving Target that becomes Increasingly More Behavior Restrictive with Age

The best preventative measure towards the mitigation of the longer-term risks of chronic end organ interstitial space inflammation is to process lifestyle retooling earlier in life *before* allowing malevolent and often addictive behaviors to become entrenched within everyday routines. The midlife implosion of chronic inflammatory rhythms and outcomes would suggest that a few decades of poor nutrition, undisciplined exercise routines and casual but self-inflicted addictions to tobacco, alcohol, drugs, sugars and salt will cause a mid-life explosion of potentially lethal end organ interstitial space disease consortiums[5,6,7,24,30]. This midlife combination of poor health habits and escorted disease consorts will unleash waves of dangerous outcomes that will be linked to clinical fatigue, chronic pain and increasing inability to being functionally dependable. As symptoms escalate and the daily calendar consumed with doctor appointments, tests, prescription drugs, and treatment interventions the freedom to live life becomes consumed within the constraints of the medical industrial complex.

When anti-inflammatory lifestyles can be incorporated within early life, midlife proinflammatory surprises can be confidently thwarted or delayed by years to decades. These changes will involve all activities of daily living from food choices and when to eat them, walking instead of driving, taking stairs instead of elevators, the rhythms of sleep and wakefulness, the management of a cranky boss and work-life balance. The implication is that anti-inflammatory decisions involving one sphere of life will tend to subliminally process similar choices across the behavioral scale that will produce a daily *anti-inflammatory rhythm*. The features of this rhythm would include a daily bedtime of 10 PM, 7-8 hours of continuous sleep, a daily AM exercise routine before eating two regular meals at 12 noon and 6 PM that are vegetable based and red meat and processed food restrictive, and the management of work and play routines that are complementary and reasonably counterbalanced to each other. If anti-inflammatory rhythm triggered, auto-perpetuated signaling and metabolic multi-end organ interstitial space chain reactions will occur that will enhance capillary cell dance step multipurpose fulfillment as they block chronic inflammatory rhythms that amalgam malignant end organ outcomes. This becomes key to midlife health as the capacity to perform anti-inflammatory end organ interstitial space surveillance diminishes due to a decreased capillary cell functional reserve that occurs from:

- a reduced infrastructure refurbishment as its nuclear chromatin is code silenced
- mitochondrial combustion cycles that increasingly favor energy over nitric oxide
- a progressively ROS code silenced nuclear chromatin

On the other hand, the continued processing of addictive behaviors has the opposite effect as they not only subliminally introduce other addictive behaviors, but make other lifestyle choices that are sloppy and maladaptive to anti-inflammatory rhythms. As maladaptive behaviors include alcohol, sugars, opioids, methamphetamines or tobacco, their subliminal processing will create poor judgement involving exercise, sleep hygiene, stress management or food choices. As stress, sleep deprivation and other social stressors increase, blood pressure, lipids, insulin resistance and BMI typically increase creating a wall of proinflammatory modifiers that will abort midlife viability. The midlife victim will be chronic inflammatory "boxed in" with an escalation of declining health and signs and symptoms that preclude premature death. When this occurs, premature and precipitous health declines are just the "tip of the iceberg" as triggered social and financial fall-out will likely include bankruptcy, divorce, homelessness, the added risk for criminal behaviors, and loss of friends and family.

Chapter Twenty

Epilogue: Avoiding a Midlife Chronic Inflammatory Signaling and Metabolic Crisis

What Makes Midlife Chronic Inflammatory Rhythms Dangerous

The enduring quality of midlife (ages 40-65) health becomes a bell weather for the prevention of most late life end organ diseases that are associated with escalating fatigue and pain. The persistence of beneficial midlife health habits will couple with systemic anti-inflammatory signaling and metabolic rhythms, that are paced by the capillary and downstream endothelial cell dance steps, will postpone or even prevent many types of intervening disease consorts for years to decades [5,6,7]. On the other hand, the escalation of midlife pain and fatigue becomes a clinical flashing red light reflection that signals a systemic chronic inflammatory resolve whose rhythms become the underbelly of anti-organ outcomes that are directly proportional to the increasing inability of all endothelium to perform their counterbalanced pivot and swing dance step rhythms.

The transitioning of multicentric end organ chronic interstitial space inflammation becomes a collision of pesky vascular inflammatory free radical impingements, increasing ineptitude of funneled inflammatory mediators to eliminate them, the inability of mesenchymal cells to convey an anti-inflammatory message to the capillary cell's basement membrane, the conversion of immune arsenal to proinflammatory rhtyhms, and the progressive degradation of the capillary and allied cell infrastructure that manifests from an ineffectual dance step rhythm and increasingly intentional anti-organ purposed execution. The recurring cycles of vascular inflammatory free radical interstitial space impingements, that are typically derived from addictive obsessions, will co link to make chronic inflammatory signaling and metabolic momentum even more likely.

There is plenty of room for public health forums regarding these largely preventative chronic inflammatory disease outcomes as early education in public school systems should help to supplant social pressures from peers or parents that would otherwise support the indiscriminate abuse of addictive substances. Public health initiatives should not stop in the school systems but should also be aggressively pursuing cleaner air and water and higher quality food with less sugar, animal fats and processing. Within urban communities there should be increased tree density, bike paths and walking trials and incentives for vehicles and home heating systems to emit zero carbon emission. Without a more aggressive posturing of public health, the microenvironment becomes increasingly vascular inflammatory free radical risk adverse with escalating chronic inflammatory interstitial space fall-out to follow.

Without intervening public health initiatives, midlife becomes a mine field for increasing chronic inflammatory risks. As proinflammatory signaling and metabolic pressure mount within end organ interstitial spaces and the capillary and downstream endothelial cell dance step rhythm deescalates, chronic fatigue and pain that often accompany high blood pressure, insulin resistance, dyslipidemia and incipient weight gain, will signal the posturing of anti-organ disease prerogatives. The escalation of pain and fatigue will contribute to increasing stress and sleep deprivation which incentivize subliminal posturing towards insulation that manifests as a "circling of the wagons effect" that will include increasing social isolation and other habitual "comfort measures" that actually make the chronic inflammatory multi end organ interstitial space processing worse as salty and highly processed snacking become habitual and sleepless nights preclude and less daytime energy to perform necessary tasks. It is in this escalation of midlife chronic inflammatory rhythms where a "piling on effect" emerges as it becomes tempting to abuse alcohol, smoke or inject stimulants, ask health care providers for opioid pain relief and buy highly processed "comfort food".

It becomes clear, that if left to subliminal urges that are under the influence of acquired addictions, the midlife response to increasing pain and fatigue is to pile on additional behaviors that will increase chronic inflammatory risks. The midlife mindset, that is already under considerable duress, will demand a "quick fix" from a health care provider to fix all the pain and fatigue from the chronic inflammatory assault but without necessarily adjusting any of the behavioral overtures that have led to these outcomes. The knee-jerk *quick fix* approach will often involve prescriptions to treat pain, fatigue, insomnia and anxiety, orthopedic referrals to intervene on pain from weight bearing joints and other workups to evaluate for cancer, autoimmune disease and heart disease. The quick fix never truly addresses chronic inflammatory root causes that have engineered the midlife pain and fatigue or that have instigated the maturation of anti-organ disease venues. The knee jerk midlife "adjustments" to pain and fatigue that allopathic medicine tends to support, can be considered as superficial interventions that provide temporary symptom relief but actually just kick the chronic inflammatory can down the road as modifying or preventing disease venues within interstitial spaces becomes an afterthought to alleviating pain and fatigue[4,5,6,7]. Unfortunately these midlife "coping" mechanics will often only lead to a harsher chronic inflammatory interstitial space mosaic of unpleasant anti-organ surprises.

A Valid Midlife Alternative towards Behavioral Choices: Becoming Anti-Inflammatory Mindful

The key to a midlife chronic inflammatory reversal it to become intentionally mindful about behaviors that condone anti-inflammatory interstitial space benefits while at the same time out maneuvering the previously adopted maladaptive addictive behaviors involving salt, sugars, processed gluten derivatives, alcohol, drugs and tobacco. This acquisition of anti-inflammatory *mindfulness* is not easy as it requires both motivation and intentionality to change proinflammatory behaviors that have become engrained and are intimately linked to both pleasure/reward and painful withdrawal symptoms. Crucial to this understanding is that anti-inflammatory mindfulness is a long-term process that could have short term setbacks as it is not easy breading away from the friendship of long-term addictions at a time when midlife circumstances may want them more than ever. Becoming acquainted with daily anti-inflammatory rhythms can be a useful starting point such as routinely getting to bed at 10 PM, arising at 6 AM, exercising in the morning before eating and having two routine vegetable-based meals a day at 12 noon and 6 PM. In this example, habits involving sleep and wakefulness as well as when and what to eat when firmly ritualized will help subliminally message other anti-inflammatory behaviors [5,6,7,8,9].

Being midlife mindful will intuitively require a sustained capacity to break addiction cycles, whose pleasure overtones and painful withdrawal features have become part of a powerful coping mechanic in the management of everyday stressors. The link between addictions, pleasure and stress management particularly if patterned over decades of abuse makes anti-inflammatory mindful behavioral transitioning cumbersome [5,6,7,8,9,10,11,21,24,30]. What becomes midlife clear is that the anti-inflammatory unwinding of longer term addictive behaviors that subliminally appear to be "self-protecting" in the coping of life's stressors may actually increase stress due to the coping void that is left unfulfilled and which is made worse by the unpleasant withdrawal symptoms of the addicting substance. Breaking the addictive chronic inflammatory hubris in midlife takes a special mindfulness that is often psychologically and physically increases short term pain while creating voids in the management of environmental stressors. On the plus side, addiction reversals will reduce vascular inflammatory free radical end organ interstitial space impingements that will enable the previously disabled capillary and downstream endothelial cell to reacquire some semblance of their dance step rhythm. This should facilitate restoration of interstitial space anti-inflammatory signaling and metabolic rhythms that will bode well for longer term interstitial space hygiene and subsequent disease prevention in late life[5,6,7]. With sufficient midlife anti-inflammatory mindfulness, the vascular endothelium generally and capillary cells specifically will be able to reprocess their dance steps to coincide with dispensing a magnified anti-inflammatory end organ interstitial space purpose. This midlife anti-inflammatory reinvigoration will postpone end organ disease outcomes in late life as chronic inflammatory interstitial space overtures become less dynamic from the lack of addiction related free radical support[4,5,6,7].

The *Underestimation* of Longstanding Proinflammatory Midlife Health Habits: The Bulls-Eye of Denial

When it comes to the auto perpetuation of midlife chronic inflammatory interstitial space signaling and metabolic rhythms, their virulence and purposed identity are f often underestimated as the behaviors precipitating their ascent are not considered to be serious to the processing of disease constellations. In some instances, there is so much denial that repetitive addictions could often be considered as beneficial as the pleasure-reward system of the addiction cycle blocks rational thinking to the risk to benefit equation[4,5,6,7]. When the substance abuse problem is confronted with the painful psychological and physical effects of withdrawal plus the void that is created in the management of life's stressors, substance abstinence is often rendered a moot point with the development of contrarian yet irrational points of view that enable further usage. The inability to be midlife decisive or to follow through with addiction abstinence becomes a virilizing chronic inflammatory modifier as a plethora of vascular inflammatory radical interstitial space impingements obtain free reign within end organ interstitial spaces to enable the processing of anti-organ prerogatives. When this occurs, the capillary and downstream endothelial cell dance steps cave to irrepressible chronic inflammatory signaling and metabolic pressures. When addiction denial becomes full blown, there is no rational argument that can be given to the abuser that will change the trajectory of the addiction as deteriorating health becomes inconsequential to the addict's prerogatives.

What makes addiction cycles so difficult to manage is how innocuous initial behaviors appear. Something as simple as smoking that first cigarette, sipping on that initial mixed drink or having a sticky bun becomes a signaling and metabolic memory of pleasure that will process a craving for more of the same. These addiction responses are also prone to comingling so that the nicotine, alcohol and sugar components become addiction additive and frequently interchangeable. When this occurs, free radical interstitial space displays are augmented, diversified and increasingly more anti-organ virile. As addictive proinflammatory habits co link they disrupt anti-inflammatory circadian rhythms that are processed through the capillary cell dance steps. The ascension of multicentric addiction recycling will process additional proinflammatory behaviors that on the surface appear to be addiction unrelated that include increases in sexually risky behaviors, disruption of the sleep wake cycle, increasing stress, depression, anxiety, binge eating, weight gain, insulin resistance and hypertension. The penchant for these proinflammatory behavioral add-ons will enable the piling on of additional addictive drugs to alleviate symptoms that include sleeping pills for insomnia, anxiolytics, stimulants for energy and opioids for pain[5,7].

The combination of the proinflammatory momentum derived from the accumulation of a multicentric addiction numerator will process rhythms that in midlife sharply diminish the capacity to be anti-inflammatory willful as their anti-organ functional outcomes that accompany additional substance craving become much easier to let enable than to resist. In this manner, cancers, infections, thrombotic events, scarring and autoimmune predispositions become multi end organ expected.

Is there any Hope for Midlife Anti-Inflammatory End Organ Rhythm Maintenance?

Auto perpetuated anti-inflammatory lifestyle choices and their beneficial multi end organ outcomes in mid and late life become increasingly more difficult to maintain due to an increasing proclivity for proinflammatory disruption and a less than optimal capacity of the capillary and downstream endothelial cell to anti-inflammatory dance step perform. The ladder occurs as increased nuclear chromatin cross linkage and subsequent code silencing prevents the cell from obtaining a full refurbishment capacity that would enable optimal anti-inflammatory multipurpose fulfillment even when the dance step rhythm is sufficiently two step counterbalanced[5,6,7]. In this manner, the capillary cell dance step rhythm can be functionally two step optimal and signal/metabolic counterbalanced yet its operational capacity will be limited as infrastructure refurbishment becomes handicapped form less than optimal protein replacements. This will make the collective dance step pace, stem, ricochet and backwash anti-inflammatory responsive but less purpose comprehensive. The reduced dance step derived anti-inflammatory processing will increase the potential for chronic inflammatory interstitial space inroads even when anti-inflammatory lifestyle choices are optimized. While pristine midlife anti-inflammatory lifestyles do marginalize chronic inflammatory outcomes, they will not permanently postpone them.

When properly lifestyle facilitated and capillary endothelial cell dance step executed, anti-inflammatory multipurposed processing of effective fulfillment will occur that will disease prevent and pain/fatigue abort for much longer periods in late life that would be expected or that would otherwise occur given the alternative. The implies that the back-and forth capillary endothelial cell dance step rhythm even if functionally less comprehensive, will maintain a functional impetus to where it can keep chronic inflammatory interstitial space rhythms at bay for much longer than expected periods even when anti-organ disease consorts have become coparticipants within the interstitial space milieu. If the capillary cell dance step rhythm can maintain its anti-inflammatory multipurpose and signaling control of the interstitial space, it should have enough functional reserve to mitigate anti-organ disease progression.

The Maintenance of the Capillary-Endothelial Cell Anti-Inflammatory Dance Step Rhythm will Serve as a Chronic inflammatory Risk Modifying Mid and Late Life Buffer

The longer-term maintenance of upstream capillary and downstream endothelial cell dance step rhythms from lifestyle, medicinal, herbal and supplement nurturing, will outcome an enduring systemic anti-inflammatory resilience that reduces end organ disease outcomes while limiting pain and fatigue. When strategically incorporated into daily routines the anti-inflammatory interstitial space chain reactions they support become a powerful midlife buffer that increases resistance to late life anti-organ surprises. The inclusion of all endothelium within this midlife anti-inflammatory resolve becomes a powerful holistic bridge that both prevents and resists disease progression [5,6,7]. When endothelium are universally exercising an integrative dance step fulfillment, they will accentuate a rhythmic pace, stem, ricochet and backwash that pulses a precise anti-inflammatory and interlocked compilation of chain reactions that transcellular rejuvenate, immune enhance and disease suppress as their rhythms process an endearing end organ functional resolve. In this manner a trans endothelial cell *functional holism* can be defined as the sum total of pulsed dance step anti-inflammatory chain reactions that collectively multitask anti-inflammatory fulfillment throughout the arterial tree.

This level of endothelial cell functional integration requires a pulsed signaling and metabolic hierarchy that is paced from the ultra-equipped outer membrane complex of upstream capillary cells. Unlike other endothelium downstream, the capillary cell's functionally sophisticated continuous outer membrane, luminal glycocalyx and anatomically variable abluminal basement membrane enable the processing of a complex and integrative sequencing of signaled and metabolic rhythms that outcome a multifaced anti-inflammatory performance. Of the three membranes, the most sophisticated and purpose integrative is the continuous outer membrane. It is here that infrastructure proteins process the activation of luminal exposed adhesion receptors, pores, and transport vesicles that are functionally attached by selectin receptors to the highly reactive gap junction orifice and channel. The capillary cell's continuous outer membrane becomes the processing membrane of functional interstitial space outcomes as it pulses a purpose precise *anti-inflammatory immune funneling composition* into the interstitial space whereby various forms of inflammatory breach are circadian removed. This interstitial space fulfillment will set up "cytokine inhibitory" chain reactions within the interstitial space that are hosted by mesenchymal cells that integrate the message with outcomes from interstitial space lymphocytes, monocytes, macrophages and platelets. The interstitial space "all clear" signal will feedback loop to the capillary cell's basement membrane to signal a reversal of outer membrane complex permeability to sharply limit further immune funneling and begin the processing of the next capillary cell's pivot and swing dance step. The functional outcome of the next dance step produces an entirely different yet complementary anti-inflammatory purpose fulfillment within the context of the two-step rhythm as the generated backwash through the capillary cell and into the systemic circulation will process a systemic anti-inflammatory immune enhancement while communicating the switch in dance step purpose to downstream endothelium. In this manner the recurring two step dance rhythm will pace a *pulsed, counterbalanced, quality assured* and *integrative* execution of multipurpose while making sure the end organ cell's functional resolve is included within the dance step hierarchy.

Within this interstitial space context, the ramifications of pan-endothelial cell functional holism can be construed as being *doubled edged* meaning that facilitated chain reactions to and from the interstitial space and through the capillary cell could momentum either a pro or anti-inflammatory interstitial space outcome depending on what entity (capillary cell or anti-organ) controls the interstitial space signaling hierarchy. This means that interstitial space rhythms can be as destructive as they are beneficial to the end organ cell depending on what entity is controlling them.

The Anti-inflammatory Power of Endothelial Cell "Holism"

The concept of *holistic health* should become synonymous with the anti-inflammatory confirmation of the capillary cell's two step dance rhythm and how it's multipurpose is conveyed and processed through its downstream endothelial cell brethren. The power of these two step dance rhythms is determined by the functional integrity of their outcomes with the downstream endothelial cell network. Capillary cell dance step rhythm operability is determined by how effective it can timely process the removal of vascular inflammatory free radical interstitial space impingements. When this occurs within a recurring, integrative and circadian two step dance rhythm, the outcome will confer a powerful anti-inflammatory immune holism that will foster both remission and prevention of end organ interstitial space disease outcomes. In this context, executed dance step expression becomes an anti-inflammatory code for optimizing end organ cell functional resolve and disease resistance.

In midlife executed anti-inflammatory dance step multipurpose becomes innately compromised as aggregate ROS cross linkages increasingly code silence nuclear chromatin to where the capillary cell's outer membrane complex does not refurbish completely as it progressively loses its functional lattice. The processing of ongoing proinflammatory interstitial space and backwashed rhythms will impose progressive losses to dance step anti-inflammatory functional integrity over time as chronic inflammatory rhythms consolidate interstitial space purpose and signal pirate immune content from the systemic circulation towards its disease consorts within the interstitial space[7]. The decay of the endothelial/capillary cell dance step rhythm becomes an undeniable stimulus to a chronic inflammatory interstitial space precipice of purpose consolidation and the transitioning towards nurtured disease consorts.

To counter this midlife chronic inflammatory interstitial space assault anti-inflammatory lifestyle intentionality must take root. Interventions must be deployed before end organ interstitial spaces become irreversible signaling and metabolic black holes to rampant disease consorts. Even with aggressive "anti-inflammatory" midlife interventions their capacity to reverse previously entrenched chronic inflammatory interstitial space rhythms may not be possible. This will likely mean that some manner of a chronic inflammatory precipice may remain dormant within the interstitial ready to escalate if anti-inflammatory resolve diminishes. This implies that anti-inflammatory lifestyle remediation must be steadfast, comprehensive and even more stringent with the aging process. Doing so will produce anti-inflammatory dividends that will involve a constituency of multiple end organs in preventing the escalation of interstitial space disease consorts.

The anti-inflammatory momentum of multi end organ interstitial space disease prevention becomes contingent upon how much *cognancy* the capillary cell dance steps have within their nuclear chromatin to continue processing a comprehensive infrastructure rejuvenation that will enable signaling and metabolic control over embedded chronic inflammatory attempts to usurp their counterbalanced rhythms and multipurposed fulfillment. In this scenario, cancers, infections, emboli and thrombosis, end organ ischemia, scarring and autoimmune phenomena may attempt to find interstitial space signaling loopholes but will be beaten back by the power of the dance step anti-inflammatory immune funneling and their precision purposed execution. This becomes particularly relevant in midlife as seeded disease venues attempt to find interstitial space traction.

Anti-Inflammatory Mindfulness as an Intentional Chronic Inflammatory Midlife Modifier

Midlife lifestyle, medicinal and supplement interventions become part of a willful "anti-inflammatory" consciousness that becomes multi end organ interstitial space pervasive as vascular inflammatory free radical impingements are eliminated and dance step rhythm and multipurposed execution remains robust. When this does not occur, due to ongoing proinflammatory lifestyle crescendos, medicinal, supplement non-compliance or both, end organ interstitial spaces become vulnerable in a midlife chronic inflammatory enhancement and proliferation of disease consorts. It turns out, that due to increasing midlife capillary cell dance step irregularities, anti-inflammatory lifestyle, medicinal and supplement support are required to overcome lack of dance step outcome comprehensiveness as increasing chronic inflammatory interstitial space intrusion pester and fester. It is this understanding about the pervasiveness of chronic inflammatory interstitial space rhythms that requires the postured but diminished anti-inflammatory presence to be increasingly mindful of their purposed executions. A pervasive anti-inflammatory interstitial space mindfulness implies that in midlife these rhythms need back up help to continue their sustainability that would include a more "routinized" daily lifestyle rhythm (involving vegetarian based diet, AM exercise on an empty stomach, 12 noon and 6 PM eating and a 10 PM to 6 AM sleep cycle). This anti-inflammatory lifestyle rhythm is further supported by appropriate medicinal, vitamins and herbs that will further augment the anti-inflammatory interstitial space capacity to immune respond.

The enablement of mid and late life anti-organ end organ interstitial space prodromes will coincide with:

- ❖ the increasing pervasiveness of vascular inflammatory free radical interstitial space impingements
- ❖ the increasingly less than adequate anti-inflammatory immune responses against their penetrations
- ❖ the increased prevalence of anti-inflammatory immune funneling blunders that are predisposed to proinflammatory cause and effect conversion
- ❖ the emergence of an increasingly anti-inflammatory disengaged capillary and downstream endothelial cell
- ❖ the *consolidation* of chronic inflammatory interstitial space signaling and metabolic rhythms that will coincide with *siignal pirating* the capillary cell's outer membrane complex for their purpose execution
- ❖ the increased capacity for chronic inflammatory interstitial space *scaling of intent* to process anti-organ disease expressions[6,7].

In the midlife context, increasing anti-inflammatory lifestyle maneuvering becomes a critically important processor of interstitial space outcomes as its intentionality will overcompensate for an increasingly less than ideal capillary and downstream endothelial cell dance step rhythm[7]. The anti-inflammatory interstitial space signaling and metabolic consortium that is generated from these "external contingents" will help process additional anti-inflammatory momentum to overcome capillary cell dance step disengagement of the advancement of already present anti-organ disease consortiums. From this perspective, mid and late life anti-inflammatory lifestyle mindfulness becomes the 5th wheel towards the enhancement of function al outcomes from the capillary and downstream endothelial cell dance step rhythm.

Robert L Buckingham, MD, FACP

The Mid and Late life Repercussions from an Anti-Inflammatory Capillary Cell Dance Step Compensated Backwash

When the capillary cell's pivot and swing dance step rhythm is timely, precision executed and multipurpose comprehensive, its circadian interstitial space ricochet and exocytic backwash in the systemic circulation become bullish anti-inflammatory signaling and metabolic rhythms that further augment multipurpose fulfillment. When complemented by lifestyle, medicinal and supplement mid and late life intentionality, the anti-inflammatory immune enhancements can mimic those seen that are decades younger in suppressing interstitial space exposures to anti-organ outcomes[6,7]. In mid and late life the compensated and lifestyle fortified anti-inflammatory dance step *backwash* becomes an important systemic anti-inflammatory enhancer as it simultaneously induces a chronic inflammatory *immune deterrence.* The compensated anti-inflammatory interstitial space ricochet and exocytic systemic backwash will immune enhance to further make the capillary cell's dance step rhythm multipurpose fulfilled even when the capillary-endothelial cell's infrastructure is less capable of optimally processing the mechanics of dance step execution.

This type of mid and late life lifestyle anti-inflammatory overcompensation can make all the difference to interstitial space outcomes when a diminished capillary cell dance step functional reserve becomes incapable of suppressing chronic inflammatory rhythms. In this dance step context, its dance step backwash must couple with medicinal and supplement integration to process a systemic anti-inflammatory immune enhancement that keeps a reduced dance step immune funneling rhythm purpose precise (Figures 10 and 20, appendix). This anti-inflammatory compensated dance step backwash can be critical in mid and late life as incipient capillary cell outer membrane complex pseudocapillarization will not by itself provide for a sufficient immune funneling rhythm to process the timely elimination of a diversified portfolio of inflammatory breach.

The capillary cell's compensated dance step backwash becomes anti-inflammatory immune complementary as pulsed waves of cytokines couple with medicinal and supplement support to become enhanced blood plasma anti-inflammatory *influencers* towards the execution of interstitial space outcomes[7]. This occurs in earnest when the backwashed circulating and medicinal supported aggregates process a molecular tweaking of the outer membranes of immune cell and protein derivatives to anti-inflammatory enhance their funneled interstitial space purpose. When aggregate trans endothelial cell backwashes couple these immune enhancing effects, future interstitial space anti-inflammatory resolve is enhanced. Their continued dance step derived backwash will scale a full cadre of persistent systemic immune enhancements that maintain a robust capillary cell two step multipurposed outcome as the interstitial space sanitation is optimized for a longer-term end organ cell functional endearment. The mid and late life lifestyle compensated capillary endothelial cell dance step derived ricochet and backwash becomes additive towards the disinclination for cells and their interstitial spaces to stop processing aging dynamics (Figures 10 and 20, appendix).

Mid and Late Life Allopathic Disease Treatments: *Often "Too Little and Too Late" to Stop Capillary and Endothelial Cell Dance Step Functional Hemorrhaging*

Over the past many centuries, medical practitioners have collected a myriad of information about signs, symptoms, environmental vectors, diagnostic interventions and increasingly complex treatment protocols, which on first blush, appear clinically disconnected. While the effort to so deserves merit, the disease treatment outcomes have been at best look warm effective as they either result in too many side effects, the secondary processing of other diseases or more serious longer term unexpected harms. In these scenarios, infections may end organ interstitial space recur or breed other types of infections, cancers may go into remission only to recur months to years later or the treatments themselves may encourage other types of cancers to unfold. Treatment interventions for abnormal clotting, autoimmune compromise or inordinate end organ scarring events can be successful only to enable the propagation of other disease consorts within a chronic inflammatory congested interstitial space. What treatment paradigms have failed to realize is that root cause matters and that unless the integrity of the capillary cell's dance step rhythm is included in the disease treatment calculus, the interstitial space expression of disease consorts will continue unabated. This treatment gist requires that the dysfunction of the capillary cell and its downstream endothelial cell brethren be addressed in order to gather a sufficient treatment threshold in the mastering of underlying chronic inflammatory interstitial space signaling and metabolic rhythms.

The implication to current disease treatment is that protocols that directly assault the disease but don't collaborate to undermine underlying chronic inflammatory signaling rhythms will eventually fail. It becomes obvious, that these underlying rhythms will increase the likelihood of disease treatment resistance and will likely foster the development of other concurrent disease consorts. The archaic process of *waiting* to treat a fully matured interstitial space disease, that has garnered a significant amount of signaling and metabolic mastery over the involved end organ interstitial space, must be revamped.

In order to incentivize a genuine anti-organ interstitial space remission, not only must the disease venue be directly attacked with the force of an authentic immune brigade but other functional dynamics of the chronic inflammatory interstitial space lattice must also be addressed. Vascular inflammatory free radical interstitial space impingements must be intentionally removed so that the capillary-endothelial cell's dance step rhythm stands a chance to be operationally revived. The potability of free radical declines must include a full-frontal assault on elevated blood pressures, insulin resistance, dyslipidemias, and intransigent addictions from smoking tobacco, the imbibing of alcohol, or the use of other addictive substances that reliably supply free radical into the interstitial space to blunt the anti-inflammatory effectiveness of the trans endothelial dance step rhythm. When chronic inflammatory fundamentals are uniformly addressed, not only are newly acquired disease consorts end organ interstitial space suppressed, but disease treatment of an existing disease venues is enhanced[6,7].

The implication from this discussion is that prevailing chronic inflammatory interstitial space signaling and metabolic rhythms have biased treatment failures if only directed at the disease entity. This loss of capillary cell dance step driven anti-inflammatory interstitial space resolve makes a direct attack on a disease entity such as a cancer or infection less effective as immune funneling into the interstitial space through a dysfunctional capillary endothelial cell will signal conform to chronic inflammatory outcomes rather than to their resistance and removal. Without effectively disrupting the signaling and metabolic rhythms of chronic inflammatory interstitial space infrastructure disease treatment will have varying levels of success[7].

In summary the full range of anti-organ chronic inflammatory interstitial space prerogatives will include the utilization of vascular inflammatory free radicals as processing fuel, an increasingly disabled capillary cell outer membrane complex as an incoming immune conduit towards its functional intent, and an increasing interstitial space signaling and metabolic collective that will facilitate the engineering of the anti-organ infrastructure that enables the growth and development of disease consorts. It is within this chronic inflammatory interstitial space infrastructure buildout that treatment protocols fail to address or at the very least are not directly connected to successful outcomes.

In more desperate disease treatment situations, treatment protocols can get very aggressive based on the clinical gravity of the situation. In these treatment settings, aggressive interventions that "nuke" the disease entity but by doing so it creates a large interstitial space signaling and metabolic void that will come under risk for the propagation of chronic inflammatory rhythms from other establishing disease consorts. The treatment hope is that end organ interstitial space disease debulking will provide a sufficient shock to the signaling and metabolic interstitial space infrastructure to where it will once again become harnessed to anti-inflammatory directives. Without addressing the underbelly of chronic inflammatory interstitial space signaling and metabolic rhythms, disease debulking will not be long term successful as it will either recur or other disease venues will take its place[7].

In these chronic inflammatory interstitial space settings, the anti-organ has a leg up on its nascent cell end organ competitors. Regardless of which disease entity is expressing intent, it will utilize signaling and metabolic rhythms that are available within the interstitial space that the true end organ cell can't or won't. It is within this metabolic interstitial space context of deteriorating oxygen tensions or increased insulin resistance whereby cancers, infections, scar tissue, and hypercoagulable states find mid and late life impetus making them harder to treat and less likely to recoil from anti-inflammatory resistance[6,7]. In this manner the signaling and metabolic constitution of the interstitial space frames the success of the disease consort as it makes the end organ cell increasingly less functional. This should behoove treatment protocols against escalating disease consorts to pay much closer attention to these predisposing chronic inflammatory rhythms within interstitial spaces when planning a comprehensive treatment strategy.

As Resistance to Treatment of End Organ Interstitial Space Disease Consorts Increase, Secondary Disease Expressions will Escalate

Current disease treatment protocols may not only confer a less than optimal conclusion to a disease expression, but by their nature of causing a loss of counterbalanced anti-inflammatory functional rhythms (for example, increasing the effect of killer lymphocyte T cells may lessen the functional impact of unbalanced lymphocyte T helper cells), they will enable an inherent risk for the expression of other disease venues within the end organ's interstitial space[6,7]. Within the context of treatment protocols, the emphasis is always on a direct confrontation of the disease consort without understanding the cascades of unbalanced chain reactions that it may outcome that subsequently increase stress to other anti-inflammatory interstitial space functional rhythms. Within this potentially harrowing situation, the end organ's interstitial space may get an edge on one disease entity (for example cancer treatment) only to then become vulnerable to the emergence of another (another type of cancer, infections or scar tissue development). Within the disease treatment format, pushing immune funneling and purposed fulfillment excesses in one direction will likely contribute to functional anti-inflammatory deficiencies from its unbalanced counterpart. Thus, effective treatment of a cancer or infection may induce anti-inflammatory immune vulnerability within the interstitial space that will enable a different type of infection or cancer to occur or even the development of an entirely different disease entity such as a thrombosis or scar tissue. When this happens, disease treatment(s) outcomes will make them complicit towards a variety of secondary interstitial space disease consorts that are both caused or effected from anti-inflammatory immune imbalances that are residuals from the scale and directives of initial disease treatment.

As disease venues partner with the preexisting chronic inflammatory interstitial space signaling and metabolic hierarchy, not only does this create disease treatment resistance, but it simultaneously lessens the impact of anti-inflammatory rhythms generated from funneled immune elements and the external support they subsequently derive from disease treatment protocols. This makes interstitial space anti-inflammatory mechanics less effective in neutralizing disease expression while also trivializing what might be left of the capillary cell's dance step rhythm. This loss of anti-inflammatory capacity to resist a disease venue coupled with the increasing virulence of the disease consort to express its own willfulness, makes treatment protocols less effective and prone to increasing treatment resistance. These anti-organ interstitial space renderings increase the stakes of treatment protocols as they become increasingly more invasive, expensive, side effect prone yet less likely to cause a disease remission[5,6,7]. Until disease treatment includes a plan to mitigate preexisting chronic inflammatory interstitial space signaling and metabolic rhythms and predict the anti-inflammatory chain reactions and unbalanced fall-out these intervention will subsequently cause, disease treatment renderings will continue to be less than ideal[7].

One critical feature to all disease treatment should be the facilitation of a revitalized capillary and downstream endothelial cell dance step rhythm. Not only will this help facilitate a more effective anti-inflammatory immune response to the offending disease venue, but when harnessed to an externally derived direct attack on the disease consort, it should become more capable of lessening the impact of subsequent loss of anti-inflammatory functional counterbalance that the external treatment may likely induce. cause. Keeping the capillary cell's dance step rhythm functionally facile may allow the dance steps to compensate for extreme shifts in immune purpose that will occur when treatment protocols are aggressively pursued. For example, when treatment initiatives enable a killer T lymphocyte cell push into the interstitial space to process a direct attack on a disease consort, a healthy capillary cell dance step rhythm should be able to compensate for this T cell push by extending signals to luminal outer membrane complex for the interstitial space funneling of additional *helper T cells* to affect a functional counterbalance. This capillary cell response will make longer term viability of the anti-inflammatory response more intentional and purpose fulfilled. In treatment vernacular, this would counter the possible deterioration of anti-inflammatory vulnerable interstitial space rhythms that would otherwise preclude towards the expression of other disease entities. When disease treatment *includes* the invigoration of the capillary and downstream endothelial cell dance step rhythm, the involved interstitial space stands a better chance of making the necessary anti-inflammatory signaling and metabolic adjustments that are required due to the aggressive posturing of externally derived disease treatment protocols.

As the interstitial space is anti-inflammatory remastered from the combination of a purpose precise treatment protocol and an invigorated capillary and downstream endothelial cell dance step rhythm, the anti-organ's interstitial space signaling and metabolic lattice becomes disrupted making additional disease seeding and propagation unlikely. Disruption of the underlying anti-organ interstitial space signaling and metabolic cues and functional interface, while simultaneously being able to kindle anti-inflammatory functional counterbalance through the reenergized capillary cell dance step rhythms, becomes a powerful anti-organ antidote as anti-inflammatory interstitial space expressions find a leg up to chronic inflammatory prerogatives.

Incorporating an invigorated capillary cell dance step rhythm into external disease treatment protocols must have an "all-hands on deck" approach that should include anti-inflammatory medicinals, supplements for vitamin and mineral deficiency states, and a comprehensive lifestyle anti-inflammatory rhythm reset. The ladder must intentionally incorporate ideal sleep rhythms, stress mitigation, appropriately timed eating intervals of a plant-based diet and a consistent daily AM exercise routine. Bringing a comprehensive anti-inflammatory lifestyle reset into disease treatment paradigms will enhance outcomes through the inherent improvement of the capillary and downstream endothelial cell dance step rhythm, as the aggregate interstitial space signaling and metabolic profiles they enlist, removes the chronic inflammatory free radical lattice while simultaneously disrupting the execution of proinflammatory purpose fulfillment[7].

Robert L Buckingham, MD, FACP

The Mechanics of Mid and Late Life Anti-Inflammatory Interstitial Space Retooling

With aging, skeletal muscle mass, which includes sarcomere thickness and mitochondrial volumes and size shrink as abdominal adipose, clinical fatigue and muscle-joint achiness increase. This typically translates into a reduced capacity to move or perform physical tasks as becoming chair or bed bound becomes increasing self-fulfilling and even walking a few feet becomes at risk for falling. This transition is often accompanied by a "multi end organ slide" that includes varying levels of dementia, sleep disturbances, loss of reflexes, vision and hearing, and insidious increases in breathlessness with mobilization. As muscle mass shrinks, abdominal fat deposition increases and in aggregate are associated with increasing insulin resistance, hypertension and lipid disorders. All of these age-related "physical adjustments" a part of the multi end organ interstitial space chronic inflammatory makeover that processes disease consorts as they destroy the multipurposed functional continuity of endothelial cell anti-inflammatory dance step "circadian rhythms".

One of the most important disrupters of the capillary and downstream endothelial cell dance step rhythm, is the signaling momentum generated from the fusing of chronic inflammatory interstitial space signaling and metabolic rhythms. When this occurs in mid and late life it does not bode well for the involved end organ's long erm viability. As compilations of cognitive decline, reduced physical endurance, and generalized pain, fatigue and weakness escalate, they are typically accompanied with the multi end organ interstitial space processing of disease venues. These outcomes are commonly connected to reduced upstream end organ oxygen delivery but could be tethered to other equally disruptive chronic inflammatory anti-organ processes involving oncogenesis, infections, scarring or displaced immunoglobulin attachments. When one or more of these build out a chronic inflammatory interstitial space lattice, they will cause and effect incipient clinical pain and fatigue. If their evolving lattice is left unchecked or unmitigated, a progressive multi-end organ chronic inflammatory interstitial space assault will stake claim to the available signaling and metabolic resources at the expense of end organ cell function. When this occurs, the capillary and downstream endothelial cell become "functional pawns" towards the servicing of chronic inflammatory anti-organ intent,[5,6,7,8,9,10,11].

The midlife mitigation of these overt chronic inflammatory interstitial space rhythms cannot occur soon enough as specific assaults require an increasing awareness of adjusted lifestyle consciousness that will preclude their progression. Central to this theme is the reinvigoration of anti-inflammatory interstitial space circadian rhythms that are pulsed from the capillary cell's two step dance rhythm and coordinated with their downstream endothelial cell brethren. When this occurs in earnest, midlife interstitial space signaling and metabolic rhythms may actually reverse purpose to become once again anti-inflammatory driven.

One important midlife implication to the resuscitation of anti-inflammatory circadian rhythms is how imbedded proinflammatory rhythms have already become within the end organ interstitial space signaling and metabolic apparatus. The extent to which this has occurred will largely determine if and how much capillary cell dance step resuscitation will occur regardless of how much external "treatment help" is supplied. With a permanent chronic inflammatory interstitial space compromise, anti-inflammatory resuscitation can cordon off chunks of interstitial space functional resolve but may not be able to achieve a complete infrastructure remission making the interstitial space vulnerable to anti-organ relapses given the right signaling or metabolic prodromes. This will always make mid and late life end organ interstitial spaces at risk to anti-organ relapses given the reintroduction of proinflammatory interstitial space signaling or metabolic rhythms. This often becomes "self-fulfilling" as capillary cell dance step counterbalance becomes misappropriated from a declining capacity of the outer membrane complex to distribute into the interstitial space a purpose precise immune contingency that will completely remove a prevailing inflammatory breach. As the capillary cell becomes functionally biased to lose its dance step counterbalance its increasing senescence becomes self-fulfilling towards chronic inflammatory interstitial space outcomes.

To prevent this mid and late life anti-organ debacle, the anti-inflammatory processing of lifestyle decisions becomes narrower as there is less margin for making behavioral mistakes. Securing an end organ interstitial space microenvironment that will be supportive to a a less than optimal capillary cell dance step rhythm becomes the counterbalancing recipe that is required to keep the dance steps form spiraling out of rhythm. This lifestyle approach in effect secures an intentional anti-inflammatory *consciousness* within end organ interstitial spaces that lengthens the viability of the anti-inflammatory interstitial space signaling and metabolic window that will foreshadow outcomes that disease prevent for much longer periods of time even when the capillary cell cannot operate at full dance step capacity.

Central to this increased mid and late life anti-inflammatory preemptive consciousness are behaviors that sharply reduce vascular inflammatory free radical interstitial space impingements. In this manner, even with a functionally disabled capillary cell dance step rhythm, it will be compensated for by a more pristine interstitial space microenvironment. The chain-reacting interstitial space processes that result from a mid and late life behavioral anti-inflammatory consciousness include:

- the resuscitation of specific immune funneling rotations through the capillary cell's outer membrane complex for the removal of specific types of interstitial space inflammatory breach which becomes compensatory to a previously compromised capillary cell pivot and swing dance step rhythm.
- the interstitial space signaling and metabolic blueprint transitions to become anti-inflammatory marketable and chronic inflammatory subversive.
- the restoration of the circadian capillary cell dance step process will in turn have functional implications to its downstream endothelial cell brethren, as well as to the anti-inflammatory purposed rehabilitation of its allied interstitial space cellular partners such as the mesenchymal, connective tissue and end organ cells.
- the capillary cell dance step rhythm anti-inflammatory realignment will chain react a pulsed metabolic amplitude which will facilitate a continuum of counterbalanced intracellular processes involving fermentation (glycolysis/gluconeogenesis), liposomal lipolysis/lipogenesis and the mitochondrial counterbalanced combustion precursor pyruvate and fatty acids in the production of combustion hub molecule-acetyl co A.
- The extension of mitochondrial combustion counterbalance will include dance step derived energy and nitric oxide production, the subsequent membrane purposed attachment and redox of combustion exhaust (ROS/RNS) products, and where newly minted hub molecule acetyl co A is shuttled (Krebs cycle or ribosomes)
- Pulsed interstitial space anti-inflammatory dance step derived metabolic alignments will include timely and purpose precise fluctuations in pH, the hybridization of concentration appropriate glucose/pyruvate and fatty acid levels, the optimal diffusion of oxygen/carbon dioxide tensions, and the precise pulsing of dance step derived osmolality and hydrostatic pressure gradients
- with sufficient return of dance step anti-inflammatory signaling and metabolic operatives, favorable interstitial space outcomes are restored which incentivizes further anti-inflammatory dance step success as a rhythmic multipurposed fulfillment is achieved. This in turn will process the dance two step-*pace, stem, ricochet* and backwash effects.

- the increasing resurgence of anti-inflammatory dance step resolve will assist in clarifying the functional intent of nearby mesenchymal cells as they receive immune funneling input form the capillary cell that is purpose dynamic. This in turn will elicit and clarifying mesenchymal cell "all clear" or "all hands-on deck" signal that will either inhibit or expand immune funneling into the interstitial space *(Figures 10 and 20, appendix)* [6,7].

Even with less functional reserve from the irreversible loss of infrastructure, the mid and late life capillary and downstream endothelial cell can still induce a functionally counterbalanced dance step rhythm provided that innate interstitial space hygiene has been suitably compensated for. As the dance steps shift back and forth rhythms of outer membrane complex permeability gradients and mitochondrial combustion swings, it will escort resonating salvos of anti-inflammatory multipurpose that when fulfilled will chain react an interstitial space ricochet and exocytic cytokine backwash the qualifies and quantifies the purpose to their dance step rhythms[6,7]. In this manner and even with some level of functional compromise, the capillary cell's dance step rhythm can still resonate an anti-inflammatory responsiveness that will pinnacle end organ cell functional resolve as anti-organ disease venues are aborted or sidelined (Figure 10, appendix).

How Endothelial Cell Dance Steps Remain Multipurpose Durable

Dance step rhythm durability requires that it's resonating rhythms and executed anti-inflammatory multipurpose remains accurately timed, signal and metabolically *counterbalanced and* functional*ly quality assured.* The implication is multifaceted but serves as a reminder that dance step outcomes are codependent on each other's successful purpose fulfillment7. This means that the dance step outcome itself has biased intracellular and interstitial space chain reactions that have processed the signaling and metabolic framework for the successful execution of the next dance step's anti-inflammatory outcome.

The dance step *metabolic processing* within the capillary cell is just as important as corresponding anti-inflammatory signaling salvos as the combination is required to harvest dance step anti-inflammatory multipurpose. As each dance step executes its purpose, the comprehensiveness of its *fulfillment* will in turn process signaling and metabolic rhythms that will equally incentivize a similar fulfillment capacity of the next dance step. The degree to which a dance step is purpose fulfilled will determine the degree to which the next step fulfills its purpose. stion.

When the capillary cell's each dance step is signal and metabolically counterbalanced and comprehensively purpose fulfilling, the anti-inflammatory rhythm and momentum it generates becomes dance step regenerative and rhythm outcome predictable. The process of reproducing dance step anti-inflammatory rhythms becomes automatic as the level of purpose fulfillment of each consecutive dance step fortifies a similar level of fulfillment to the next step [5,6,7]. All of this anti-inflammatory multipurpose recycling becomes vulnerable within the mid and late life context as chronic inflammatory interstitial space rhythms erode the integrity of consecutive dance step purpose fulfillment.

The Streaming Rhythms of Interstitial Space Contested Cytokines, Free Radicals, Enzymes and Electromagnetic Wavelets: Anti-Inflammatory Friend or Foe?

Within the context of mid or late life, the intent of interstitial space signaling and metabolic rhythms becomes inextricably linked to what underlying purpose is controlling their intent. In the case of a chronic inflammatory interstitial space lattice, the sway of such rhythms will favor the evolution of disease consorts and their favored interests[7]. This conversion of an end organ's interstitial space purpose from anti to proinflammatory can occur at any age based on prevailing health habits and underlying genetics but in mid and late life is biased to occur from increasing capillary cell senescence from nuclear chromatin code silencing. When this occurs, compensatory mechanics both within its infrastructure and outer membrane complex become insufficient to cope with even modest volumes of vascular inflammatory interstitial space free radical infringements. Thus, the interstitial space becomes chronic inflammatory rhythm biased even when vascular inflammatory free radicals have been considerably interstitial space restricted. The increasingly senescent capillary cell will inherently manifest delays in dance step rhythm execution with subsequent loss of functional counterbalance and executive quality assurance. The interstitial space will suffer with this decline as signaling and metabolic chain reactions will favor anti-organ prerogatives.

The signaling and metabolic reverberations become chronic inflammatory self-fulfilling as they consolidate and consume the purpose identity of vulnerable mesenchymal and funneled white blood cells, immunoglobulins, platelets and their released cytokine, enzyme, free radical and electromagnetic expressions. Without a consciously designed reversal of overcompensating anti-inflammatory functional design, the mid and late life end organ outcomes are met with often severe compromise and potentially fatal expressions.

Two Competing Clocks, Rhythms, and Organs (True or Anti) Battle for Control of One Interstitial Space: Aging Favors Anti-Organ Prerogatives

How Dancing Really Stops the Clock, is about how end organ interstitial space signal and metabolic rhythms transition over time to eventually favor disease entrapment unless there are intentional and aggressive anti-inflammatory compensatory mechanics in place to subvert their incipient intrusions. If anti-inflammatory circadian rhythms and lifestyle choices become instituted early on, they become end organ interstitial space beacons that keep the capillary and downstream endothelial cell dance step rhythm perfunctory as the systemic aging clock, that is a manifestation of this two-step rhythm, slows down precipitously. In this restrictive chronic inflammatory scenario, the cells that compose the end organ slow the aging clock as their functional aptitude and longevity become inextricably linked to the functional effectiveness of the capillary and downstream endothelial cell's dance step rhythm which connects interstitial space immune effectiveness to its anti-inflammatory circadian two-step pivot and swing clock. The relationship between the postponement of transcellular aging and interstitial space immune effectiveness to the pivot and swing capillary cell dance step rhythm crosses all cell lines and end organs regardless of functional purpose or relationship to the capillary cell's basement membrane. When the capillary and downstream endothelial cell lines are executing a counterbalanced two step dance rhythm to multipurpose fulfill, interstitial space anti-inflammatory immune expression in all end organs will manifest which in turn will optimize end organ cell functional reserve. The rhythms of each dance step will also support the functional outcomes of the next step thereby auto perpetuating the outcome integrity of sequential steps as long as they remain signal, metabolic and purpose counterbalanced. To the extent that this rhythm becomes dismantled is to the extent that chronic inflammatory interstitial space rhythms will find a signaling and metabolic resolve that will eventually portend adverse interstitial space outcomes.

Whereas anti-inflammatory interstitial space rhythms emanate from capillary cell dance steps, proinflammatory rhythms disburse and organize into rhythms from an interstitial space that has become chronically inflamed with persistent vascular inflammatory free radicals and complemented with increasing funneled arrays of purpose confused and signal vulnerable immune contingents. Collectively they form an interstitial space paradigm that incentivizes chronic inflammatory signal and metabolic organization to where disease consorts become expected outcomes. In contrast, anti-inflammatory rhythms will optimize interstitial space hygiene while nurturing the functional utility of the end organ cell as it facilitates dance step derived infrastructure rehab to the capillary cell and its allied interstitial space cellular partners. If the dance step rhythm remains purpose counterbalanced, its anti-inflammatory functional disbursements will stay operationally effective for extended periods before its nuclear chromatin becomes too far removed from its capacity to code for a comprehensive protein synthesis infrastructure refurbishment.

The capacity to inhibit the capillary and downstream endothelial cell's *"aging clock"* becomes a reflection of how these cells can keep their dance step multipurpose counterbalanced over time when compensatory mechanics are required within its rhythm in the management of excessive vascular inflammatory free radical interstitial space impingements, when precise immune funneling does not go as planned or when the end organ cell requires unusual oxygen support for uneven combustion requirements. Anti-inflammatory dance step rhythm persistence is codependent on many ancillary and ossifying rhythms that first and foremost in mid and late life rely on aligned lifestyle choices and the execution of daily anti-inflammatory rhythms. In this context it is not just about what you eat, drink, sleep, exercise and how stress is mediated that matters, but *when* these processes are instituted as part of a daily anti-inflammatory rhythm. This implies that lifestyle decisions are also part of a daily anti-inflammatory circadian process, that when "timed correctly", become anti-inflammatory additive to the execution of anti-inflammatory end organ interstitial space rhythms and the functional utility of the capillary and downstream endothelial cell dance steps. When sleep is initiated at 10PM and goes undeterred until 6 AM, the sleep cycle will process potent brain refurbishment as it enhances anti-inflammatory immune rhythms. The same holds true when exercise becomes a daily AM routine prior to eating breakfast as fatty acids are extracted from abdominal adipose and utilized for skeletal muscle energy thereby reducing insulin resistance. Eating two vegetarian based meals at 12 noon and 6 Pm while avoiding processed foods, sodas, red meat, most gluten and lactose, desserts and alcohol will process similar anti-inflammatory benefits from enhancing the functional utility of the intestinal microbiome and reducing leaky gut derivatives into the portal circulation thereby protecting the liver from becoming fatty.

The proclamation of these behaviors into daily rhythms becomes even more anti-inflammatory categorical in mid and late life as the capillary cell's nuclear chromatin loses capacity to code for maximum cellular restitution thereby limiting its functional resolve to transact anti-inflammatory interstitial space outcomes. This is turn reduces the margin for error that the capillary cell and its interstitial space domain procures in preventing chronic inflammatory anti-organ outcomes.

Would the Real "Master Facilitator" of Anti-Inflammatory Immune Identity Please Stand UP!

For anti-inflammatory functional resolve to remain end organ interstitial space robust, preventing the "aging" of capillary cell infrastructure should be enabled for as long as possible. By keeping the capillary and endothelial cell dance two-step rhythm counterbalanced, multipurpose execution remains tidy and efficient as its nuclear chromatin remains free of coding restraints caused by excessive ROS cross linkages. Keeping the dance step rhythm fully anti-inflammatory multipurpose resilient for as long as possible will incentivize pivot and swing purpose executed timeliness, signal, metabolic and functional counterbalance and quality assurance of purpose execution going dance step forward. The dance two-step counterbalanced reverberation becomes the basis for purpose precise immune choreography into the interstitial space which keys the timely processing of vascular inflammatory free radical degradation. The sanitized interstitial space enables the next dance step Ito process optimal oxygen delivery to an end organ cell ready to maximize its functional aptitude. The reverberating rhythm auto perpetuates anti-inflammatory resolve thereby making chronic inflammatory signaling overtures interstitial space irrelevant. When successful the mid and late life rewards become substantial as anti-inflammatory immunity remains robust thereby facilitating less aging, pain and fatigue as chronic disease signaling precedence hibernates[4,5,6,7].

Within any given end organ interstitial space there is the potential for two different clocks and rhythms with two potential end organ outcomes competing for signal and metabolic controlling interest. "To the victor lies the spoils". Within the context of mid and late life, or even earlier if vascular inflammatory free radical impingements have successfully overrun end organ interstitial spaces, the signal controlling bias will eventually favor anti-organ prerogatives. However, when a concerted midlife anti-inflammatory effort is mounted, vascular inflammatory free radical impingements will interstitial space decrease enabling the capillary and downstream endothelial cell to retool a counterbalanced two-step dance rhythm. When this occurs, the interstitial space and end organ cell become anti-inflammatory resuscitated thereby transacting a rekindled functional vigor that becomes self-sustaining within the cadence of the robust and counterbalanced capillary cell dance steps. This reverberating anti-inflammatory interstitial space hierarchy is in stark contrast to the darker signaling and metabolic rhythms of the mid and late life processing of anti-organ intent whereby escalating pain and fatigue become introductory markers of cancer, infections, autoimmune mishaps, thrombosis and end organ scarring. In the grand scheme of life and death and everything in between, choice matters with the margin for error narrowing with advancing age. Whereas, repetitively poor lifestyle choices accelerate the "aging clock" by degrading anti-inflammatory rhythms that would ordinarily be generated from the capillary cell's dance steps, decisions that cadence anti-inflammatory rhythms by limiting vascular inflammatory free radical interstitial space impingements, will position the capillary cell dance steps to process multipurposed outcomes that will either prevent, delay or even reverse the aging clock.

Appendix

Color and Abbreviation code (which are used in all of the corresponding twenty figures):

Brown-(OM)-End Organ Cell *Outer Membrane*, Yellow/Orange-(EOC)-*End Organ Cell*, Blue-(M)-*Mesenchymal Cell*, Black Line-(CC)(COM) and (M)(MOM)-Capillary Cell *Continuous Outer Membrane and Mesenchymal Cell Outer Membrane* respectively , Bright Yellow-(IS)-*Interstitial Space*, Powder Blue-*Mitochondria*, Red-(MIM)-*Mitochondria Inner Membrane*, Yellow-(CCC)-Capillary Cell *Cytoplasm* or (CC)-*Capillary-Endothelial Cell,* Purple-(BM)-Capillary Cell *Basement Membrane,* Light Green-(VIFRs)-*Vascular Inflammatory Free Radicals,* Orange-(G)-*Glycocalyx,* White Space between capillary cells and/or within its cytoplasm will correspond to the (GJC),(GJO), (TTC), (BV) or the *Gap Junction Channel, Gap Junction Orifice, Transcellular Transport Channel, Budded Vesicle* respectively, Spotted Orange with Irregular orange Lines-(L)-*Lumen,* Dark Green (CAMs)-(CC)(COM) or *continuous outer membrane adhesion receptors,* Olive Green-(IA)-*Immune Arsenal* will be either proinflammatory (cater to chronic inflammatory signaling rhythms) or anti-inflammatory/precision purposed-(CC) (COM) choreographed), → with arrow (*transcellular movement*) → with arrow (movement through the *gap junction, budded vesicle or transcellular transport channel*),--//→ demonstrates a blocked , blunted or aborted effect between different *membrane surfaces,* Brown-(DV)-*Anti-Organ "disease venue",* very dark forest green –(CC) (N) or Capillary Cell *Nucleus,* Pink within the Lumen (L) reflects a backwashed and *systemic immune suppression.* The (CC) (COM) refers to the capillary cell *continuous outer membrane* whereas the (CC)(OMC) refers to the *three capillary cell outer membranes, the abluminal basement membrane, continuous outer membrane and luminal glycocalyx.*

Figure One

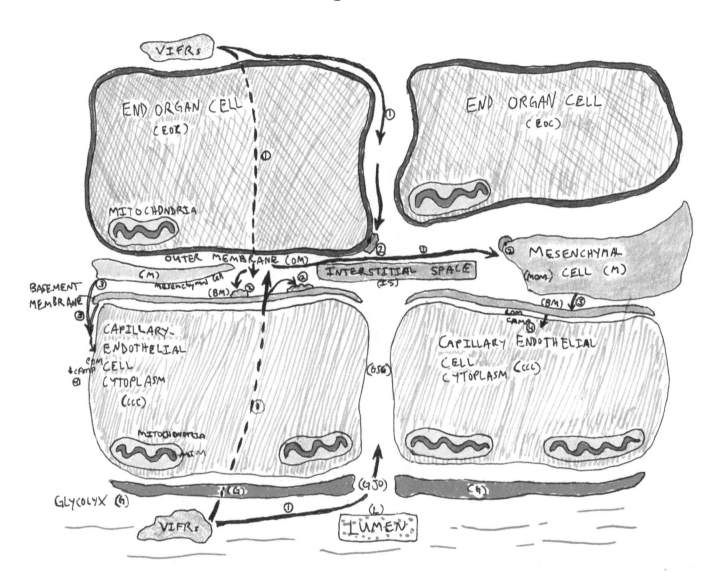

Interstitial Space (IS) Vascular Inflammatory Free Radicals (VIFRs) and the Capillary Cell's (CC) Continuous Outer Membrane (COM) Permeability Pivot

Descriptive:

(VIFRs) **are ubiquitous vascular inflammatory free radical proinflammatory expressions that can penetrate into an end organ cell's interstitial space** *(EOC) (IS).* **Depending on their size, solubility (fat or water soluble), physical properties (solid, liquid or gas) and molecular configurations, many will have an affinity to attach or disrupt membrane surfaces or integrate into its infrastructure to alter the membrane's function. Some of these membrane attachments will involve the capillary cell's basement membrane** *(CC) (BM).* **(VIFRs) can be more or less permeable to various membranes based on their physical characteristics.**

Once attached or membrane penetrated, they can disrupt the membrane function either directly or indirectly depending on how their attachment or penetration into the membrane skews its function.

Much will depend on how thoughtful and precise the immune arsenal *(IA)* response is towards the attachment. The failure of that response to timely eliminate the (VIFR) is what initiates signaling and metabolic processes within the (IS) changes that portend to chronic inflammatory reverberations and delays in the sequential (CC) pivot and swing dance step.

In the case of toxic gas *(IS)* intrusions such as carbon monoxide, its capacity to passively diffuse through membranes by following concentration gradients, gives them easy access to most transcellular infrastructure. In mitochondria, these gases may disrupt the cross connected and signal counterbalanced interplay of combustion gases such as oxygen, nitric oxide, and carbon dioxide. When this occurs, energy and nitric oxide combustion cycles could be further delayed or their output rendered less efficient.

(VIFRs) can enter end organ cell (EOC) interstitial spaces (IS) by two different pathways; either through the (EOC) (1) or capillary cell (CC) (1) outer membranes. In the case of (EOC) penetration (IS) incursions will stem from contact with the external environment such as from skin, mucous membranes, intestines or lung tissue. This will typically occur from being directly inhaled, ingested, injected, inserted, smoked or sublingually absorbed.

(VIFRs) will also enter the (IS) through the systemic circulation (1) whereby they can use their molecular and physical properties to penetrate through the downstream endothelial and capillary (CC) *(OMC)* (1). This penetration could be completely membrane passive (following concentration gradients from one side of the membrane to the other) or can be facilitated by utilizing several other transport endocytic instruments that include mobilization through the gap junction orifice *(GJO)* (1) and gap junction channel *(GLC)* (1) or being actively transported from vesicles or transcellular transport channels (not pictured) as the freeload into the (IS) with a transported albumen or other protein.

Once deposited in the (IS), (VIFRs) (2) may membrane attach and if not timely removed can fester a chronic inflammatory immune response towards their attachment (2). Their persistent membrane presence becomes akin to a antigen-antibody complex that has gone awry, as increasing numbers of immune aggregates fail to reduce the (VIFR) to its elemental charge neutral forms. As (VIFR) attachments fester they disrupt membrane function and become antagonists to the circadian (CC) dance step rhythm.

When (VIFRs) penetrate the (IS) and membrane attach (2), their presence becomes immediately identifiable from nearby mesenchymal cells *(M)*. M (3), in conjunction with adjoining and confirmatory signals from other (IS) (IA) or the (CC)*(BM)*, will send a surveillance message about the (VIFR) to the (CC) *(COM)* (3) in the form of an "all hands-in deck" signal that is commensurate with the extent of (VIFR) (IS) membrane involvement. The signal will help facilitate the (CC) outer membrane complex (OMC) to choreograph a funneled and specific purposed immune arsenal (IA) contingency from the central circulation *(L)* into the (IS) to timely eradicate/reduce the (VIFR).

The (VIFR) signal from the mesenchymal cell outer membrane *(MOM)* to the (CC) (OMC) will reflex a reduction in master switch (CC) (COM) *cAMP* (cyclic adenosine monophosphate) (4) which will cause (CC)(COM) chain reactions involving infrastructure switches, routers and gates that will adjust the CC (COM) permeability to become attractive towards specific (IS) (IA) funneling. This will involve the luminal exposures of (CC) (COM) *(CAMs)* that will facilitate specific (IA) attachments (not pictured in the figure).

Figure Two

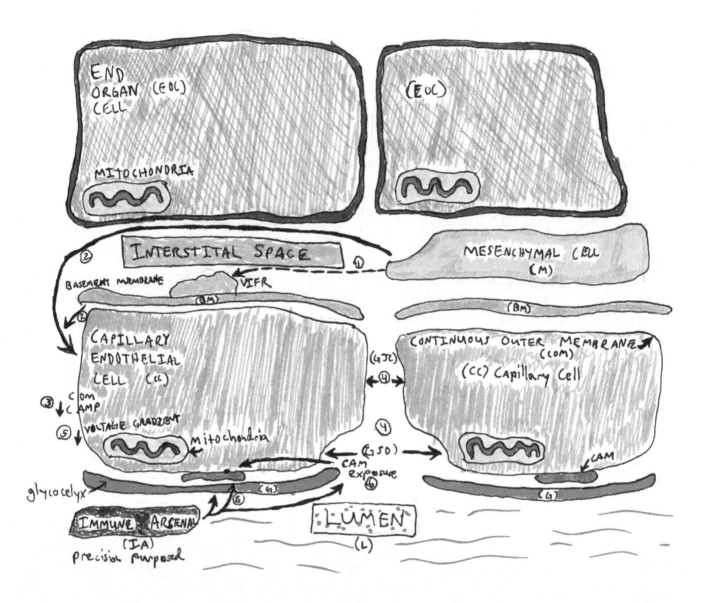

(IS) (VIFR) Induced (CC) (COM) Chain Reactions

Descriptive:

(M) and (CC) (BM) will partner to facilitate a proper identification and (IA) response to the (BM) attached (VIFR) (1). They do this through the exchange of specific salvos of signaling (and metabolic) streams that will get transmitted to the (CC) (COM) (2). These signaling streams will help formulate a specific expression of (IA) funneling into the (IS) that will identify and eliminate the (VIFR).

The (CC) (COM) will respond to the (M) (BM) membrane "all hands-on deck" signal by decreasing master switch cAMP (3). This will cause a flurry of (CC)(COM) switch chain reaction and other

infrastructure paraphernalia (unlocking of gates and routers that expose (L) (COM)(CAMS)) which increase permeability of funneled and precision purposed (IA) into the (IS) to target the (VIFR) removal.

The funneling of precision purposed (IA) into the (IS) could involve the entirety of the (CC) (OMC). Circulating (IA) consisting of neutrophil white blood cells or platelets could be initially affixed to the *(G)* weblike interface (6) and then processed for attachment to the (CC) (COM) (CAM)s (6). They can then be mobilized to the aperture widened *(GJO)* (4) and *(GJC)* (4). The (IA) (CC) (COM) permeability pivot is further accomplished by reducing the (CC)(COM) voltage gradient (5) from the interaction of calcium ions with the sodium/potassium "pump" thereby enabling a more liberal membrane penetration of circulating cytokines and other smaller molecules via facilitated diffusion (not pictured in the figure).

Figure Three

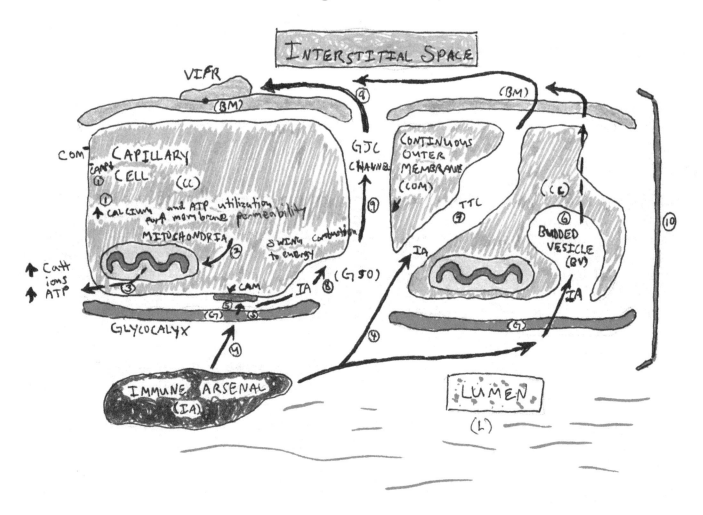

The (CC) (COM) Permeability Pivot Will Facilitate the Combustion Swing of (CC)-Mitochondria to Produce Either Nitric Oxide (NO) or Energy (ATP) as the (CC) (COM) Makes Multiple Dance Step Related Adjustments to Increase or Decrease its Permeability to Funneled (IS) (IA)

Descriptive:

The (CC) (COM) increased permeability to inflammatory mediators from its luminal surface into the (IS) will increase in response to (IS) generated signaling cues regarding (VIFR) penetration. The (CC) (COM) cAMP master switch will be triggered to process the permeability adjustment (1). Its transmembrane reduction will set off a series of signaling and metabolic chain reactions that will cascade through the (CC) (COM) infrastructure to increase (COM) permeability to funneled and purpose precise inflammatory mediators into the (IS) to remove (VIFRs). To achieve an optimal (CC) (OM) complex permeability adjustment, the process will require surges of (Ca++) (2) and ATP (2) from nearby mitochondria (3) to the (CC) (COM) to provide the necessary support to reduce voltage gradients and increase active transport capacities that will facilitate the (IA) (IS) funneling mechanics.

The signaled feedback loops from the (CC) (COM) to adjust its pulsed permeability will be directed towards nearby mitochondria for as they signal for more or less energy (*ECC*), (Ca++), (Mag++)

and alternatively for nitric oxide (*NOCC*) gas production (3). Both (Ca++) and (Mag ++), the ladder of which stabilizes the negatively charged molecular configuration of newly minted ATP to enable its transport out of mitochondria, will be utilized by the (CC) (COM) to facilitate multiple different permeability mechanics that enable the funneling of purpose precise (IA) (4) into the (IS).

The sequential and precise funneling of circulating (IA) leukocyte and platelet (CC) transport into the (IS) will start with an anti-inflammatory conferred cell within the blood or lymph plasma that is directed to adhere to the endothelial cell glycocalyx (G) (4) where it is configured to then adhere to specific adhesion receptors (CAM) on the (CC)(COM) (5). From there, these purpose-virulent (IAs) will be shuttled to (COM) selectin receptors (not pictured in the figure) towards the aperture widened (GJO) (8) where they are then mobilized into the (GJC) (9) to be prepared for (IS) dispersal (9). In the (GPC), (IA) are further sequenced by different gates, receptors, connexins and inhibitory proteins. In other instances, large or bulky (IA) proteins, such as immunoglobulins, albumen or inflammatory proteins, may enter the (IS) staging area (4) via *active transport* from the (CC) (COM) into the (IS) via budded vesicles (*BVs*) (6) or transcellular transport channels (*TTCs*) (7) as they typically buck up against transmembrane osmolar gradients.

Bulky protein (IA) endocytic transport through (CC) (BVs) and (TTCs) typically requires *energy* for its transcellular execution as their endocytic mobilization processes into the (IS) will likely be against variable concentration gradients or their molecular size, shape or solubility make them unlikely to use diffusion or facilitated diffusion transport mechanics. Other types of funneled (IA) (smaller in size and more lipid soluble) into the (IS) may require little if any energy to facilitate their funneling mechanics as they rely on reduced (COM) permeability related voltage gradients, facilitated ligand connections, or other transmembrane processes involving fluid, electrolyte or oncotic concentration gradients that engineer diffusion or facilitated diffusion (not pictured in the figure).

The (CC) (COM) mechanics of enhanced (IA) funneling into the (IS) is further reconciled by the reconfiguration of its (OMC) from *flat to oval* (10).

Figure Four

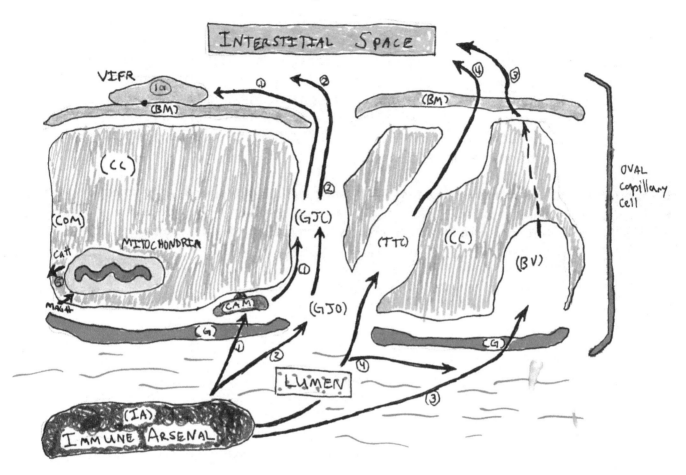

The Mechanics of (CC) (COM) Funneled, Sequenced and Precision Purposed (IA) Choreography

Descriptive:

Precision sequenced and (CC) (OMC) choreographed and (IA) funneling into the (IS) will be composed of different renditions of immune cells, immunoglobulins, activated cytokines, enzymes, free radicals and other inflammatory proteins, clotting factors and complement. All of part of these (IA) constituents may be funneled into the (IS) to mediate a (VIFR) related inflammatory breach and are brought to the (IS) based on intelligence operatives sent to the (CC) (OMC) and (BM) from the mesenchymal cell (*M*) as part of an "all hands-on deck" signal (not pictured in the figure).

The (IS) (IA) funneling efforts will involve a transluminal effort that is organized through the downstream endothelial and (CC) (OMC). Desired (IA) will initially adhere to the web-like (G) membrane (1) where typically white blood cells or platelets are configured for (CC) (COM) (CAM) attachment (1). Once attached to a (CAM), these cells will enter the (IS) through the (GJO) (1,2) and (GJC) (1,2), the ladder of which becomes a highly regulated transport canal for specific (IA) (IS) facilitated funneling.

Large bulky proteins, immunoglobulins, albumen or inflammatory proteins will require active transport into to the (IS) via (*BVs*) (3) or (*TTCs*) (4).

Once funneled (IA) (1,2) through the (CC) they will enter into the (IS) *staging area* they will be signal or metabolically maneuvered towards the (VIFR) target (1a). In this figure, the (VIFR) (1a) has attached to the (CC) (BM) but different VIFRs can affect, incorporate or attach to a variety of different membranes.

The timely (VIFR) removal, will often require a sequence of identification, immune response, and a chemical reduction followed by a molecular recycling of its electron neutral elemental constituents. The process will facilitate an (IS) anti-inflammatory signaled and *metabolic rhythm* which cues the nearby (IS) (M) (not pictured in the figure) to facilitate a cytokine inhibitory *"all clear signal"* that will resonate to include the (CC) (BM). The all-clear signal becomes the resonating stamp that ushers in the next (CC) pivot and swing dance step.

As (IA) are being funneled into the (IS) for (VIFR) removal, (CC) mitochondria are releasing (Ca++) (5) into the (CC) cytoplasm (in exchange for (Mag++) as they combust ATP through its cytochromes to facilitate the active transport of a full throttle compilation of inflammatory mediator (IS) mobilization.

Figure Five

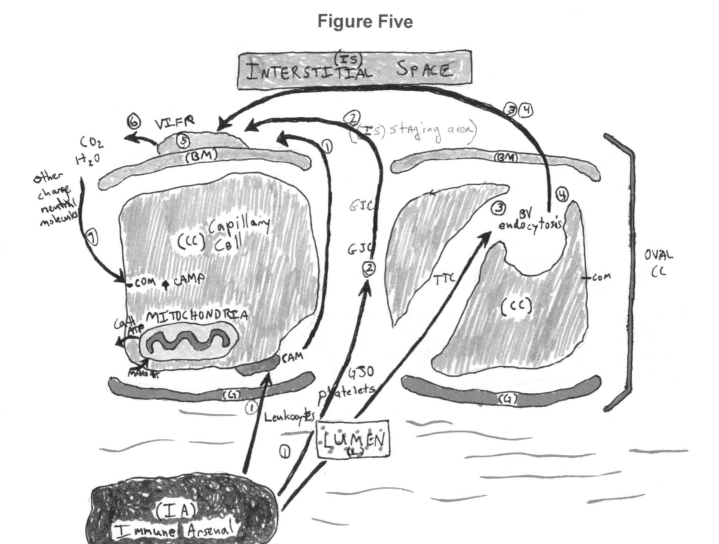

The (CC) Dance Step Rhythm is Dependent upon the Timely (IA) Execution of (VIFR) Removal

Descriptive:

Sequential and precision purposed anti-inflammatory (IA) contingents (1) from blood and lymph plasma, are funneled into the (IS) staging area from (G) (1) to specific (CC) (COM)(CAM) attachments (1) where they are dispatched to the (GJO) and (GJC) (1,2). In other instances, they may enter the (IS) via diffusion or facilitated diffusion or by active transport through the (CC) (COM) (TTCs) (3) of (BVs) (4).

Once precision purposed (IA) are positioned within the (IS) staging area (1,2,3,4), their purposed execution will be further incentivized from anti-inflammatory signaling streams consisting of previously activated cytokines, enzymes and electromagnetic rhythms (not pictured in the figure) that will direct the (IA) towards the (IS) (VIFR)(5).

Timely (IS) (VIFR) reduction and molecular recycling of its elemental electron neutral constituents (CO^2, H^2O, nitrogen, et al) (6) will metabolically rhythm to (M) to facilitate the (IA) inhibitory "all clear signal" (not pictured in the figure). This signal, if well clarified, will stream to the (CC) (BM) and (OMC) to cause an increase in master switch cAMP (7) that will cause switch chain reactions within the (CC) (COM)'s infrastructure that will trigger reductions in permeability of funneled (IS) inflammatory mediators (not pictured in the figure) and the initiation of the next dance step.

Figure Six

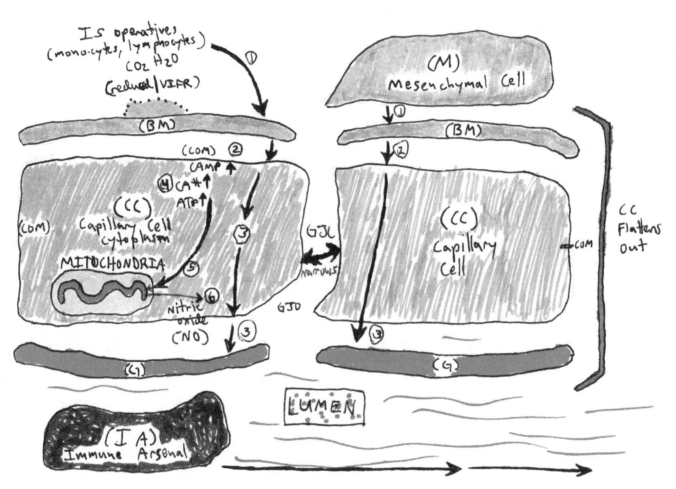

How the (CC) Outer Membrane Complex (OMC) and (COM) in Particular
Responds to the (IS) Mesenchymal (M) "All Clear" Inhibitory Signal

Descriptive:

(M) cells (1), in conjunction with other anti-inflammatory (IS) (IA) operatives, will have successfully reduced (VIFRs) to carbon dioxide, water, nitrogen etc. (1), will aggregate an (IS) (IA) funneling inhibitory "all clear signal". This will consist of the release or activation of inhibitory cytokine(s)) (1) that will interact with the (CC) (BM) to trigger a (CC)(OMC) permeability adjustment (2)(3).

This will require that the (CC) (COM) surge cAMP (4) which will cause switch chain reactions that will diminish the requirement for (Ca++) and ATP utilization at the (CC) (COM) (4). (Ca++) and ATP will transmembrane accumulate to form concentration gradients within the (CC) cytoplasm (4) which will easily transgress through the porous mitochondrial outer membrane (5). Once in the intermembrane space they will engage with the voltage potent inner membrane (5) to feedback loop a swing in

mitochondrial combustion away from energy as ATP synthase in cytochrome V is inhibited (not pictured in the figure) and nitric oxide synthase (*NOS*) is activated within the mitochondrial matrix. The ladder will induce the production of nitric oxide (NO) gas (6) and the initiation of the (NOCC).

The back-and forth dance step rhythm of (CC) (OMC)permeability pivots and the subsequent swinging of (CC) mitochondrial combustion between the (ECC) and (NOCC) becomes a *pulsed-counterbalancing anti-inflammatory rhythm* that paces and connects multipurpose (CC) execution within its infrastructure, (IS) domain and to its (IS) cellular partners (not pictured in the figure).

Figure Seven

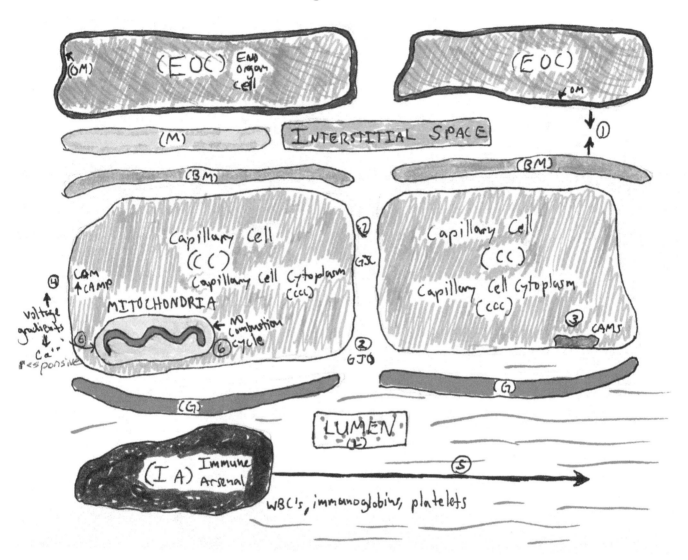

Pulsed Anti-Inflammatory Signaling Streams and Metabolic Rhythms Chain React a Back-and Forth Pivot and Swing of (CC) (OMC) Permeability and Mitochondrial Combustion that Redirects a Counterbalanced Dance Step Multipurpose

Descriptive:

As (CC) (COM) and (OMC) permeability is reduced, the (CC) (OMC) *flattens out* (1) to allow for a substantial increase in (BM) surface area exposures to the end organ cell (*EOC*) (OM) (1). This increase in transmembrane intimacy provides opportunity for greater functional exchanges between these membrane surfaces, which along with increased capillary cell driven nitric oxide (IS) oxygen delivery, will incentivize enhancement of (EOC) functional capacity.

When this permeability shift occurs, circulating (IA) will be become resistant towards adhering to a less adhesive (G) (5).

In this dance step permeability reversal, the corresponding (CC) (COM) (GJO) and (GJC) will become less (IA) reactive and will narrow (2) their widths as part of the collective effort to reduce (IA) (IS) funneling. In addition, (CC) (COM) (CAMs) will have limited exposure and less likely to engage with luminal (G) (3).

(CC) (COM) voltage gradients will increase (4) during this pulsed dance step cycle as (CC) (COM) cAMP increases and ATP and (Ca++) accumulate and engage with the mitochondrial inner membrane to block ATP combustion (6) while enabling the (NOCC) (6).

Figure Eight

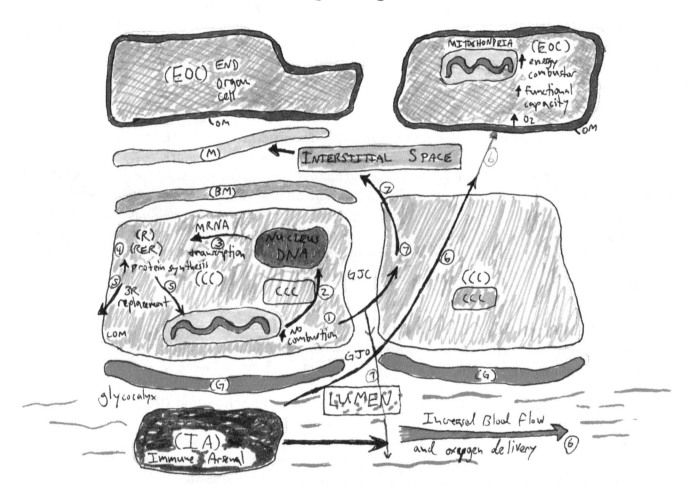

The Pulsed Anti-Inflammatory (CC) Mitochondrial (NOCC) and (ECC): A Rhythmic Signaling, Metabolic and Functional Back-and Forth Counterbalance, that Combines with The (CC) (OMC) Permeability Pivots, to Precision Execute Multipurpose

Descriptive:

The (CC) mitochondrial (NOCC) (1), when timely, sufficiently robust and synchronized within the (CC) dance steps, will produce sufficient quantities of pulsed (NO) gas that will distribute into the (CC) cytoplasm (1) to cause and effect chain reactions of signaling and metabolic rhythms which redirect organelle purpose(s) away from the mitochondrial (ECC). Within the (CC) nucleus (2) (NO) gas, in combination with activated growth and other factors, will initiate chromosomal DNA transcription (3) to mRNA for purposes of inducing protein synthesis at the (R) and (RER) (4).

The newly minted proteins will be distributed within the cell's infrastructure, including the (OMC) and mitochondria, to *quality assure* future (CC) dance step multipurposed execution as they refurbish worn out or malfunctioning (OMC) conglomerates (5) as they replenish, via replacement, fusion and replication, mitochondrial mass, volumes and size *(5)* (not pictured in the figure).

The dispersal of (CC) produced (NO) gas will also diffuse through the (OMC) via diffusion by following concentration gradients into the (IS) (7) where it will feedback loop a redirected (IS) purpose with (M) (7) and residual (IA). When (NO) diffuses into the (L) space, it will facilitate smooth muscle relaxation from downstream arterioles that in turn will pulse increases in blood flow and oxygen delivery (6) to the upstream (CC) and (EOC). This oxygen surge will enhance (EOC) functional reserve (6) as the (EOC), unlike its (CC) partner, is mitochondrial combustion and oxygen dependent for optimizing its functional requirements (6).

The (3R-*repair, replacement and replication*) off (CC) infrastructure rejuvenation that occurs during the (NOCC) (CC) dance step (5) becomes a quality assurance benchmark towards the optimal maintenance of (CC) functional management. In the case of the (CC) outer membrane complex (OMC), the quality of its infrastructure function is dependent on the reliable optimization of repair and replacement of infrastructure proteins. Without a dance step resuscitated (BM), (G) and (COM), the execution of each dance step's purpose will not be comprehensive. When this occurs, cracks form in anti-inflammatory resilience, with subsequent delays in eliminating VIFRs, and a subsequent proclivity for chronic interstitial space signaling and metabolic rhythms to sprout (not pictured in the figure).

The (CC) (NOCC) will also facilitate the activation of telomerase and the subsequent lengthening the protective telomeres on nuclear chromosomal DNA (represented in the figure as a larger more prominent nucleus) which lessens the impact of possible ROS cross linkage.

The genuine (CC) (OMC) permeability pivot and completed mitochondrial (NOCC) will enable the comprehensive execution of (CC) infrastructure refurbishment while at the same time increasing the (EOC) functional reserve with additional (IS) oxygen delivery. When sufficiently (CC) dance step executed, the prevailing outcomes form the signaling and metabolic rhythms it produces will become introductory precursors to the successful fulfillment of the next dance step.

In this manner the (CC) dance steps reverberate a timely signal, metabolic and purpose counterbalance that is mandated through its rhythm and that permeates through the (IS) (M) (7) and (EOC) (6) as an operational homeostasis of anti-inflammatory executed multipurpose.

Figure Nine

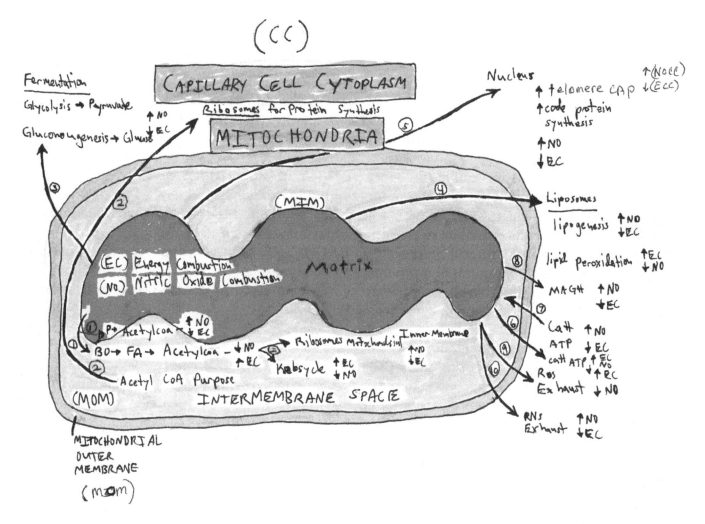

(CC) Counterbalanced Mitochondrial Combustion Signaling and Metabolic Rhythms, within the Context of the (CC) Dance Step, will Facilitate and Quality Assure (CC) Multipurposed Execution

Descriptive:

Within the context of a counterbalanced and precision executed (CC) (OMC) permeability pivot and swinging mitochondrial combustion dance step, the reliable (CC) mitochondrial (NOCC) will chain react signaling, metabolic and functional rhythms that redirect the cell to a different purpose while simultaneously discontinuing rhythms that would otherwise occur during its mitochondrial (ECC). In this metabolic about face, the (CC) mitochondrial (NOCC) will favor the utilization of *pyruvate* rather than *fatty acids (FA)* (or ketone bodies) as a substrate in the production of its combustion hub molecule *acetyl CoA* (1).

On the other hand, within the context of a counterbalanced (CC) dance step rhythm, the mitochondrial (ECC) will favor (FAs) rather than pyruvate in the production of acetyl CoA, as mitochondria process longer chained (FAs) through beta oxidation (*BO*) during this cycle. This occurs as cytoplasm liposomes lipolyze even longer chained (FAs) to 14 carbons or less in order to facilitate the mitochondrial (BO)

(1) process. During (CC) (NOCC) liposomes will induce lipogenesis of shorter chained (FAs) to longer ones in order to facilitate lipoprotein synthesis from nearby ribosomes (R) within mitochondria (2) and within the (CC) cytoplasm.

During the (CC) mitochondrial (NOCC), fermented pyruvate (from glycolysis) will enter the mitochondrial matrix to mint acetyl CoA, which will then be prevented from entering the Krebs cycle to instead be shuttled to mitochondrial *ribosomes* (2) as fodder for protein synthesis and the mitochondrial refurbishment of roughly 29 proteins for which its refurbished DNA clumps will subsequently code for 3R (repair, replacement, replication) infrastructure rejuvenation.

Within the dance step rhythm, and in the context of the mitochondrial (ECC), lipolyzed (FAs) of 14 carbons or less will be ushered into the mitochondrial matrix whereby they are (BO) processed to produce acetyl CoA which will then be preferentially shuttled to the *Krebs cycle* (2) (and not to ribosomes). Its Krebs cycle reduction to carbon dioxide and water will yield abundant hydrogen ions (not pictured in the figure) that will be picked up by FAD and NAD hydrogen transport molecules and delivered to the mitochondrial inner membrane (*MIM*) and inner membrane cytochromes (not pictured in the figure) where they will subsidize cytochrome electron transport mechanics for the production of energy surges through cytochrome V.

The (CC) dance step counterbalance mechanics are also inextricably linked to its cytoplasmic fermentation processes (3). During the (CC) mitochondrial (NOCC), metabolic and signaling rhythms preferentially utilize *glycolysis* to reduce glucose to pyruvate which is then utilized within the mitochondrial matrix in the production of acetyl CoA (3). During the (CC) mitochondrial (ECC), *gluconeogenesis* becomes the preferred (CC) fermentation cycle (3) as pyruvate gets converted to glucose (3) while cytoplasmic liposomes (4) are signaled to reduce longer carbon chained (FAs) to 14 carbons or less (lipid peroxidation) (4) so that they can be (BO) utilized (1) within the mitochondrial matrix in the production of acetyl CoA.

Depending on (CC) (COM) permeability pivot and mitochondrial (NOCC) or (ECC) combustion swing, each mitochondrial combustion cycle will correspondingly pulse signaling and metabolic rhythms that predicate a much different exclusionary purpose that becomes signal and metabolic inclusionary to the introduction of the next dance step when purpose fulfilled. As these rhythms reverberate purpose transitions throughout the (CC) they will shift the purpose of the cell's entire organelle infrastructure to conform with the assigned dance step shift in purpose (not pictured in the figure).

This purpose shift can be demonstrated within the (CC) nucleus (*N*) (5). During the (CC) (NOCC), chromosomal DNA translation and mRNA transcription will occur that in turn will mobilize to ribosomes (R) and rough endoplasmic reticulum (RER) to initiate growth factor assisted protein synthesis and subsequent (CC) infrastructure refurbishment (5). It is also during the (CC) (NOCC) that telomerase is activated which re lengthens the telomeres that protect the nuclear chromosomal DNA form free radicals (5).

During the (CC) (ECC), calcium ions (Ca⁺⁺) followed by magnesium (Mag++) stabilized ATP are released from the mitochondrial matrix (6), penetrate and/or are exchanged through the (MIM), and follow facilitated diffusion/concentration gradients through the porous (MOM) into the (CC) cytoplasm where they will be utilized by the (CC) (OMC) to increase permeability to funneled inflammatory mediators into the (IS). These (CC) (COM) permeability mechanics, that are facilitated by both (Ca++)

and ATP, will include a voltage gradient reduction, the widening of the aperture and width of its (GJO) and (GJC), and the activation of active transport mechanics via (BVs) and (TTCs) (not pictured in the figure).

(CC) mitochondrial (Ca++) and ATP will go in a reverse direction during the (CC) (NOCC) (7) as they will no longer be necessary for (CC) (OMC) (IS) immune funneling. As such, they will reaccumulate within the (CC) cytoplasm and form concentration gradients that will impinge on the mitochondrial (MIM) (7) and matrix to feedback loop a shutdown of the (ECC) while activating nitric oxide synthase and the (NOCC) (7).

To facilitate the dance step driven and recurring mobilization of (Ca ++) through the (MIM), (Ca++) will be (MIM) exchanged with (Mag++) (8), whereby the ladder will be utilized to molecularly stable the newly minted charge negative ATP. During the (CC)(NOCC), the reverse will occur at the (MIM) (8) as (Mag++) is no longer required in the mitochondrial matrix to stabilize ATP as its production has been shut down. In this manner, (Mag++) will (MIM) exchange with (Ca++) with the ladder reaccumulating within the matrix to be stored or utilized as a cofactor for other (NOCC) combustion operatives (7).

(CC) Mitochondrial ROS (reactive oxygen species) combustion exhaust (9) will increase during the (CC) (ECC). Within the context of the (CC) dance step rhythm, ROS will have its own transmembrane attachment purpose to further enhance (IS) (IA) funneling prior to its subsequent degradation by antioxidants and the completion of dance step fulfillment. As ROS production precipitously declines during the (NOCC) the production of RNS (reactive nitrogen species) (10) exhaust increases and will have its own membrane attachment sphere of influence to help magnify the (NO) effect.

Both ROS and RNS, in the context of the (CC) dance step rhythm fulfillment could be considered as activated *cytokines or anti-inflammatory enzymes* whose membrane attachments further facilitate the execution of dance step performance before being systematically reduced by antioxidants (9,10).

Figure Ten

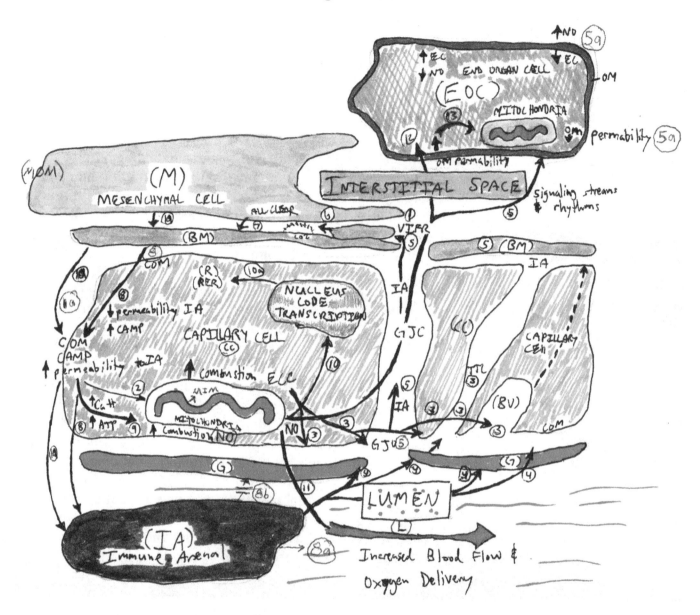

Counterbalancing a Sequential (CC) Dance Step Rhythm Requires the Timely Execution of Each Sequential Dance Step Purpose

Descriptive:

Effective (CC) dance step counter-pulsed purpose execution will have a timely beginning and end whereby each step pulses anti-inflammatory signaling streams and metabolic rhythms that execute purpose while laying the signaling and metabolic framework for the successful transition to the execution of the next dance step's purpose(s).

In the figure, the increases in (CC) (OMC) (IA) (IS) funneled permeability and the swinging of mitochondrial combustion to the (ECC) is initiated by (IS) (VIVR) (1) recognition which is helped along from (M) recognizance. The signaling aggregate then formulates a message about the (VIFR) to the (CC) (BM) (1a) which gets transcribed to the (CC) (COM) (1a) that will sort out what type and how much (IA) gets funneled from the blood or lymph plasma into the (IS) (1a) to facilitate (VIFR) removal.

This sequencing of information through the (CC) (OMC) becomes the "VIFR elimination blueprint" (1a). The (CC) (OMC) coordinates that facilitate the precision choreographed (IA) (IS) funneling blueprint are facilitated in part by (CC) (COM) master switch cAMP (1a) and the subsequent switch chain reactions it elicits through the (CC) (COM) and mitochondria (2) that will facilitate the execution of the choreography process.

The choreography of (IA) (IS) funneling through the (CC) (OMC) will in many instances require surges of energy that will be produced from (CC) mitochondria (3) as anaerobic fermentation alone is too inefficient to provide for a sufficient surge. To accommodate the different types of (IA) (IS) active transport the (CC) (OMC) will activate adhesion (CAMS) and selectin receptors that will facilitate (IA) transport through the (GJO) (GJC) (3) as well as through the energy dependent budded (BVs) (3) or (TTCs) (3)). In this dance step context, specific circulating anti-inflammatory (IA) are chemotactically selected to adhere to the (CC) (G) web (4) where they are then prepared for (CC) (COM) (CAM) attachment (not pictured in the figure) or processed for (IS) transport via other (CC) (COM) funneling mechanics (3).

The (CC)(OMC) permeability pivot that liberalizes (IA) (IS) funneling will signal loop with (CC) mitochondria via sharp reductions in cytoplasmic (Ca++) and (ATP) concentrations as they are incorporated into the (CC) (COM) mechanics of (IA) transport into the (IS) (not pictured in the figure). Their reductions will feedback loop with the (CC) (MIM) to chain react a brisk combustion swing towards the (ECC) to begin the process of resupplying the sudden drop of cytoplasmic ATP (3) while also releasing (Ca++) from its matrix as it exchanges with incoming (Mag++) to enable the surge of purpose choreographed (IA) into the (IS) via the various (CC) (COM) funneling mechanics (4).

The (Ca++) surge to the (CC) (COM) from the mitochondrial matrix (3) will bias reductions in (COM) voltage gradients as well as contract actin-myosin fibrils to produce an oval rather than flat (CC) (OMC). This in turn will bias an increase in the width of the (GJO) (5) aperture and (GJC) (5) which will potentially increase the pace and distribution of (IA) into the (IS) (5).

As (IA) arrives into the (IS) staging area its purpose identification of (VIFR) elimination will be facilitated by preexisting activated anti-inflammatory cytokine, enzyme and electromagnetic signaling streams that have been strategically expressed from (IS) pericytes and (M) (not pictured in the figure). (IA) (IS) mobilization towards the (VIFR) will also be nurtured from pulsed dance step derived *metabolic derivatives* that involve (IS) subtle but effective fluxes in pH, osmolality gradients, glucose and fatty acids concentrations and oxygen and carbon dioxide tensions (also not pictured in the figure).

These pulsed (CC) dance step derived signaled and metabolic aggregates will virilize purpose specific (IA) towards a (VIFR) elimination (5). As the (VIFR) is reduced, its metabolic outcome (water, carbon dioxide, nitrogen, etc.) (6) of primarily electron neutral byproducts becomes signaling fodder for the induction of next (CC) dance step as their residues readjust (IS) pH, osmolality and oxygen and carbon dioxide concentration gradients within the (IS) microenvironment. The (IS) "metabolic adjustment" becomes a triggering signal to the nearby (M) to activate a cytokine inhibitory "all clear" signal (7) which will permeate through the (IS) to signal loop with the (CC) (BM) to initiate the next (CC) (OMC) permeability pivot and mitochondrial combustion swing.

The (IA) (IS) (VIFR) reduction, as well as reverberating signaled and metabolic rhythms from the capillary cell dance steps, will also signal feedback loop with the (EOC) (5) to cause a *juxtaposed* outer membrane permeability adjustment and mitochondrial combustion swing that is diametrically opposed to that of the (CC) (OMC) and mitochondria. The juxtaposed (EOC) effect will make its outer membrane less permeable to (IS) anti-inflammatory activity (5a) thereby using this (CC) dance step cycle to do its own (NOCC) infrastructure refresh. This in turn will be associated with a distancing between the outer membranes of the (EOC) and (CC) as the ladder focuses on (VIFR) elimination and (IS) sanitation rather than enhancing (EOC) functional reserve.

With the activation of the (M) all clear signal, the (CC) (COM) (IS) (IA) funneling will be sharply reduced (8). The (CC) (COM) master switch cAMP will surge at its transmembrane-cytoplasm interface (8) to cause the (OMC) to decrease its permeability mechanics towards (IA) (IS) funneling (9). When this occurs, (CC) cytoplasmic (Ca++) and ATP (9) will surge an increased concentrations gradient that will easily penetrate the mitochondrial (9) (MOM) to interact with the (MIM) to transition combustion towards the (NOCC) and (NO) gas production (9). When this occurs, an inhibitory cytokine backwash from the (IS) into the blood plasma, coupled with a resistant (CC) (OMC) towards (L) (IA) attachment will cause circulating (IA) (8b) (--//->) to bypass (G) attachment (8a).

As the (CC) (OMC) permeability to (IA) (IS) funneling decreases, the (G) adhesive properties become muted (8b). In addition, the (CC)(COM) (CAM) exposures (not pictured in the figure) to (G) will diminish and the (BV) and (TTC) channels will become less (IA) transport responsive as the width of the (GJO) and (GJC) narrow. All of the (CC) (COM) adjustments along with the return of a robust voltage gradient will restrict (IA) access to the (IS) (not pictured in the figure).

The subsequent (CC) dance step mitochondrial (NOCC) will in turn chain react streams of intracellular cytokines, enzymes and growth factors that will be accommodative to the redirected dance step purpose. This will include growth factor induced signaling rhythms that will facilitate nucleus transcription (10a) for the induction of protein synthesis as mRNA is transported to (R) and (RER) (10a) to initiate cellular infrastructure repair or replication.

With a dance step completion of the (CC) (NOCC) there is a completed (CC) infrastructure refresh that would include the entirety of the (CC) (OMC) as well as replacement, fusion and replication of nearby mitochondria. The (NOCC) refresh will help maintain the functional integrity of the (CC) infrastructure so that its dance steps remain multipurpose crisp.

(CC) (NOCC) dance step cycle will also diffuse (NO) gas into the lumen (L) (11) where it will facilitate increases in blood flow and oxygen delivery to the (CC) (EOC) (12). The increased oxygen delivery to the (EOC) will increase its functional reserve as it increases (EOC) mitochondrial energy combustion (13).

Figure Eleven

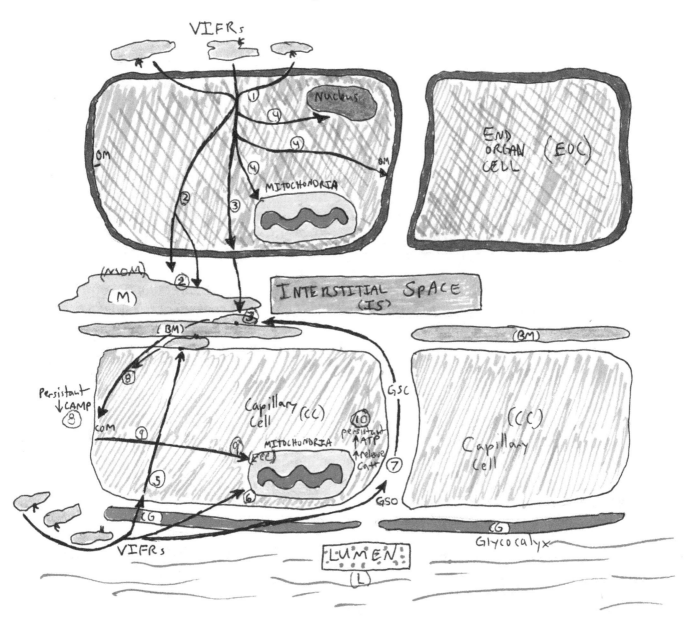

The Linchpin of a Persistent Chronic Inflammatory (IS) Signaling and Metabolic Crescendo: Too Many (IS) (VIFRs) that Cannot be Timely (CC) Dance Step Removed

Descriptive:

❖ **The Numbers of VIFRs within the (IS) that are Capable of Achieving this Decreases with Age as the (CC) loses Capacity to Funnel the Appropriate Type and Volume of (IA)**

(VIFR) arrival into an end organ's (IS) can be bidirectional, either through (EOC) epithelial membranes (1) or from blood or lymph plasma through the endothelial and (CC) (OMC) (5,6,7). (VIFR) (IS) penetration through the (EOC) will usually occur from end organs that have direct expose to the external environment such as the skin, mucous membranes, gums, lung tissue, intestinal tract, nose

and sinuses. As (VIFRs) penetrate and reverberate into the (IS) they can predispose to a variety of intra and extracellular membrane and organelle disruptions.

Within the (EOC), depending on (VIFR) solubility characteristics, molecular size, configuration and whether they are a solid, liquid or gas, can impact organelle function via direct attachment to or integration within membranes or how they interfere with the mechanics of organelle function. In the figure, (VIFRs) from the external environment that penetrate the (EOC) before the reach the (IS) can attach or influence the function of the EOC (OM) (4) mitochondria (4), nucleus (4) or other organelles.

When (VIFRs) penetrate into the (IS) from either the (EOC) or (CC), they too can disrupt membrane or organelle function of cells within the (IS). In the figure, (VIFRS) can also attach to and effect the function of (M) (2) or penetrate the cell to affect the functional mechanics of organelles within its cytoplasm. Other cells within the (IS), such as white blood cells or platelets (not pictured in the figure) can also be (VIFR) effected to disrupt or divert their purpose. They can also attach to the (CC) (BM) (3) to adversely affect its purposes to the (IS), (EOC) and as (CC) (OMC) facilitator.

Similar to what can occur within the (EOC) infrastructure, (VIFRs) can bidirectionally enter the (CC) cytoplasm via non energy (diffusion, facilitated diffusion), or in some cases, energy driven processes (endo or exocytic transport) to attach or integrate with different membranes that include the (CC) (OMC) (5). Within the (CC) cytoplasm, they may attach to or enter organelle outer membranes or penetrate their infrastructure to adversely affect their function which in the figure is depicted by (VIFR) penetration into (CC) mitochondria (6).

When (VIFRs) penetrate the (IS) through the (CC) from the blood plasma (5,7), they too can affect the functioning of (M) or other immune cells that are harbored there (not pictured in the figure). Some can also attach to cellular outer membranes including the vulnerable (CC) (BM) (5)(7). When the (VIFR) (IS) attachments are allowed to fester there will likely be delays in their (CC) dance step removal. When this occurs, the anti-inflammatory circadian effect of the (CC) dance step rhythm gets disrupted, loses counterbalance and becomes multipurpose ineffectual.

The persistence of (IS) (VIFRs) and their proclivity to membrane attach and disrupt cellular function by creating a chronic inflammatory (IS) immune cell response (5)(7) will process a persistent decrease in (CC) (COM) cAMP (8) which keeps the (CC) dance step at a fixed increase in outer membrane permeability to (IS) funneled inflammatory mediators that is feedback loop coupled to a persistent (CC) mitochondrial energy combustion (9). In the figure, the persistent (CC) mitochondrial (ECC) (9) will persistently keep (Ca++) (10) ions out of its matrix to facilitate the (CC) (COM) (IA) funneling processes into the (IS) (not pictured in the figure).

With aging and increased (CC) functional senescence, fewer (IS) (VIFR) penetrations will have the same chronic inflammatory effect of disrupting the functional integrity of the (CC) dance step rhythm. This will occur from different functional mechanics with the principle one being the reduced capacity of the (CC) nucleus to code for a comprehensive protein synthesis for infrastructure refurbishment due to aggregate cross linkages of its DNA (not pictured in the figure).

Figure Twelve

The Loss of (CC) Dance Step Rhythm, Functional Counterbalance and Multipurpose Execution will Increase (CC) (IA) (IS) Funneling Mistakes from Combinations of (CC) (OMC) Pseudocapillarization, Reduced (CC) Mitochondrial Functional Reserve and the Silencing of its Nuclear Chromosomal DNA Coding Capacity (As its Protective Telomeres Shorten)

Descriptive:

With a persistent cause and effect disruption of (IS) VIFRs (1), the (CC) dance step rhythm unravels and becomes associated with a deteriorating capacity for (M) and the (IS) funneled (IA)s to remove them. In this scenario, the (CC) (BM) becomes an increasingly dysfunctional hub of miscommunication (2?) which prevents the (CC) (OMC) from effective (IS)(IA) funneling to process (VIFR) removal.

The (CC) (BM) bungling occurs in part due to the chronic inflammatory effects of (VIFR) attachments to its membrane surface (1) but also from the lack *surveillance clarity* from (M) and (IS) (IA) about what is required from the blood or lymph plasma (VIFR) removal. This enables a proinflammatory

(IS) recycling of (VIFR) misinformation that limits the utility of (IA) (IS) anti-inflammatory purposed immune funneling.

This recycling of inadequate (IS) immune surveillance, and an increasingly efficient (IS) (IA) anti-inflammatory product will increasingly disable the (CC) dance step rhythm, reduce its (NOCC), and cause increasing (OMC) pseudocapillarization, reduced mitochondrial combustion reserve and code silencing of its nuclear chromosomal DNA. The proinflammatory momentum will cause the (CC) to become increasingly senescent and an eventual blood plasma funneling vehicle for pirated chronic inflammatory (IS) purposes as funneled (IS) (IA) increasingly purpose convert from preexisting chronic inflammatory signaled (IS) rhythms (IA) (6).

The (CC) (COM) pseudocapillarization effect matures when its infrastructure atrophies from lack of replacement. (CC) (COM) luminal (CAMs) (3), pores, voltage gradients (4) and GJO (5) and GJC (5) lose capacity to (IS) funnel precision purposed anti-inflammatory (IA) that a capable of executing a timely rhythm of (IS) (VIFR) removal.

In this corrupted chronic inflammatory rhythm of recycled, increasingly virile and intentional proinflammatory (IS) edicts, (CC) dance step deterioration escalates as its (OMC) (3) (4a) and (COM) (3) increasingly fail to deliver purpose precise ant inflammatory (IA) (6) into the (IS). When purpose neutral (IA) are (IS) funneled by a less than adequate GJO (5) and GJC (5), they will be easily purpose converted in the (IS) to preexisting chronic inflammatory signaling rhythms that will be antagonistic towards (VIFR) removal and protagonists to chronic inflammatory intentional escalations (not pictured in the figure).

As the (CC) (OMC) processes *pseudocapillarization, its* (G) will thin as its (BM) thickens. As this is occurs, the (CC) mitochondria (7) are cannibalizing their infrastructure with increased fission and autophagy as its combustion remains stuck in the (ECC). The bias excessive mitochondrial (ECC) will increase risk for reductions in mitochondrial size, volumes and mass within the (CC) (7). As purpose misaligned (IA) continue to get (IS) funneled (6), they will purpose convert to support (IS) signaling rhythms that increase chronic inflammatory virility and intentionality.

Figure Thirteen

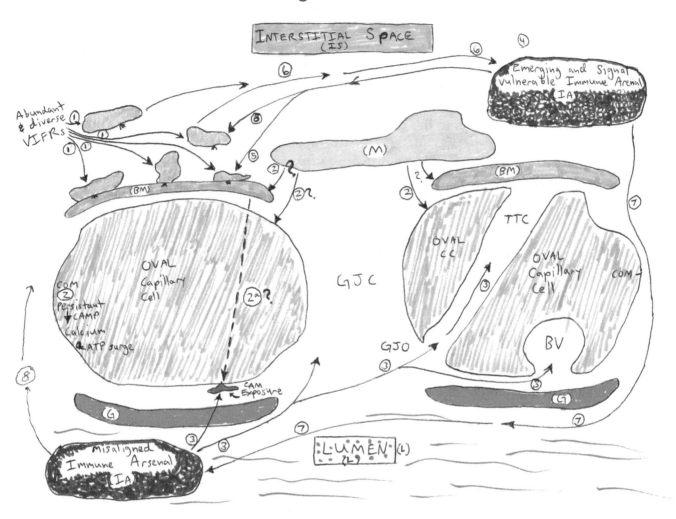

The Misappropriated (IS) (IA) Funneling through the Functionally Compromised (CC) (OMC) will Outcome an (IS) Purpose Misalignment that will Further Deter (CC) Dance Step Rhythm and Enable the Further Expression of Chronic Inflammatory Intent

Descriptive:

When (VIFRs) (1) are not timely (IS) removed, the counterbalanced (CC) dance step rhythm of its (OMC) permeability pivot (2) and mitochondrial combustion swing will falter causing to eventually cause the cell to become senescent. The loss of (CC) (OMC) functional utility will escalate the enablement of (IS) proinflammatory signaling and metabolic momentum that will diminish (IS) (EOC) capacity to function as the (IS) becomes increasingly chronic inflammatory purpose driven (not pictured in the figure).

The (IS) conversion process will always involve (M) as they succumb to escalating chronic inflammatory signaling cues and convert their rhythms to synergize with those of chronic inflammation. Their subsequent anti-inflammatory "all hands-on deck and all clear" signaling apparatus becomes increasingly muted and subject to misreads from the also disabled (CC) (BM). The outcome is to funnel (IS) (IA) that have a good chance of becoming proinflammatory signal converted (2?). The transitioning process makes (VIFR) removal less capable as (IS) cytokines, enzymes, electromagnetic wavelets and free radicals increasingly cater to chronic inflammatory overtures (3).

When proinflammatory (IS) (IA) funneling momentum is coupled with increasing (CC) (OMC) pseudocapillarization, diminished mitochondrial volumes and silenced nuclear chromatin, the combination will yield an (IS) (IA) proinflammatory resolve that incentivizes chronic inflammatory functional outcomes. In the figure, the already compromised (IS) (M) will disperse muted anti-inflammatory signaling messages to the disabled (CC) (BM) and (COM) (2a?) that will favor chronic inflammatory (IS) (IA) funneling (2a,3). (CC) (COM) (CAM) attachments from blood and lymph plasma of circulating (IA) (3) will more likely be anti-inflammatory purpose misaligned thereby making them increasingly more disruptive to the (CC) dance step rhythm as they antagonize (IS) VIFR) removal.

With (CC) pseudocapillarization, the entire (IS) (IA) funneling apparatus within the (OMC) decays. This includes the (IA) selection and pacing mechanics through the functionally compromised (GJO) (3), (GJC)(3), TTCs(3) and (BVs)(3), as these (IA) transporters have become less anti-inflammatory reliable from the increased loss of infrastructure refurbishment from a diminished dance step (NOCC).

Once in the (IS) staging area, the proinflammatory inclusive (IA) (4) will signal convert to become part of the signaling and metabolic momentum that will incentivize chronic inflammatory intent (5). As this occurs, the process will disincentivize anti-inflammatory (IS) (IA) signaling streams that would eliminate (VIFRs) (not pictured in the figure). Instead, the (VIFR) (IS) presence is enabled (5) to incentivize further expression of chronic inflammatory (IS) rhythms (6).

As chronic inflammatory (IS) (IA) consolidates (IS) purpose fulfillment (5,6), their rhythms and functional outcomes will virilize and signal pirate intent as backwash through the disabled (CC) (OMC) (7). When in the central circulation, dispersed chronic inflammatory cytokines, enzymes and free radicals will molecularly tweak circulating (IAs), that when (CC) (OMC) (IS) funneled, will conform to a virilized chronic inflammatory intent (8).

This chronic inflammatory (IS) backwash into the central circulation will involve multi end organs simultaneously as their (IS) is being chronic inflammatory signal and metabolically consumed by similar compilations of (VIFRs), (IA) signaling transitions and increasingly anti-inflammatory senescent capillary cell dance steps (not pictured in the figure). This multi end organ chronic inflammatory (IS) debacle will yield a systemic backwash that becomes increasingly anti-inflammatory immunosuppressive.

Figure Fourteen

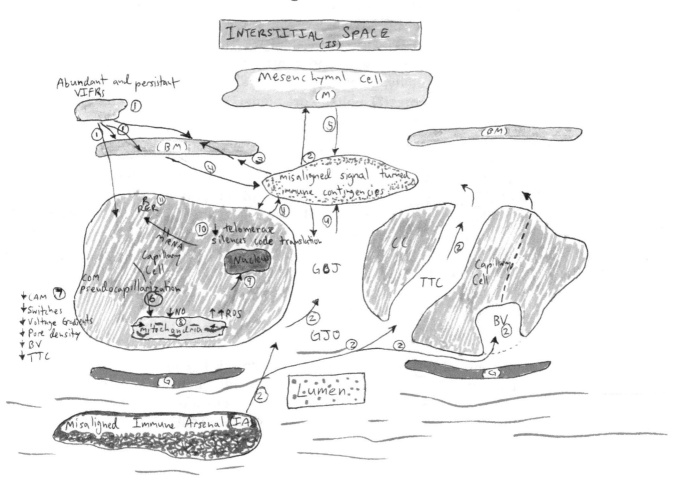

The Reverberation of Chronic Inflammatory (IS) (IA) Signaling and Metabolic Rhythms will Abort the (CC) (OMC) Dance Step Permeability Pivot which Marginalizes the (CC) Mitochondrial (NOCC) to Result in Loss of (CC) Signaling, Metabolic and Multipurpose Execution

Descriptive:

The expression of persistent (IS) (VIFRs) (1) become proinflammatory fuel for the expansion, consolidation and sub specialization of an increasingly purpose intentional chronic inflammatory (IS) operative.

As misappropriated (IS) (IA) funneling increases (2) their converted signaling rhythms become chronic inflammatory (IS) facilitators (3) which will couple with chronic inflammatory converted (M) to momentum consolidation of chronic inflammatory (IS) expression (4). These emitted (IS) (IA) and (M) chronic inflammatory messages (2,3,5) get transmitted to the functionally compromised (CC) (BM) (4) and (OMC) (4) to pirate future purpose fulfillment of chronic inflammatory intent.

This expression of a chronic inflammatory intent (2,3,4,5) will transition the (IS) away from (CC) dance step anti-inflammatory signaling and metabolic rhythms and towards chronic inflammatory derived disease venues (not pictured in the figure).

When the (CC) dance step rhythm decays, the mitochondrial (ECC) escalates and its (NOCC) (6) diminishes as mitochondria losses their signaling, metabolic and functional counterbalance. Coinciding with (CC) mitochondrial functional shrinkage (8) is an (OMC) that becomes increasingly pseudocapillarized (7). Together and along with reduced nuclear chromatin coding capacity, from the combination of increased ROS cross linkage and shortened nuclear telomeres, the (CC) will lose its anti-inflammatory functional utility. Most important, the (CC) (COM) becomes functionally senescent as (CAMs)(7), switches(7), pores(7), voltage gradients(7), (TTCs)(7) and (BVs) (7) become less precision (IA) choreograph capable.

Corresponding with CC (OMC) pseudocapillarization is a loss of mitochondrial functional reserve (8) as their volumes, mass and size (8) shrink from excessive (ECC) that will generate increases in mitochondrial fission and autophagy and less fusion and replication (typically occurring during the NOCC). Within this context, the functionally diminished (CC) mitochondria combustion will underperform which will further negate precision of anti-inflammatory (IS) (IA) funneling.

One important outcome of cascading chronic inflammatory (IS) rhythms is the increased production of (CC) mitochondrial ROS combustion exhaust from its persistent (ECC) (9). The excessive ROS becomes a toxic (CC) free radical as it exhausts antioxidant reduction, lingers within the cell and crosslinks various unsuspecting membranes and nuclear chromosomal DNA surfaces.

The increased (CC) mitochondrial (ECC) and reduced (NOCC) will hasten the shortening of the protective nuclear chromosomal DNA telomeres (10) as telomerase activity (10) gets aborted. In addition, mRNA translation (10) of nuclear chromosomal DNA becomes quiescent as (CC) stimulus for protein synthesis for repair of infrastructure from (R) and (RER) will substantially diminish (--//→) (11).

Figure Fifteen

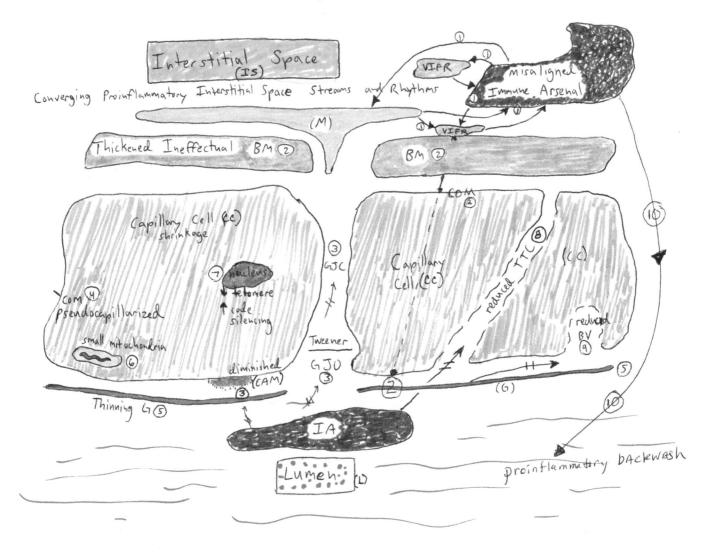

Persistent (IS) Chronic Inflammatory Signaling Streams and Metabolic Rhythms will Dismantle the Anti-Inflammatory (CC) Dance Step Rhythm and its Execution of Multipurpose

Descriptive:

The convergence of persistent chronic inflammatory (IS) signaling streams and metabolic rhythms from abundant (IS) (VIFRs) and anti-inflammatory misaligned /proinflammatory signal converted (IA) (1) will bias (M) (1) to signal convert towards their expression. The combination creates a chronic inflammatory signaling and metabolic (IS) momentum that progressively disables (pseudocapillarizes) the function of the (CC) (OMC) (2,4) to include abluminal (BM) (2), (COM) (2) and luminal (G) (2).

As the (CC) (OMC) transition's purpose towards a chronic inflammatory (IS) functional conduit (4), the adhesion receptor diminished (CC) (COM) (CAMs) (--//→) become increasingly incapable of delivering anti-inflammatory (IA) to the (GJO) (3) (3). The GJO (3) (--//-> and GJC (3) (--//→) likewise become refractory towards processing a sequential anti-inflammatory (IA) constituency into the (IS).

At the (CC) (COM) is derailing anti-inflammatory purpose execution, the (CC) (G) is likewise deteriorating as its thick web like interface progressively thins (5) making it less capable of executing (IA) attachment mechanics that would be directed towards an anti-inflammatory (IS) purpose (IAs) (=//→(3)).

As the (CC) (OMC) becomes an anti-inflammatory functional pariah, the (CC) mitochondrial functional reserves are also pressured to fail (6) as their size, mass and volumes shrink from the lack of fusion, replication and (NOCC) derived infrastructure resuscitation (not pictured in the figure).

The (CC) pivot and swing dance step functional decline will also block telomerase from keeping the length of nuclear chromosomal DNA telomeres (7) suitable to protect the chromatin from ROS cross linkages. In addition, the crosslinked DNA will become prone towards being code silenced for translation and transcription (7) to mRNA and subsequent protein synthesis for infrastructure repair of the (CC).

At the same time, the capacity for (CC) (OMC) (TTCs) (8) and (BVs) (9) to engage in the active transport of large or bulky (IAs) (immunoglobulins, albumen, inflammatory proteins) will also diminish (--//→).

Collectively the transition of (IA) funneling into the (IS) from anti to proinflammatory purpose will exocytic backwash (10) through the disabled (CC) cytokines, enzymes and free radicals into the blood and lymph plasma that will tweak circulating (IAs) towards becoming anti-inflammatory immunosuppressive (10). When coupled with similar backwashed (IS) rhythms from other end organs, the collective aggregate will induce a potent (IA) immunosuppression and subsequent proclivity towards accelerating multi end organ disease venues (DVs) (not pictured in the figure).

Figure Sixteen

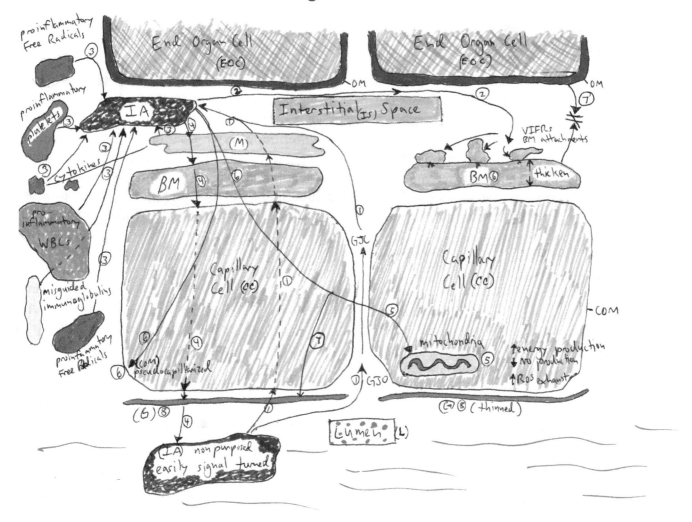

(IS) Chronic Inflammatory Signaling and Metabolic Consolidation and the "Pseudocapillarization Effect" on (CC) (OMC) Enables the Chronic Inflammatory (IS) Matrix to Pirate (IS) Intent

Descriptive:

(CC) (OMC) pseudocapillarization (6) enables (IS) funneling of anti-inflammatory purpose inept (IA) that become signal converted towards proinflammatory signaling initiatives from existential chronic inflammatory rhythms that have previously assembled within the (IS) (1).

Their simulation will increase the expression of chronic inflammatory (IS) virulence that will stoke additional chronic inflammatory (IS) momentum as they simultaneously enable (VIFRs) (2) to pester and fester the (IS) by preventing their reduction. As (VIFRs) enable the expression of chronic inflammatory signaling and metabolic rhythms, (M) immune surveillance falters as the (CC) (BM)) (2) becomes increasingly incapable of providing the necessary detail to the (CC) (COM) about what anti-inflammatory (IA) from the blood and lymph plasma is required to process (VIFR) and inflammatory breach resolution.

The (IS)(IA) signal conversion to a proinflammatory purpose will occur when (IS) proinflammatory signaling streams from previously converted WBCs (3), immunoglobulins (3) and platelets (3) release their cytokines (3), enzymes and free radicals (3) into the (IS) signaling pool that will in turn transmit their intent on the recently (IS) funneled and purpose confused (IA).

The additional chronic inflammatory momentum generated from purpose converted (IAs) will impart their effects to (M) (4) and the increasingly pseudocapillarized (CC) (BM) (4) and (OMC) in what becomes a revolving door of chronic inflammatory (IS) momentum and purpose clarity. Their conveyance will over time become increasingly *purpose intentional* to where their signaling impulses breach the (CC) (OMC) to pirate a chronic inflammatory message (4) to the blood and lymph plasma as to what specific (IA) is required for a manifested chronic inflammatory (IS) intent. As these chronic inflammatory (IS) signaling messages mature purpose specificity, the (IA) (IS) funneling they procure will mature a more reticent chronic inflammatory (IS) intent. The initial phase of pirating the (CC) (OMC) to transition a chronic inflammatory (IS) outcome is known as the *chronic inflammatory matrix*.

Once the chronic inflammatory matrix reaches a certain signaling and metabolic (IS) threshold, the power it conveys to steer influence will auto perpetuate the recycling of chronic inflammatory rhythms (1->2->3->4 and 4>3>2>1) that will redirect (IS) purpose fulfillment away from (VIFR) removal and (EOC) functional optimization to instead cater to the maturing of chronic inflammatory outcomes (not pictured in the figure). This expression of chronic inflammatory (IS) outcomes will further decimate (CC) dance step functional counterbalance, reduce its restorative mitochondrial (NOCC) (5) and auto perpetuate the ongoing degradation of the (OMC) (6) and mitochondrial combustion reserves.

As the (CC) and downstream endothelial cell thicken their respective (BMs) from chronic inflammatory (IS) residuals, anti-inflammatory crosstalk within the (IS) or to and from the (EOC) becomes increasingly muted (7) (←//→).

Other (CC) (OMC) pseudocapillarizes its luminal (G) thins out (8), rendering it less capable of procuring anti-inflammatory (IA) adhesive attachments. This becomes one more chronic inflammatory nail of anti-inflammatory (CC) (OMC) disengagement.

Figure Seventeen

The Maturing of Chronic inflammatory (IS) Signaling and Metabolic Purpose towards Anti-Organ Disease Venues (DVs)

Descriptive:

Accumulating proinflammatory (IS) (IAs) (1) will cytokine stream momentum towards additional chronic inflammatory signaling and metabolic rhythms that overwhelm (IS) (M) to where they conform to and identify with their rhythms (1).

The aggregate of maturing proinflammatory (IS) signaling and metabolic rhythms (1) will consolidate chronic inflammatory intentionality towards the nurturing of (IS) (DVs) (1). Within this chronic inflammatory (IS) signaling and metabolic hierarchy, (DVs) and (VIFRs) become increasingly anti-inflammatory (IA) ignored (2) (--//->) as their (IS) (IA) contingents with in the (IS) diminish which in

turn reduces their capacity to generate capable anti-inflammatory purposed signaling and metabolic rhythms (2) (--//->).

In this context, (VIFRs) (2a) pester and fester as anti-inflammatory rhythms that would ordinarily remove them becomes increasingly less reliable in doing so (IAs) (2) (--//→). The loss of anti-inflammatory (IS) (IA) resolve incentivizes a chronic inflammatory (IS) signaling bias that will continue generating anti-inflammatory inept (IA) (3) funneling from blood and lymph plasma into the (IS) (5) while simultaneously blocking anti-inflammatory purpose precise (IA) (2b) (--//->) from entering the (IS) staging area. This combination will allow (VIFRs) (2a) will fester within the (IS) as they continue to expand chronic inflammatory residues towards their membrane attached interfaces that will include the (CC)(BM) (2a).

With the advent of a growing (IS) (DV) presence, their crosstalk (4) will merge with other chronic inflammatory signaling rhythms to propagate a continued anti-inflammatory ineptness from the increasingly disabled (CC) (OMC) (4) and nearby shrunken mitochondria to anti-inflammatory dance step perform. As (CC) mitochondria extend their (ECC) and diminish their (NOCC) (4) the combination will extend the continued expression of proinflammatory biased (IAs) being funneled from the blood and lymph circulation into the (IS) (5).

As (VIFRs) continue to expand and express a chronic inflammatory (IS) prodrome, their purpose will couple with signals form (DVs), whereby they will cause the disabled (CC) (OMC) to *cede* signaling control of the (IS) from an anti-inflammatory prerogative to a chronic inflammatory (IS) purposed rhythm (4->3a->5). As the (CC) (OMC) pseudocapillarizes and nearby mitochondrial volumes and mass shrink, the prevailing (IS) chronic inflammatory signaling and metabolic rhythms (4) will accelerate its own purpose execution as they propagate (IS) (IA) immune funneling away from anti-inflammatory intent and towards their own purposes (IA) (5) that will support the functional operatives of (DVs).

The subsequent proinflammatory cytokine streams generated from signal converted (IS) (IA) (3a) will favor ongoing expressions of chronic inflammatory rhythms generated from signal converted (M), (VIFRs) and (DVs) (4) rather than to anti-inflammatory (IS) (IA) rhythms generated from the atrophied (EOC) or the diminished (CC) (OMC) (2) (--//>).

The net effect of this (IS) purpose transitioning from anti to chronic inflammatory rhythms is to increasingly isolate the atrophied (EOC) (OM) (6) (--//-> and <-//--) from the (CC) (OMC) such that their capacity to anti-inflammatory execute meaningful functional exchanges becomes untenable.

Figure Eighteen

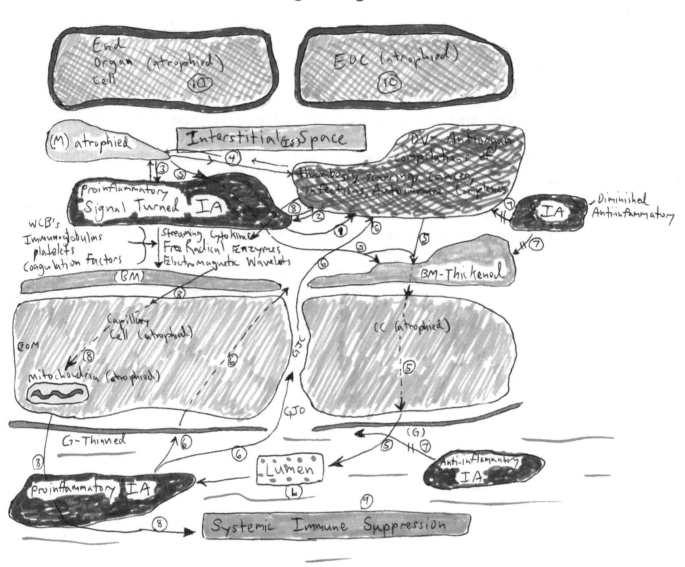

***The Full Expression of Anti-Organ (DVs): The Anti-Inflammatory (CC),
(IS) and (M) Signaling and Metabolic Capitulation that Enables the Anti-
Organ to Divert (IS) Functional Rhythms towards Its Own Purpose***

Descriptive:

As signal turned proinflammatory (IS) (IA) facilitate signaling streams (1) of support towards the evolving (DV), their emitted cytokines, enzymes and free radicals become part of the chronic inflammatory transitioning process that restructures (IS) signaling and metabolic expression towards an anti-organ roadmap of (DV) expansion. The mechanics of the (IS) purpose transitioning will involve the expansion and persistence of (VIFRs) (not pictured in the figure), the consignment of signal converted (M) (3,4,5) and proinflammatory (IA) to chronic inflammatory rhythms, and the consolidation of these efforts into a virilized (DV) expression (2,4,5,8).

In this manner, (VIFRs), signal turned (M), proinflammatory (IS) (IA) and the expanding (DV) will aggregate their signaling and metabolic rhythms to become anti-organ *purpose intentional partners* within the (IS). This partnership will include the signal and metabolic *pirating* of the increasingly senescent and (OMC) pliable (CC) (BM) (5) and (COM) (5) where the (IS) chronic inflammatory partnership will consolidate a (DV) expression (6).

The expression of chronic inflammatory signaling and metabolic rhythms to and from the (IS) (5,6,8) becomes the purpose coordinated byproduct of the expanding (DV) (8) and its signal compliant (M) and (IA) (IS) (2,3,4,5). As this occurs, the (CC) dance step rhythm becomes *persona non grata* to an (IS) anti-inflammatory presence, thereby opening the (IS) door to an undeterred chronic inflammatory signaling and metabolic expansion (7) (--//->).

As the functional effects of the (EOC) diminishes (10), the expression of (DV) purpose intentionality expands (8). As its (IS) signaling and metabolic rhythms become increasingly purpose centric, they will form a resounding proinflammatory backwash through the (CC) (8) and into the blood and lymph plasma (L) where their rhythms will facilitate a subtle molecular reconfiguration of circulating (IA), that once (IS) funneled (6), will signal convert and conform to (DV) purposes. This chronic inflammatory backwash (8) will facilitate a systemic anti-inflammatory immunosuppression effect (9) as their blood plasma rhythms integrate with those from other (EOC) (IS) backwash from other end organs.

Figure Nineteen

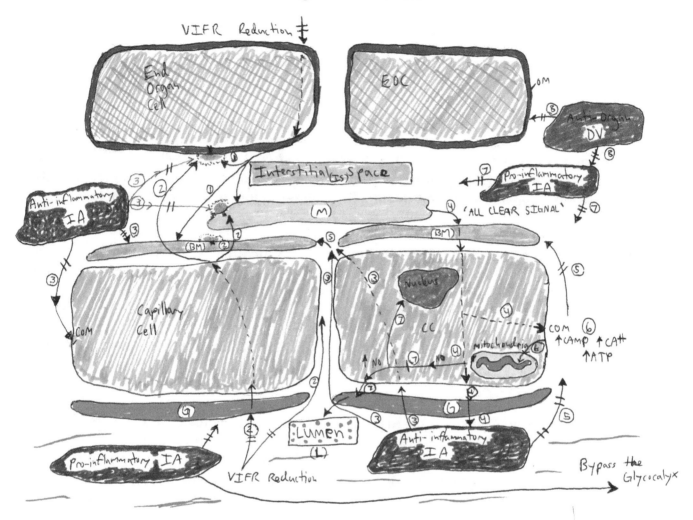

Breaking the Thread of Chronic Inflammatory (IS) Signaling and Metabolic Chain Reactions: Finding (CC) Dance Step Traction from (IS) (VIFR) Reduction and Decreased (DV) Posturing

Descriptive:

Any hope to reassembling an (IS) anti-inflammatory virilized functional rhythm, in the setting of a matured anti-organ (DV), requires a sustained-intentional effort to reduce (IS) (VIFRs) that are arriving either through the (EOC)(1)(--//->) or (CC) (2)(--//->) or both.

If (VIFR) (IS) funneling can be persistently reduced (typically from anti-inflammatory lifestyle adjustments, medicinals and supplements), the (CC) dance step rhythm might be able to posture the return of functional counterbalance whereby a resuscitated (NOCC) will become capable of retooling (CC) infrastructure to include its (OMC) and mitochondria. This can occur, when the (CC) can permeability pivot its (OMC) away from constantly funneling (IA) into the (IS) (4).

When (VIFRS) are sufficiently reduced within the (IS), the (M) "all clear signal" will enable the (CC) (COM) to permeability pivot (6). This will generate a sufficient signaling power (from accumulated

ATP and calcium ions) to feedback loop a swing in mitochondrial combustion away from its (ECC) and towards the regenerative (NOCC) (6).

The subsequent anti-inflammatory signaling and metabolic momentum generated from the *back-and forth* rhythm of the (CC) pivot and swing dance steps will rekindle (IS) anti-inflammatory transcellular multipurpose execution (3) as signaling rhythms within the (IS) retransition from proinflammatory (--//->) to anti-inflammatory (3).

When the (CC) dance step rhythm transitions sufficiently to enable anti-inflammatory signaling and metabolic reconfiguration of (IS) purpose, the (CC) mitochondrial (NOCC) (7) will become increasingly more robust as mitochondrial volumes and mass increase (not pictured in the figure) and the NOCC output becomes more consist. When this occurs, (CC) infrastructure regenerates, to include the (OM) (OMC) (7).

This resuscitated dance step derived anti-inflammatory (IS) (IA) rhythms can eventually mitigate further (IS) transitioning towards chronic inflammatory intent. These rhythms will weaken (IS) (DV) (8--//->) signaling resolve, disrupt (IS) (IA) proinflammatory (7--//->) signaling rhythms and remove anti-organ signaling blocks from strengthened (IS) anti-inflammatory (IA) rhythms (2--//->) (3--//->).

This (IS) transitioning from pro to anti-inflammatory purpose removes signaling blocks that prevent (VIFR) (3--//->) degradation while restoring functional intimacy between the EOC, anti-inflammatory (IA) and the (CC) (OMC) (3--//->).

The (IS) anti-inflammatory (IA) revival will not only increase (VIFR) removal (3) and transmembrane functional intimacy between (EOC) and (CC) (OMC) (not pictured in the figure) but it will also stoke an anti-inflammatory signaling renaissance of (M) (4) which becomes functionally capable of eliciting purpose clarity via both the "all hands-on deck" and "all clear "signals that increases or decreases (IS) immune funneling as its pushes adjustment in (CC) (OMC) (4) permeability gradients.

The return of a functionally counterbalanced (CC) dance step rhythm will facilitate the timely back and forth reduction and re accumulation of (CC) (COM) cAMP (6) whose fluxing transmembrane concentration gradients form potent switch chain reactions that percolate through the (CC)(COM) infrastructure to facilitate permeability adjustments that not only regulate endocytic (IS) (IA) funneling but also exocytic cytokine and enzyme backwash.

The execution of (IS) (IA) funneling (3) or (5) (--//->) is processed in part by the fluxing of (Ca++) and ATP concentration gradients to and from the (CC) (COM) and which are supplied by nearby mitochondria (6,7). These transmembrane (CC) (COM) permeability shifts will dance step rhythm adjustments in mitochondrial combustion efforts to backdrop either surges of ATP or NO that are combustion responsive to shifts in mitochondrial (MIM) (Ca++) and ATP concentrations gradients (6).

With a refurbished (CC) mitochondrial (NOCC), (NO) gas will transmembrane diffuse throughout the (CC)'s infrastructure (7). When it does, its concentration gradients will chain react purpose differentials within the infrastructure of the various organelles that facilitate the execution of the (CC) dance step (not pictured in the figure).

The multi organelle (NOCC) purpose adjustment will include the (CC) nucleus (7) and the subsequent stimulation of chromosomal DNA *transcription* to mRNA for (R) and (RER) derived protein synthesis (not pictured in the figure). This dance step process of stimulated protein synthesis will key the (CC) and (M) infrastructure refurbishment. When in dance step rhythm it will also facilitate a counterbalanced (EOC) refurbishment as well during the (CC) (ECC)(not pictured in the figure).

(NO) gas will also likely diffuse through the (CC) (OMC) (7) and into the (L) (7) where it can form concentration gradients to facilitate the downstream relaxation of arteriole smooth muscle. This will enhance dilatation of arteriole lumens to increase blood flow and oxygen delivery to the upstream (CC) bed, (IS) and (EOC)(not pictured in the figure).

With the improved degradation of (IS) (VIFRs) (1) (--//->), the diminishment of (DV) (8) (--//->) functional utility, and the reduction of (IA)(IS) (7) (--//->) chronic inflammatory resolve, the (CC) dance step rhythm will become increasingly more operational and multipurpose robust. This (CC) anti-inflammatory pulsed multipurposed execution will get (IS) transmitted to all (CC) (IS) partners ((EOC) and (M)) via the dance step pace, stem and ricochet effects (not pictured in the figure).

Figure Twenty

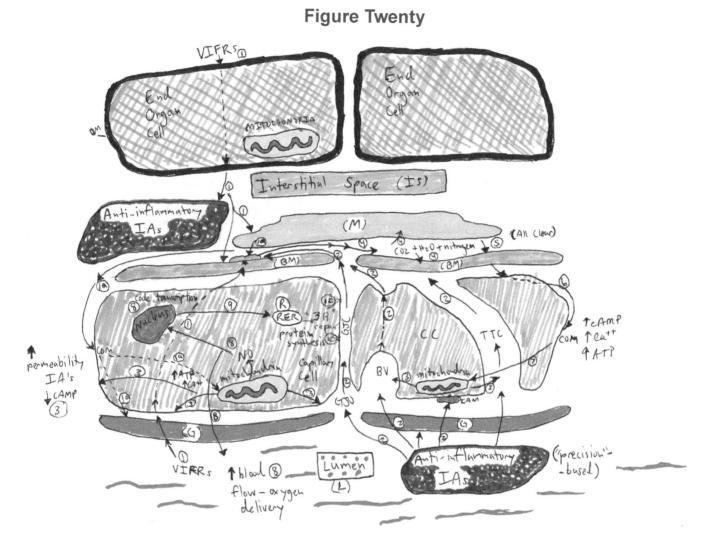

*Summarizing the Multipurpose Execution of the (CC) Dance Step Rhythm:
Integrating the Counterbalanced Anti-Inflammatory Execution of (CC), (IS),
(M) and (EOC) Purposes within the Context of (CC) Dance Steps*

Descriptive:

The (CC) Dance Steps Provide Timely Signaling, Metabolic and Purpose Execution while corresponding Cause and Effect Rhythm *Counterbalance* that *Quality Assures* Each Step's Purpose Execution. Its "In Rhythm" multipurposed Execution will Facilitate:

- **Optimal (IS) Sanitation**
- **(EOC) Functional Longevity and Reserve**
- **A Timely and Accurate (M) Signaling Exchange to and from the (IS) (IA) and the (CC) (OMC) that Facilitates an "All Hands-on Deck" or "All Clear" signal**
- **A Stout Defensive Signal and Metabolic (IS) Posturing against Potentially Invasive Chronic Inflammatory Rhythms that Preclude Matrix or Anti-Organ (IS) Organization**
- **Perpetuate a Virilized Anti-Inflammatory (IS) (IA) Circadian Multipurpose which will Backwash a Circulating (IA) Insurance Policy Against the Propagation of End Organ (IS) (DVs).**

(IS) (VIFRs) (1) can penetrate an end organ's (IS) from the blood or lymph plasma (L) (1) or externally through the (EOC) membrane interface (1). Once (VIFRs) penetrate the (IS) they can integrate with, diffuse through or impinge on various membrane surfaces that would include the EOC (OM), (CC) (BM) (1) and (M) (OM)(1). When (VIFR)s membrane attach, the molecular reconfigured (OM) and subsequent (IA) response towards them can be construed as a type of *antigen-membrane attachment complex* that in the context of a (CC) dance step rhythm will require elimination to properly sequence the next dance step.

Within the context of an (IS) (VIFR) membrane attachment, (M) will recognize the (VIFR) and emit a surveillance response (1a) (typically in the form of a cytokine stream) concerning the nature of the attachment to the (CC) (BM)) (1a). The transmission will facilitate the (BM) to communicate with the (CC) (COM) a precision-based anti-inflammatory (IA) response from the blood or lymph plasma through the (CC) (OMC) to timely dance step eliminate it.

This (VIFR) elimination process in most instances requires a specific (IS) (IA) (IS) funneling mechanic from the central and lymph circulation that pushes the (CC) (OMC) to *pivot its permeability* to bias the choreographed mobilization of (IA) into the (IS). Within the context of a functionally counterbalanced (CC) dance step rhythm, anti-inflammatory (IA) (IS) funneling to remove the (VIFR) will be precise and timely so as to produce a signaling and metabolic (IS) crescendo that favors the introduction of the next dance step.

The (CC) (OMC) choreography that details a precise (IA) funneling into the (IS) will require the (CC) (COM) to utilize a full specter of (IA) funneling options that will involve fluxing voltage gradients, the utilization of diffusion and facilitated diffusion concentration gradients, specific pore activation and the luminal exposure of specific (L) (CAMs) (2) that will facilitate a specific (IA) attachment in preparation for (GJO) and (GJC) transport to the (IS). It will also require the activation of budded (COM) (BVs) (2) and TTCs (2) that will further nuance the active transport of additional (IA) into the (IS).

As the (CC) (OMC) executes anti-inflammatory (IA) funneling into the (IS) for (VIFR) removal, the increased permeability of the (CC) (COM) has sharply reduced its transmembrane cAMP concentrations (3). Its reduction serves as a *master switch* that will cause and effect cascades of pulsed (CC) (OMC) switch operatives that will bias increases in (CC) (OMC) (IA) (IS) penetration.

The pulsed (CC) (OMC) funneling of (IS) (IA) will distribute powerful shifts in (Ca++) and ATP into the (CC) cytoplasm that form fluxing concentration gradients that become feedback loops signals to nearby mitochondrial (3) as they interact with the mitochondrial inner membrane to swing combustion towards energy (3) or NO, with the former facilitating the (IS)(IA) funneling effort (2). The (CC) (COM) ATP/(Ca++) permeability message to the mitochondrial (MIM) (1a) will also interloop with signals from (IS) (M) (1a) that will further nuance the mitochondrial (ECC) or (NOCC) rhythms. The signaling dynamics from the (CC) (COM) and (IS) (M) will collectively form a feedback loop to swing mitochondrial combustion, which in the case of increased (IA) (IS) funneling (2), will process the (ECC)(3).

When (VIFR) (IS) removal is both timely and effective, the (VIFR) gets reduced to mostly electron neutral byproducts of carbon dioxide and water (4) which become (IS) metabolic fodder that will facilitate the signaling of the next pivot and swing (CC) dance step. When coupled with other signaling streams from the timely (IS) (VIFR) mop-up, anti-inflammatory chain reactions will transact with (M) (4) to facilitate the "all clear" (IA) inhibitory signal (5) that will bring about (CC) (OMC) permeability shift that will reduce further (IS) (IA) funneling as it ushers in the next dance step.

This (CC) (OM) complex permeability pivot will be supported by a host of shifting metabolic rhythms that cause-and effect adjustments in (IS) pH, osmolality and oxygen /carbon dioxide gradients (4) and glucose/fatty acid utilization that collectively facilitate the clarity of the (M) "all clear signal" (5). The elicited (M) "all clear" cytokine inhibitory reverberation (5) will incentivize the (CC) (OMC) to suppress further (IS) (IA) funneling (6) as it initiates the re accumulation of (CC) (COM) cAMP (6). As (CC) (COM) (IA) (IS) transport mechanics stall, the utilization of (CC) (COM) ATP and (CA++) decreases (6). Their cytoplasmic accumulation will feedback loop (7) to nearby mitochondria to swing combustion to the (NOCC) (8) that will facilitate a shift in (CC) purpose from (IS) hygiene to that of infrastructure refurbishment and (EOC) functional optimizer. In terms of the ladder, (NO) gas will facilitate increases in blood flow and oxygen delivery (8) to the (CC) bed and (EOC).

When (NO) diffuses into the nucleus, it will couple with activated growth factors and other intracellular inducements to facilitate the induction of chromosomal DNA translation and transcription (8) to mRNA (9). The coded message will get transported to (R) (9) and (RER) (9) for protein synthesis and subsequent "3R" repair (10) of the cell's infrastructure. This will include the repair of its critically important (CC) (OMC) complex and its vast array of (COM) (CAMs), pores, switches, gates and interlocking infrastructure. In this manner each (CC) dance step's rhythm of multipurpose execution is both functionally *counterbalanced* and *quality assured* as each step's timely execution becomes the signaling and metabolic *framework* of the next dance step (not pictured in the figure).

Bibliography

Beltramo, E., A. Mazzeo, T. Lopatina, M. Trento, and M. Porta,"Thiamine transporter 2 is invovled in high glucose-induced damage and altered thiamine availability in cell models of diabetic retinopathy,"*Diab &Vasc Dis Res* (2019) doi.org/1479164119878427.

Bhati, P., R. Alam, J. A. Moiz, and M. E. Hussain,"Subclinical inflammation and endothelial dysfunction are linked to cardiac autonomic neuropathy in type 2 diabetes," *J of Diab and Met Disorders* (2019)18(2)419-428.

Bassingthwaighte, J. B., "Capillary permeability,"*Wiley Encyclopedia of Biomedical Engineering*(2006) doi.org/10.1002/9780471740360.ebs0211.

Buckingham, R. *Hazing Aging: How Capillary Endothelia Control Inflammation and Aging.* Bloomington, IN: iUniverse, 2015.

Buckingham, R. *Rejuvenation!: How the Capillary Cell Dance Blocks Aging while Decreasing pain and Fatigue.* Bloomington, IN: iUniverse, 2017.

Buckingham, R. *Trafficking: How Chronic Inflammation Sabotages the Immune Arsenal and Poisons the Interstitial Space of End Organs.* Atlanta, GA: Litfire Publishing, 2018.

Buckingham, R. *Rejuvenation 2.0: How the Capillary Cell Dance Paces and Stems Interstitial Space Sanitation and End Organ Rejuvenation to Resolve Disease, Pain and Fatigue.* Atlanta, GA: Lifire Publishing, 2019.

Buckingham, R. "HSCRP as a biomarker of the capillary cell pivot andswing dance," *Conference: New Developments in Biomarkers-Summit* (2018)doi.org/25616-38834.

Buckingham, R.,"Silencing neurodegeneration by reducing vascular inflammatory free radicals and unleashing the capillary cell dance," *Project:Rejuvenation2.0*(2018)doi.org/10.13140/ RG.2.2.20786.45761.

Buckingham, R.,"Particulates, inhaled toxins and breathlessness-harbingers to broken capillaries," *Project:Rejuvenation2.0*(2018)doi.org/15842-e86679.

Buckingham, R. "The blurring of interstitial space intent-the evolution of leaky gut,"*J of Clin Gastroenterology and Hepatology*(2018)doi.org/2575-7733.

Camont, L., M. Lhomme, F. Rached, W. LeGoff, A. Negre-Salvayre, R. Salvayre, C. Calzada, M. Lagarde, M. J. Chapman, and A. Kontush," Small, dense high density lipoprotein-3 particles are enriched in negatively charged phospholipids:relevance to cellular cholesterol efflux, antioxidative, antithrombotic, anti-inflammatory and antiapoptotic functionalities,"*Arteriolscherosis, Thrombosis, and Vascular Biol* (2013)33(12):2715-2723.

Chen, K., R.N. Pittman, and A.S. Popel,"Nitric oxide in the vasculature: where does ot come from and where does it go? A qualitative perspective,"*Antioxid Redox Signal*(2008)10(7):1185-1198 doi. org/10.1089/ars.2007.1959.

Chen, L., H. Deng, H. Cui, J. Fang, Z. zuo, J. Deng, Y. Li, X. Wang, and L. Zhao,"Inflammatory responses and inflammation-associated diseases in organs," *Oncotarget*(2017)9(6):7204-7218.

Cutolo, M. and R. H. Straub,"Circadian rhythms in arthritis:Hormonal effects on the immune/inflammatory reaction,"*Autoimmunity Reviews* (2008)(7)3:223-228.

Di Marco, E., S. P. Gray, and K.Jandeleit-Dahm,"Diabetes alters activation and repression of pro-and anti-inflammatory signaling pathways in the vasculature,"*Front. Endocrinol* (2013)doi.org/10.3389/fendo.2013.00068.

Greco, J.A., J.E. Oosterman, and D.D. Belsham,"Differential effects of omega-3 fatty acid docosahexaenoic acid and palmitate on the circadian transcriptional profile of clock genes in immortalized hypothalamic neurons," *Am J Physiol Regul Integr Comp Physiol* (2014)307(8)doi. org/10.1152/ajpregu.00100R1049-60.

Hasselmann, H., S. Gamradt, A. Taenzer, J. Nowacki, R. Zain, K. Patas, C. Ramien, F. Paul, K. Wingenfeld, D. Piber, S.M. Gold and C Otte,"Pro-phenotype and cell-specific steroid signaling alterations in unmedicated patients with major depressive disorder,"*Front Immunol* (2018((23)doi. org/10.3389/fimmu.2018.02693.

Huang, L-H., A. Elvington, and G. J. Randolph, "The role of the lymphatic system in cholesterol transport," *Front Pharmacol.*(2015)6:182.

Huff, T., and I. Jialal,"Physiology, cholesterol,"StatPearls.Treasure Island(Fl):StatPearlsPublishing(2019)https://ncbi.nlm.nih.gov/books/NBK470561/.

Irwin, M.R.,"Sleep and inflammation:partners in sickness and in health,"*Nat Rev Immunol*(2019)(19) 702-715doi.org/1038/s41577-019-0190-z

Javeed, N., M.R. Brown, K. Rakshit, T. Her, Z. Ye, H. Lee, T. Ordog, and A. V. Matveyenko,"Proinflammatory cytokines disrupt B-cell circadian clocks in diabetes," *Bio Rxiv*(2019)doi.org/10.1101/705210.

Koronowski, K. B. et al., Communicating clocks shape circadian homeostasis, *Science* (2021) doi:10.1126/science.abd0951.

Kim, S., N. Neuendorff, and D. J. Earnest," Role of proinflammatory cytokines in feedback modulation of circadian clock gene rhythms by satruated fatty acids," *Sci Rep* (2019)(9)doi.org/10.1038/s41598-019-45322-9.

Klodian, D., D.A. Evans, K. B. Rajan, D. A. Bennett, and M. C. Morris,"Healthy lifestyle and the risk of Alzheimer dementia, findings from 2 longitudinal studies," *American Academy of Neurol*(2020) DOI:https://doi.org/10.1212/WNL.0000000000009816.

Lancellotti, P., P. Marechal, N. Donis and C. Oury,"Inflammation, cardiovascular disease and cancer,"*European Heart journal*(2019),40(48)3910-3912

Linton, M.R.F., P.G. Yancey, S.S. Davies, et al.,"the role of lipids and lipoproteins in atherosclerosis," *Endotext)* (internet) South Dartmouth (MA)(2019)https://www.ncbi.nlm.nih.gov/books/NBK343489/

Miller, G., N. Rohleder, and S.W. Cole,"Chronic interpersonal stress predicts activation of pro-and anti-inflammatory signaling pathways six months later,"*Psychosom Med*(2009)71(1):57-62.

Montagne, A., D.A. Nation, A.P. Sagare et al.,"APOE4 leads to blood brain barrier dysfunction predicting cognitive decline," *Nature*(2020)https://doi.org/10.1038/s41586-020-2247-3.

Naviaux, R.K.,"Metabolic features and regulation of the healing cycle,"*Mitochondrion*(2019)46:278-297doi.org/10.10.16j.mito.2018.08.001.

Nyberg, S. T., A. Singh-Manoux, J. Pentti, et al.,"Association of healty lifestyle with years lived without major chronic diseases,"*JAMA Int Med*(2020),180(5)760-768.doi:10.1001/jammainternmed.2020.0618.

Pilchova, I., K.Klacanova, Z. Tatarkova, P. Kaplan, and P Racay,"The involvement of Magnesium in Regulation of Cellular and Mitochondrial Functions,"*Oxidative medicine and Cellular Longevity*(2017) doi.org/10.1155-6797460.

Rahadian, T., D. Fukuda, H.M. Salim, S. Yagi, K Kusunose, H.Yamada, T. Soeki, M. Shimabukuro, and M. Sata,'Thrombin inhibition by dabigatran attenuates endothelial dysfunction in diabetic mice," *Vasc Pharm* (2019)doi.org/106632.

Toya, T., J. D. Sara, M.T. Corban, R. Yaher, S. Godo, J.Herrmann, L.O. Lerman, and A. Lerman. "Assessment of peripheral endothelial function predicts future risk of solid-tumor cancer," *European J of Prev Cardiol* (2019)doi.org/10.1177/2047487319884246.

Verma, N., M. Liu, H. Ly, A. Loria, K.S. Campbell, H. Bush, P.A. Kern, P.A.Jose, H. Taegtmeyer, D.M. Bers, S. Despa, L. B. Goldstein, A.J. Murray, and F. Despa,"Diabetic microcirculatory disturbances and pathologic erythropoiesis are provoked by deposition of amyloid-forming amylin in red blood cells and capillaries,"*Kidney International* (2020)97(1)143-155.

Wang Y., P. Pati, Y. Xu, F. Chen, D.W. Stepp, Y. Huo, R.D. Rudic, and D. J.R. Fulton,"Endotoxin disrupts circadian rhythms in macrophages via reactive oxygen species,"*Plos*(2016)doi.org/10.1371/journal.pone.0155075.

Yao, W., Y. Li and G. Ding,"Interstitial fluid flow: the mechanical environment of cells and foundation of meridians,"*Evidence-Based Complementary and Alternative Medicine* (2012) doi.org/10.1155/853516.

Ziegler, T., F. A. Rahman, V. Jurish, and C. Kupatt,"Atherosclerosis and the capillary network: pathophysiology and potential therapeutic strategies,"*Cells*(2020) 9(1),50;doi.org/10.3390/cells9010050.

Index

G

gap junction channel 52, 232

gap junction complex 67, 69-70, 74-75, 83, 90, 109, 117-118

gap junction orifice 15, 39, 44, 50-51, 56, 62, 65, 69, 118, 201, 215, 232

ghrelin 87

gluconeogenesis 34, 57-58, 68-69, 77, 96, 101, 109, 112, 186, 194, 223, 248

gluten 86, 212, 226

glycocalyx mesh 50, 117

glycolysis 34, 57-58, 68-69, 96, 101, 147, 157, 163, 169, 223, 248

H

heavy metals 86, 137

heme 37, 57-58, 63, 67, 97, 113

highly processed foods 86

homocysteine 81, 86, 109

hydrocarbons 86, 112

hydrocephalus 136

hydrogen peroxide 26, 70, 77

hyper coagulopathies 13, 180

hypoxia and ischemia 128, 137, 151, 196

I

immune arsenal 12-15, 17-18, 23-25, 27-29, 32-35, 37-40, 43, 46, 49, 52-55, 57-59, 63-66, 69, 72, 74, 76, 82, 84-85, 87, 89-91, 94, 96-97, 100, 102, 104-107, 112, 116, 122, 124, 138, 140-141, 143-145, 147, 153, 155, 157, 160, 162, 165-166, 170-171, 176, 178, 184, 189, 192-193, 195, 196, 201, 207, 211, 232

immune funneling into the interstitial space 17-18, 24, 30, 33, 38, 47, 66-67, 81, 83, 99, 111, 175, 201, 219, 224

immune suppression 63, 85, 86, 119, 131, 143, 144, 148, 152, 156, 170, 184, 193, 229

immunoglobulins 13, 19, 20, 27, 32, 51, 61, 63, 67, 82, 90, 108, 110-111, 124, 140, 144, 160, 173-179, 181-182, 196, 201, 204, 225, 236-237, 264, 266

infectious agents 18, 20, 61, 109, 126, 127, 130, 139, 140-149, 151, 157, 165, 168, 176, 204

inflammatory mediators 11-12, 16, 26, 90, 95-96, 100-111, 173, 182, 211, 235, 240, 248, 256

Inflammatory Mediators 9, 184

insulin resistance 13, 18, 24, 34, 36, 40, 69, 77, 84-88, 109-111, 113, 115-116, 118, 120, 123,

126-127, 129-131, 135, 138, 139, 141-142, 146, 148, 150-151, 152, 154-158, 161-162, 165-167, 169, 170, 177, 181, 186, 193, 206, 209, 212, 214, 219-220, 222, 226, 285

Insulin Resistance 109, 169

interstitial space hygiene 18-20, 22, 41, 43-45, 49, 53, 65, 89, 92, 128, 152, 159, 164, 180, 190, 195, 199, 204-206, 213-224, 226

interstitial space sanitation 21, 47, 50, 54, 60, 74, 90, 99-100, 101-102, 164, 195, 199, 218

K

kinins 111-112

L

lactose 86, 226

lead 17, 19, 24, 27, 38, 67, 82, 86, 93, 109, 111, 136-137, 180, 182, 192, 212

leaky gut 79, 86, 132, 226, 279

Leptin 87

lipolysis 34, 57, 77, 101, 110, 112, 186, 194, 223

lipoprotein 68, 83, 248, 279

liposomes 34, 58, 68, 69, 161, 169, 247, 248, 285

luminal surface 235

lymphocyte 55, 130, 132, 134, 138, 139, 157, 173, 176, 220, 221

lymphocytes 130-132, 152, 160, 177, 182, 215

M

magnesium ions 16, 51, 57, 66-67

manganese 86

mast cells 111, 179

master switch 43, 51, 56-57, 59-60, 90, 95, 99, 117, 201, 232-233, 235, 240, 252-253, 276

meningeal infections 132

mercury 86, 137

mesenchymal cells 19, 27, 29, 30, 32, 38, 43, 45-46, 50, 56, 60, 65, 76, 79, 89-90, 92, 94, 106, 108, 110, 119, 123-124, 126-127, 129, 131-132, 137, 150, 157, 160, 164, 170-171, 176, 178, 181-182, 188, 192, 195, 206, 211, 215, 224, 232

metabolic counterbalance 12-13, 15, 16, 33, 34, 49, 68, 70, 72, 84, 97, 103-104, 163-164, 187

metabolic rhythms 11-14, 16-19, 24-30, 32, 38-42, 46, 50, 52, 54-55, 58-59, 61, 69-70, 74-75, 77, 82-84, 88-89, 94-95, 97-98, 100-102, 104-106, 109-111, 114, 115, 117-128, 131-133, 135, 138, 141-147, 150-151, 155-158, 162-168, 170-171, 173-174, 177-178, 182-184, 186,

188-189, 191-198, 200, 202, 204-206, 208, 211, 213, 215, 217-222, 224-225, 227, 245-246, 248, 251, 253, 261, 263, 265-268, 270, 277

midlife 20-21, 107, 158, 204, 206-207, 209-217, 222, 227

mitochondria 14-16, 19, 24, 30-31, 33, 35-37, 51-52, 54-57, 62-66, 68-69, 76, 78, 80, 83, 91, 97, 101, 112-113, 122, 144, 146, 160, 163, 166, 169, 171, 174-175, 184-185, 187-188, 191-192, 194, 198, 200, 202, 205, 232, 235-236, 238, 245, 247-248, 252-253, 256, 258, 262, 268, 271-272, 277

mitochondrial beta oxidation 68-69, 77

mitochondrial combustion cycles 31, 36, 57-60, 209

mitochondrial combustion swing 44, 47, 89, 100, 159, 160, 252-253, 259

mitochondrial fission 36, 57, 184, 262

mitochondrial fusion 97

mitochondrial inner membrane 15, 36, 44, 57, 63, 66-68, 95-96, 113, 127, 244, 248, 276

modifier effect 79

monocytes 67, 90, 131-132, 152, 160, 176, 177-178, 215

Multiplier Effect 85, 106

N

nitric oxide 12, 14-17, 19, 21-22, 24-26, 29-33, 35-37, 41-50, 52, 54, 56-58, 60, 62-63, 66-68, 71, 74, 75-77, 80, 82-83, 88, 90-92, 95-97, 100-101, 107, 112-113, 116, 122-123, 127-128, 140-142, 147, 157, 159-161, 163, 166-167, 169, 171, 175, 178, 183-184, 186-188, 191-194, 199-206, 209, 223, 232, 236, 242-243, 249

noxious gases 86, 112

O

oncogenesis 54, 61, 77, 83, 122-123, 126, 142, 151, 155, 164-165, 171, 178, 203, 222

opioids 86, 154, 209, 214

organelles 27, 35, 52, 78, 83, 101, 141, 143, 145-146, 171, 174, 182, 186, 194, 205, 256, 272

outer membrane permeability 31, 76, 91, 93-95, 100, 122, 195, 201, 253, 256, 286

outer membrane permeability gradients 122, 195

P

parasites 142, 146

pericyte 102, 109, 119, 123, 126, 134-135, 137, 140, 145, 189, 286

pester and fester effect 17, 30, 37, 71, 85, 108, 140, 164

plasma cells 175-177, 179

platelets 15, 19, 27, 32, 51, 90, 108, 124, 139-140, 144, 150-153, 155, 160, 196, 215, 225, 234, 237, 256, 266

pores 14, 26, 39, 46, 50-52, 56, 63, 67, 69, 75, 97, 117, 148, 187, 194, 201, 215, 258, 262, 277

portal circulation 86, 102-103, 132, 226

proinflammatory lifestyles 20

proton pump inhibitors 86

psychoactive medications 86

psychosis 154

pyruvate 14, 21, 34, 50, 57-58, 68-69, 77, 97, 101, 123, 161, 169, 186, 223, 247, 248

R

radical impediments 11, 13, 20, 45

ribosomes 34-36, 58, 68, 97, 171, 186, 223, 248

S

scar tissue 18, 125, 126, 130-135, 137-138, 147, 151, 157, 165, 169, 203-204, 220

selenium 86

senescence 17, 25, 48-49, 60, 85, 107, 122, 148, 157, 163-164, 178, 184, 187-190, 200, 202-204, 223, 225-256

sepsis 148

signaling loops 51

signaling streams 11, 27, 30, 46, 69, 88, 89, 95, 126, 156, 170, 174, 181-182, 189, 233, 239, 251-252, 260, 263, 266, 269, 276

simple diffusion 83, 112

sleep deprivation 87, 206, 209, 212

smokescreen effect 119, 120

sodium-potassium pump 67

solvent 54

Space of Disse 102

stem effect 93-99, 134

steroids 86, 135

superoxide 26, 70, 77

T

T cell lymphocyte 173
telomeres 97, 184, 246, 248, 262, 264
thrombosis 29, 61, 70, 83, 103, 112, 125-126, 128,
        150-153, 155, 162, 196, 203, 216, 220, 227
transcellular aging 152, 172, 225
transcellular restitution 19, 65, 71, 89, 92, 101-102,
        116, 152, 194, 199, 203
transport channels 15, 50-51, 56-67, 96, 117, 177,
        201, 232, 236
transport tubules 123
traumatic brain injury 133
triglycerides 81, 83, 87, 103, 109, 138
triple whammy effect 124
tweener effect 69, 70, 118
tyrosine kinase switches 62

V

vascular dementia 135-136
vasculitis 111-112
vasoactive molecules 179
vesicles 15, 39, 46, 50-51, 56, 63, 67, 69, 75, 96-
        97, 117, 177, 194, 201, 215, 232, 236
voltage gradient 35-37, 44, 51, 62-63, 66-67, 96,
        122, 187, 234, 249, 253

W

worms 142

Z

zinc 86

Printed in the USA
CPSIA information can be obtained
at www.ICGtesting.com
CBHW082030030924
14037CB00011B/698